Experiments in Computational Organic Chemistry

Warren J. Hehre

Wavefunction, Inc.
18401 Von Karman, Suite 370
Irvine, California 92715
and
Department of Chemistry
University of California
Irvine, California 92717

Lonnie D. Burke

Wavefunction, Inc.
18401 Von Karman, Suite 370
Irvine, California 92715

Alan J. Shusterman

Department of Chemistry
Reed College
3203 S.E. Woodstock Blvd.
Portland, Oregon 97202

William J. Pietro

Department of Chemistry
York University
4700 N. Keele
North York, Ontario
Canada M3J 1P3

Wavefunction, Inc.
(714) 955-2120
Facsimile (714) 955-2118

ISBN 0-9643495-0-7

Foreword

This manual comprises a collection of "experiments" touching on a broad area of structural and mechanistic organic chemistry. Like any laboratory manual it is intended to provide "hands on" experience in doing chemistry. The difference with conventional laboratory manuals is, of course, that the "chemistry" described here is not done with chemicals and glassware, but rather on a computer, or more precisely a graphics workstation. This aside, what we seek is no different: to impart the sense of excitement coming from uncovering new phenomena or discovering the obvious about old phenomena.

The experiments in this manual are arranged under five general subject headings: **Structure and Energetics, Conformation, Molecular Properties and Spectra, Reactive Intermediates** and **Reactivity and Selectivity**. Each experiment starts with a brief description of the chemical problem and, following that, suggests a computational approach and provides a list of questions about the results of the computations. For the most part, experiments have been kept very simple, both for clarity and more practically to save computer time. Where quantum chemical calculations are required, we have wherever possible, made use of semi-empirical rather than *ab initio* techniques. The reader may wish to repeat some of the semi-empirical experiments with *ab initio* methods to better understand the differences between the two techniques, both in terms of time required for completion and with regard to detailed results.

Most of the experiments are intended to be completed within a "normal laboratory period" of two to three hours, although some are much simpler and may be completed in under an hour, and a few are more involved and will require more time. Also, most of the experiments require only a modest amount of computer time (from a few minutes to an hour on a modern workstation), although a few require greater resources. All experiments require access to a workstation for some time during the laboratory period.

While the experiments in this manual are not specific to any given computer program, they have been developed assuming the graphical and computing capabilities of the *SPARTAN* electronic structure program. No effort has been made to describe in full the operation of *SPARTAN*. This has been provided elsewhere in **A Spartan Tutorial** and **Spartan Users Guide** which are available from Wavefunction, Inc. Some help with specific *SPARTAN* functions has been provided in **Appendix A** referenced from bold type in the margins of the experiments. This material, together with the tutorial, should provide an ample introduction to the program.

We have not attempted to provide insight or rationale into the selection of a specific computational approach for a particular experiment (other than keeping computation times to a minimum). The computational techniques employed here have all been extensively documented and assessed elsewhere.[1] In general, we have used the AM1 method for semi-empirical calculations and the 3-21G basis set for *ab initio* calculations. Molecular mechanics calculations, where they have been used in the experiments, typically employ the MM3 force field. Where other models have been used instead, we have attempted to explain why. We have also not sought to develop general strategies for the application of computational methods. Rather, we have used specific experiments to illustrate the kinds of approaches which may lead to useful information. Some general information regarding both the performance of various levels of electronic structure theory and more practically strategies for actually performing calculations has been provided in **Appendix B**.

Answers to all experiments are found in **Appendix C**.

Appendix D contains a listing of the quantities obtained from electronic structure calculations together with a number of unit conversions.

---

[1] *Ab initio* methods: W.J. Hehre, L. Radom, P.v.R. Schleyer and J.A. Pople, ***Ab Initio* Molecular Orbital Theory**, Wiley, New York (1986); semi-empirical methods: T. Clark, **A Handbook of Computational Chemistry**, Wiley, New York (1986); J.J.P. Stewart, in Reviews in Computational Chemistry, **1**, 45 (1989); J.J.P. Stewart, J. Computer Aided Molecular Design, **4**, 1 (1990); M.C. Zerner, in Reviews in Computational Chemistry, **2**, 313 (1991).

Table of Contents

Notes to the Reader:

i) We have endeavored to provide general references to the topics discussed in the experiments in this book. While some of these come from the primary literature, most have been drawn from three standard advanced organic chemistry textbooks:

Advanced Organic Chemistry, 3rd Ed.
Part A: Structure and Mechanisms; Part B: Reaction and Synthesis
F.A. Carey and R.J. Sundberg
Plenum Press, New, 1990

Mechanism and Theory in Organic Chemistry, 3rd Ed.
T.H. Lowry and K.S. Richardson
Harper Collins, New York, 1987

Advanced Organic Chemistry, 3rd Ed.
J. March
Wiley, New York, 1985

These have been referred to simply as "Carey and Sundberg A", "Carey and Sundberg B", "Lowry and Richardson" and "March", respectively, together with the appropriate page number.

ii) This revision (September, 1994) corrects a number of obvious errors and provides supplementary exercises and questions for a number of the experiments.

Chapter 1. Structure and Energetics

Very early in the study of chemistry we are introduced to the idea of a reaction coordinate diagram. This relates the energy of a molecular system to its geometry. Presented in one dimension the diagram is very easy to interpret.

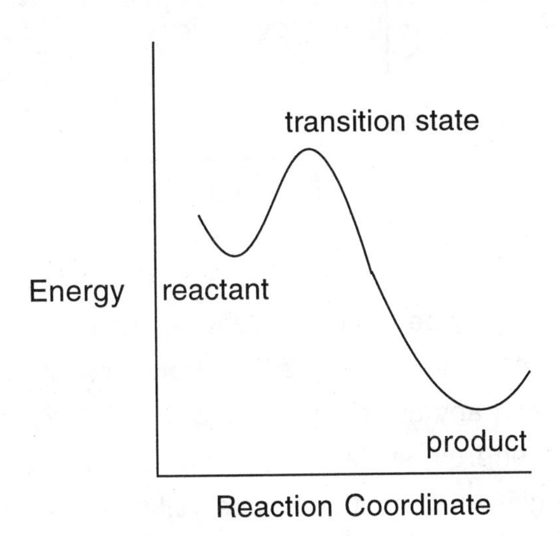

Reactant and product are stable molecules and are shown as energy minima along the reaction coordinate. They are connected by a transition state which is unstable with respect to motion along the reaction coordinate and therefore represented as an energy maximum.

This simple "reaction coordinate" diagram contains a great deal of chemically useful information. For one, it defines the geometries of reactant, product and transition state in terms of their positions along the reaction coordinate. Second, it provides information about the thermochemistry of the overall reaction. If, as shown above, the energy of the product is lower than that of the reactant, than the overall process is said to be exothermic. In this case, thermodynamics tells us that **eventually** there will be more product than reactant. If, on the other hand, the product is higher in energy than the reactant, the overall process is said to be endothermic, and in time there will be more reactant than product. Finally, the diagram tells us something about the kinetics (rate) of reaction. The higher the energy of the transition state relative to the energy of reactant (the so-called "activation energy" or "activation barrier") the slower the reaction is likely to proceed.

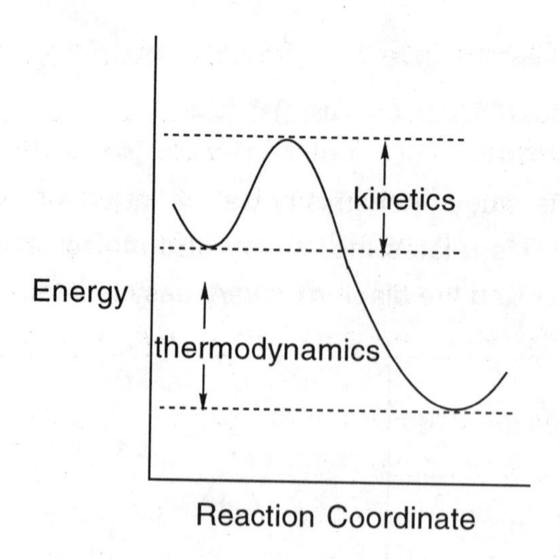

Calculations can provide a direct handle on all the important details of potential energy surfaces. They can be asked to provide geometries of stable species and short-lived reactive intermediates as well as transition states. Unlike experiment, calculations can deal with any arrangement of atoms. Calculated relative energies of minima on potential energy surfaces directly provide relative thermochemical stabilities, while energies of transition states relative to reactants relate to kinetic stabilities. Treatment is not restricted to "one dimensional" systems. While it is generally not possible to display and visually interpret multi-dimensional potential energy surfaces, their scrutiny by calculation is, at least in principle, no more difficult than consideration of the simple one-dimensional surface presented above.

The experiments which comprise this chapter all concern the structures and energies of stable molecules. They entail assigning or determining equilibrium geometry and following this establishing energy. The first two experiments examine the consequences of aromaticity in stable molecules and draw parallels between aromatic delocalization and geometry. The consequences of ring strain on the stabilities and reactivities of cycloalkanes and cycloalkenes and, closely related to this, the properties of bridgehead olefins are considered in the next two experiments. The latter leads us to an experiment which provides a general discussion of π-bond strengths. The next three experiments concern tautomeric equilibria, in nitrogen heterocycles, in amino acids and as it relates to protonation. The last experiments in the chapter examine relationships between hybridization and molecular structure, and between electronic structure and disposition for hydrogen bonding.

Experiment 1: Aromaticity in Pyrrole, Furan and Thiophene

We use semi-empirical AM1 calculations, or both AM1 and *ab initio* 3-21G calculations, to investigate the energetics of hydrogenation of pyrrole, furan and thiophene, first to molecules containing one double bond and then to fully-saturated species. We interpret differences in first and second hydrogenation energies in terms of aromatic stabilization.

Benzene possesses unusual thermodynamic stability relative to what might be expected for "1,3,5-cyclohexatriene", an unknown molecule [see **Experiment 2**]. A consequence of this is that hydrogenation of benzene to 1,3-cyclohexadiene is actually slightly endothermic, while the corresponding hydrogenation reactions taking 1,3-cyclohexadiene to cyclohexene and finally cyclohexene to cyclohexane are both significantly exothermic.

$+ H_2$ endothermic → $+ H_2$ exothermic → $+ H_2$ exothermic → (1)

The usual interpretation is that addition of hydrogen to benzene "trades" one carbon-carbon double bond for two carbon-hydrogen bonds, but in so doing destroys the aromaticity, whereas addition of the second hydrogen molecule (to 1,3-cyclohexadiene) does the same bond "trade" but does not have to contend with any loss of aromaticity. Therefore, the difference in the heats of hydrogenation of benzene and 1,3-cyclohexadiene corresponds to the aromatic stabilization of benzene. Experimentally, this difference is approximately 33 kcal/mol.

This is by no means the only or even the "best" measure of the aromatic stabilization in benzene.[1]

Far less is known about the consequences of aromaticity on the properties of heterocycles.[2] There is still argument as to whether molecules such as thiophene are really aromatic. The same analysis applied to benzene is also appropriate here. All

---

[1] Carey and Sundberg A, p. 499; March, p. 37.

[2] March, p. 42; N.D. Epiotis, W.R. Cherry, F.Bernardi and W.J. Hehre, J. Am. Chem. Soc., **98**, 4361 (1975).

we need to do is to compare "first" and "second" hydrogenation energies for the heterocycles, e.g., for pyrrole, furan and thiophene,

NH → H_2 → NH → H_2 → NH (2)

O → H_2 → O → H_2 → O (3)

S → H_2 → S → H_2 → S (4)

In principle, the required thermochemical data might be obtained from experiment. Here, however, we get it instead from calculations, carried out either entirely at the semi-empirical AM1 level or alternatively at the *ab initio* 3-21G level using AM1 equilibrium geometries.

Before we perform calculations on these heterocycles, it is important to calibrate the performance of both semi-empirical AM1 and *ab initio* 3-21G models with regard to the description of the "known" aromatic stabilization in benzene.

Such an approach, calibration of methods using known experimental facts, followed by application where experimental data are unavailable or are subject to uncertainties, is fundamental to the proper use of computations in solving chemical problems.

Hydrogenation energies for the relevant reactions are provided in the table below.

AM1, 3-21G and experimental hydrogenation energies (kcal/mol)			
	AM1	3-21G	Expt.
benzene + H_2 → 1,3-cyclohexadiene	1	4	6
1,3-cyclohexadiene + H_2 → cyclohexene	-22	-40	-26
cyclohexene + H_2 → cyclohexane	-23	-40	-28
aromatic stabilization	24	44	33

They suggest that the AM1 calculations underestimate the aromaticity of benzene by about 10 kcal/mol, while the 3-21G calculations overestimate it by about the same amount.

Procedure

Build and optimize at the AM1 level all the molecules required to evaluate the first and second hydrogenation energies of pyrrole, furan and thiophene, i.e., all the heterocycles involved in reactions (2)-(4). If you decide to run 3-21G *ab initio* calculations (3-21G(*) for the molecules containing sulfur), then use the AM1 optimized geometries, and employ direct SCF methods. The heat of formation for H_2 at the AM1 level is -5.18 kcal/mol, and its total energy at the 3-21G level is -1.22296 hartrees. [1]

Record your data in the table below.

AM1 heats formation (kcal/mol) and 3-21G (3-21G(*)) energies (hartrees)				
		X=NH	X=O	X=S
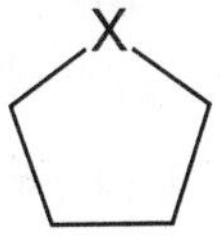 X	AM1			
	3-21G			
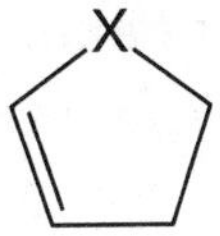 X	AM1			
	3-21G			
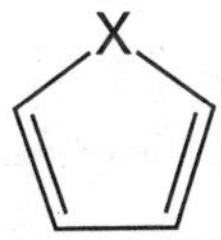 X	AM1			
	3-21G			

Work out the thermochemistry for reactions (2)-(4), and record your results below.

AM1 and 3-21G (3-21G(*)) hydrogenation energies and aromatic stabilization energies (kcal/mol)				
		X=NH	X=O	X=S
	AM1			
	3-21G			
	AM1			
	3-21G			
aromatic	AM1			
stabilization	3-21G			

Subtract the "second" hydrogenation energy from the "first" to provide a measure of the aromatic stabilization for each heterocycle. Record these differences in the table above. How do they compare with the stabilization found for benzene? Can you account for the differing degree of aromatic stabilization calculated for each heterocycle?

Optional

Do you observe significant variations in calculated carbon-carbon bond lengths for the single and double linkages incorporated into pyrrole, furan and thiophene relative to their hydrogenation products? AM1 CC bond lengths (in Å) in benzene and 1,3-cyclohexadiene are provided below for comparison.

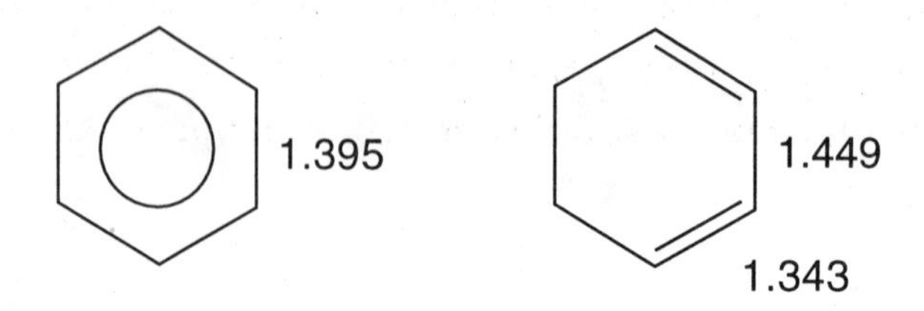

Are the variations you observe in the heterocyclic molecules more or less extreme than those found in going from benzene to 1,3-cyclohexadiene?

Experiment 2: 1,3,5-Cyclohexatriene

We use either AM1 semi-empirical or 3-21G *ab initio* calculations to examine the energy and charge distribution in the hypothetical molecule 1,3,5-cyclohexatriene relative to the energy and charge distribution in benzene.

1,3,5-Cyclohexatriene with alternating double and single bonds,

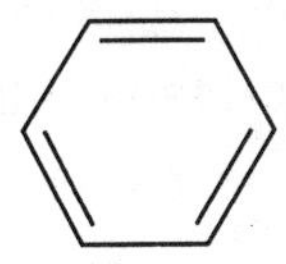

is not a stable molecule, that is, it is not a minimum on the C_6H_6 potential energy surface. Therefore, it cannot even be detected, let alone characterized. Nevertheless, 1,3,5-cyclohexatriene may be examined computationally, and its energy and other properties compared with those of benzene. This allows us to answer a number of interesting questions. Is geometrical reorganization (going from a structure with alternating single and double bonds to one in which all carbon-carbon bonds are equivalent) the full cause of aromatic stabilization, or are other factors involved? Is the distribution of charge in 1,3,5-cyclohexatriene similar to that in benzene or is it very different?

Procedure

Build benzene and optimize at the AM1 level. Optionally, recalculate the energy at the 3-21G level using the AM1 geometry. Build 1,3,5-cyclohexatriene as a planar molecule with alternating single and double bonds. Perform a single-point AM1 **[2]** calculation (alternatively, a single-point direct 3-21G calculation). Were you to attempt **[1]** to optimize the geometry of 1,3,5-cyclohexatriene, both AM1 and 3-21G procedures would lead directly to benzene. Record your data in the table below.

AM1 heats of formation (kcal/mol), 3-21G energies (hartrees) and relaxation energies (kcal/mol)		
	AM1	3-21G
benzene		
1,3,5-cyclohexatriene		
"relaxation energy"		

Compute the difference in energies between benzene and 1,3,5-cyclohexatriene and record this value in the table as the "relaxation energy". How does the "relaxation energy" compare with the "aromatic stabilization energy" of benzene (33 kcal/mol)? Does your result suggest that geometrical changes play a minor or major role in the overall stabilization of benzene?

For both benzene and 1,3,5-cyclohexatriene, generate electron density isosurfaces onto which electrostatic potentials have been encoded.

> The electrostatic potential is the energy of interaction of a point positive charge with the nuclei and electrons of a molecule. It provides one measure of overall molecular charge distribution. See also **Experiments 22** and **23**.

Use either the AM1 or 3-21G method, depending on the method previously used to calculate the wavefunction. When the calculations have completed, display the two [**3**] surfaces side-by-side and on the same scale. The surface you obtain for benzene should show a uniform distribution of charge, the region over the carbons (the π system) being negatively charged, the region around the hydrogens being positively charged. Describe the image you obtain for 1,3,5-cyclohexatriene. What do these maps tell you about the delocalization of charge in cyclohexatriene relative to that in benzene?

Optional

Build all *trans*-1,3,5-hexatriene and optimize at the AM1 level. (Optionally, [**1**] perform a single-point (direct) energy calculation at 3-21G using the AM1 geometry.) Generate an electron density isosurface onto which the electrostatic potential has [**3**] been encoded. Display this surface simultaneously and on the same scale with those of benzene and cyclohexatriene. Describe the extent of charge delocalization in this (acyclic) system relative to those in the two cyclic molecules.

Experiment 3: Ring Strain in Cycloalkanes and Cycloalkenes

We use the semi-empirical AM1 method to calculate heats of hydrogenation of cycloalkanes and cycloalkenes. The heats of hydrogenation are used to derive ring strain energies for each type of ring system, and to assess the extra strain present in cycloalkenes. We also examine the reactivity of strained cycloalkanes (relative to n-alkanes) using electrostatic potentials.

Small-ring cycloalkanes are thermodynamically less stable than the corresponding n-alkanes. This is due to a variety of factors, most notably distortion of CCC bond angles away from idealized tetrahedral values, and *eclipsing interactions* between CH bonds in cycloalkanes that are unable to assume fully *staggered* arrangements.[1]

The destabilization of cycloalkenes is referred to as **ring strain** and ring stain energies can be calculated using reactions (1) and (2). Since we expect n-alkanes to be unstrained, hydrogenation of a strained cycloalkene releases ring strain along with energy normally released by hydrogenation of a CC bond. Hydrogenation of n-butane, on the other hand, only releases the energy normally released by hydrogenation of a CC bond. Thus, the extra energy released by reaction (1) relative to reaction (2) is the strain energy of the cycloalkane.

$$\text{cyclo-}[(CH_2)_n\text{—}CH_2\text{—}CH_2] \xrightarrow{H_2} CH_3\text{—}(CH_2)_n\text{—}CH_3 \qquad (1)$$

$$CH_3CH_2\text{—}CH_2CH_3 \xrightarrow{H_2} 2\ CH_3CH_3 \qquad (2)$$

Small-ring cycloalkenes are likely to be even more strained than the corresponding cycloalkanes.[1] The main reason for this is that sp^2 hybridized carbons (which prefer bond angles of 120°) experience more bond angle distortions in a small ring than sp^3 hybridized carbons (which prefer bond angles of 109.5°). Another reason is that small rings may force a nonplanar geometry around the alkene This is particularly evident when the cycloalkene incorporates a *trans* double bond.

---

[1] Carey and Sundberg A, p. 157; March, p. 130.

The difference in strain energy between a cycloalkene and the corresponding cycloalkane can be estimated using the heats of hydrogenation for reactions (3) and (4).

$$\text{cyclo-}[(CH_2)_n\text{-}CH{=}CH] \xrightarrow{H_2} \text{cyclo-}[(CH_2)_n\text{-}CH_2\text{-}CH_2] \quad (3)$$

$$cis\text{-}H_3C\text{-}CH{=}CH\text{-}CH_3 \xrightarrow{H_2} CH_3CH_2CH_2CH_3 \quad (4)$$

Reaction (3) not only releases the energy usually released during hydrogenation of a CC double bond, it also releases the extra strain energy stored in the cycloalkene. Reaction (4), on the other hand, only releases the energy usually released during hydrogenation of a CC double bond. Thus, the extra energy released by reaction (3) relative to reaction (4) is the strain energy of the cycloalkene relative to the corresponding cycloalkane.

In this experiment we calculate the energies of reactions (1) and (3) for the smallest cycloalkanes and cycloalkenes, respectively, and we use these values to determine the relationship between ring size and ring strain.

Procedure

Build and optimize at the AM1 level each of the cycloalkanes and alkanes listed in the table below. Try to select a conformer for cycloheptane which minimizes obvious steric interactions (in an optional exercise, we perform a complete conformation search on cycloheptane). Construct the alkanes so that each has an all *trans* carbon backbone. Record all heats of formation in the table below.

AM1 heats of formation (kcal/mol)	
cyclopropane	propane
cyclobutane	n-butane
cyclopentane	n-pentane
cyclohexane	n-hexane
cycloheptane	n-heptane

Calculate energies of reactions (1) and record below. You will need the heat of formation of hydrogen at the AM1 level (5.18 kcal/mol). Also, calculate the energy of reaction (2); you have already calculated the heat of formation of butane, but you will also need the heat of formation of ethane at the AM1 level (-17.41 kcal/mol). Use the energies of reactions (1) and energy of reaction (2) to calculate the ring strain of each cycloalkane and record this below.

AM1 hydrogenation energies and ring strain energies (kcal/mol)		
	hydrogenation energy	ring strain energy
cyclopropane		
cyclobutane		
cyclopentane		
cyclohexane		
cycloheptane		
butane		

Compare these strain energies with the "experimental" strain energies (based on experimental heats of hydrogenation)[2] given in the table below.

[2] N.S. Isaacs, **Physical Organic Chemistry**, Wiley, New York, 1987, p. 283.

Experimental strain energies (kcal/mol)			
cyclopropane	27	cyclopropene	54
cyclobutane	26	cyclobutene	34
cyclopentane	7	cyclopentene	7
cyclohexane	0	cyclohexene	2
cycloheptane	6	*cis*-cycloheptene	7
		trans-cycloheptene	27

Are there any significant deviations between the AM1 and experimental values? What is the relationship between strain energy and ring size? Examine the AM1 geometries of each of the cycloalkanes. Point out any significant deviations from tetrahedral CCC bond angles (angle strain) and any eclipsing CH bonds (torsional strain). How do the CC bond distances in the cycloalkanes compare to those in the analogous n-alkanes? Try to explain why some bond distances, bond angles, and torsional angles are similar in cycloalkanes and alkanes, and why some are different.

Construct electrostatic potential maps of the electron density isosurfaces for [**3**] each of the cycloalkanes and alkanes. Display surfaces using the same color scale. Do you observe significant differences in the electrostatic potentials of different cycloalkanes? Do you observe significant differences in the electrostatic potentials of a cycloalkane and the corresponding n-alkane? Large negative potential indicates a local buildup of electron density and suggests vulnerability toward attack by electrophiles. Which sites in which compounds are the most vulnerable to electrophilic attack? Large positive potential indicates a local depletion of electron density and suggests vulnerability toward attack by nucleophiles. Which sites in which compounds are the most vulnerable to nucleophilic attack? Is reactivity towards electrophiles or nucleophiles correlated with ring strain?

Build and optimize at the AM1 level each of the cycloalkenes listed in the table below. There are two distinct stereoisomers for cycloheptene corresponding to a *cis* and a *trans* arrangement about the double bond. (*trans* stereoisomers of the smaller ring cycloalkenes are also possible, however, they are much higher in energy than the *cis* isomers and need not be considered here.[3]) Build and optimize both stereoisomers of cycloheptene. Try to select conformers for each ring which minimizes obvious steric interactions (we will perform a complete conformation search in an optional exercise). Record all heats of formation in the table below.

[3] For a discussion and a tabulation of experimental results see: Carey and Sundberg A, p. 160.

AM1 heats of formation (kcal/mol)
cyclopropene
cyclobutene
cyclopentene
cyclohexene
cis-cycloheptene
trans-cycloheptene

Work out the hydrogenation energies of each cycloalkene, i.e., the energies of reactions (3). You already have heats of formation for the required cycloalkanes and hydrogen. Also calculate the heat of hydrogenation of *cis*-2-butene, reaction (4). You already have the heat of formation of n-butane; the AM1 heat of formation of *cis*-2-butene is -2.28 kcal/mol. Record your results in the table below. Finally, calculate the strain energy of each cycloalkene relative to the cycloalkane and enter your result in the table under "excess strain energy".

AM1 hydrogenation energies and excess strain energies (kcal/mol)		
	hydrogenation energy	excess strain energy
cyclopropene		
cyclobutene		
cyclopentene		
cyclohexene		
cis-cycloheptene		
trans-cycloheptene		
cis-2-butene		

Is there excess strain energy in the cycloalkenes relative to the cycloalkanes? Is there a correlation between the excess strain energy in a cycloalkene and the strain energy in the corresponding cycloalkane? Examine in detail the AM1 geometry of each cycloalkene. Point out any large distortions away from ideal bond distances, bond angles, or torsion angles which might account for the excess strain energy. Pay particular attention to the planarity of the double bond in *cis*- and *trans*-cycloheptene.

[3] Construct electrostatic potential maps of the electron density isosurfaces for each of the cycloalkenes and for *cis*-2-butene. Display surfaces using the same color scale. Do you observe significant differences in the electrostatic potentials of different cycloalkenes? Do you observe significant differences in the electrostatic potentials of a cycloalkene and *cis*-2-butene toward attack by an electrophile [see **Experiment 38**]?

Optional

1. [4] Inspection of cycloheptane and of *cis*- and *trans*-cycloheptene suggests that there may be several conformational minima for each. Repeat your calculations to see if this is the case. Starting with the conformer which you originally built for each system, perform a conformational search at the AM1 level. When the calculations are completed, examine the list of conformers located in the search. Are there multiple conformational minima? Have any of the conclusions you have previously drawn regarding strain energies in cycloalkanes and cycloalkenes changed? How does the difference in stabilities you calculate for *cis*- and *trans*-cycloheptene compare with the experimental difference in strain energies of 20 kcal/mol?

2. [3] The electrostatic potentials obtained to examine the reactivity of strained olefins toward electrophiles also may be put to other use. Bring onto the screen electrostatic potentials (encoded onto electron density surfaces) which you earlier calculated for the cycloalkanes. Put all onto the same scale. Examine the regions around the hydrogens. Do you see a trend in the electrostatic potential in going from the small strained systems to the larger unstrained systems? It is well known that small-ring cycloalkanes are significantly more acidic than acyclic alkanes[4], and as shown in **Experiment 23**, electrostatic potentials correlate with hydrocarbon acidity.

---

[4] Lowry and Richardson, p. 293.

'Experiment 4: Bredt's Rule

We use either AM1 or a combination of AM1 and 3-21G calculations to verify Bredt's rule, "elimination to give a double bond in a bridged bicyclic system always leads away from the bridgehead". We also compare highest-occupied molecular orbitals of molecules containing a bridgehead double bond with those of isomers in which the double bond is not at a bridgehead position for evidence of the origin of instability of bridgehead olefins.

Bredt observed that elimination of water from a bicyclic alcohol such as **1** gave **2**, an olefin in which the double bond does not involve the bridgehead position, rather than the bridgehead olefin, **3**.

OH

2

3

The preference is known to diminish with increasing ring size, which suggests that its origin is ring strain associated with incorporation of a double bond into a bridgehead position.[1] In this experiment, we use calculations to test such an hypothesis. We also examine the highest-occupied molecular orbital in bridgehead olefins for evidence of the origin of their instability.

---

[1] Carey and Sundberg A, p. 161; March, p. 138.

Procedure

Build **2** and **3**, and minimize at the semi-empirical AM1 level. Optionally, [1] perform single-point direct 3-21G *ab initio* calculations using the AM1 equilibrium geometries. Record the AM1 heats of formation and (optionally) 3-21G total energies in the table below.

AM1 heats of formation (kcal/mol), 3-21G energies (hartrees) and energy differences (kcal/mol)		
	AM1	3-21G
2		
3		
ΔE		
4		
5		
ΔE		
6		
7		
ΔE		
8		
9		
ΔE		

Identify the more stable isomer and work out and record the relative energy of the higher energy form. Do the results of your calculations support Bredt's rule? What is the magnitude of the energy difference between bridgehead and non-bridgehead isomers? Do you see evidence for the instability of **3** in its equilibrium structure? Examine the C=C bond distance. Do you see significant deviations away from a normal double bond length (1.30-1.32Å) or away from an idealized planar geometry. Obtain and display the highest-occupied molecular orbital for **2** and **3**. What evidence do they provide suggesting distortion of the olefin?

Repeat the calculations with the isomeric olefins **4** and **5**, **6** and **7**, and **8** and **9**.

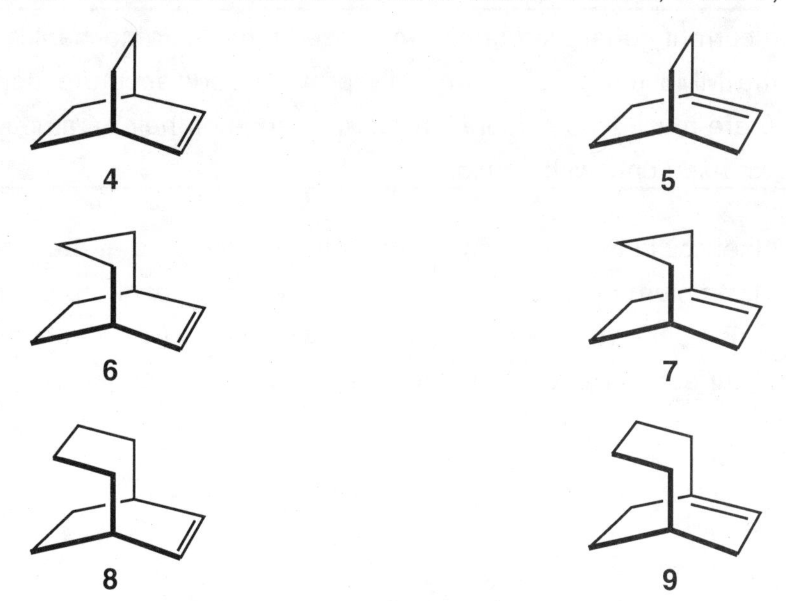

For the larger systems try to chose conformers which minimize obvious steric interactions. (As an optional exercise, we'll perform full conformational searches on these systems.) Record the heats of formation in the table above. Identify the more stable form and work out and record the energy difference to the higher-energy structure. Are the trends (differences in energies and equilibrium structures) for these compounds relative to those for **2** and **3** consistent with a steric origin for Bredt's rule? Is the highest-occupied molecular orbital in the larger-ring systems less distorted than that in the smaller systems?

Optional

Olefins **6** and **7** incorporate seven-membered rings and olefins **8** and **9** incorporate eight-membered rings. Such rings are conformationally flexible. Let's locate the "best" (lowest-energy) conformers for each of these to see if they are the same as you have already chosen and, if not, whether any of your results have significantly altered. We'll use MM3 molecular mechanics to do the conformer searching, as this should provide as accurate a description as semi-empirical methods.

The best of the current generation of parameterized molecular mechanics force fields, for example, the MM3 force field, generally provide very accurate descriptions of structure. They are much less reliable outside the range of their parameterization and should always be used only with caution.

One after the other, build **6-9**, perform conformational searches at the MM3 level and [**4**] perform an AM1 structure optimization on the lowest energy conformer for each. You [**1**] can, if you like, also perform single-point 3-21G calculations (use direct methods) and obtain graphical surfaces. Have any of the conclusions you reached earlier changed?

Experiment 5: π Bond Strengths in Olefins and Olefin Analogues

We apply the MP2/6-31G* model (using 3-21G equilibrium structures) and a simple method proposed by Benson to measure the π-bond strengths in ethylene, silaethylene and (optionally) acetylene.

Ethylene and other olefins adopt planar geometries. This maximizes overlap of the out-of-plane p-type atomic orbitals which combine to form the π bond. "Puckering" or "twisting" of the carbon skeleton requires significant energy. In the limit where the two p orbitals are twisted into a perpendicular arrangement, they no longer overlap at all and a π bond cannot be formed. This suggests that one way to determine the π-bond strength in olefins is to measure the energy for the thermal *cis-trans* isomerization, for example, in ethylene,

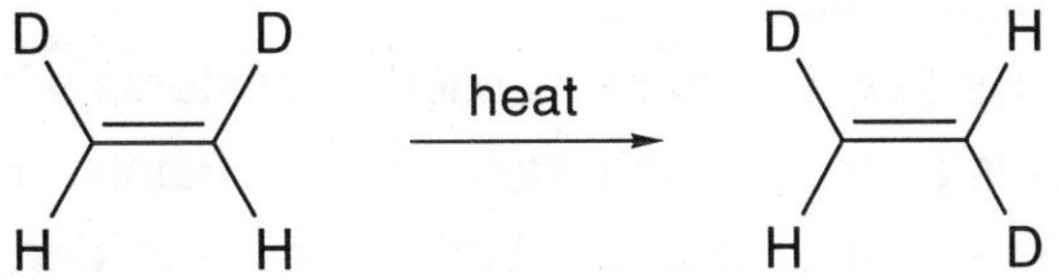

(Here the deuteriums simply act as labels, serving to indicate that isomerization has actually occurred.) Isomerization must necessarily proceed through a dimethylene biradical,[1] in which the π bond has been completely severed, and one electron is localized on each of the carbons, i.e.,

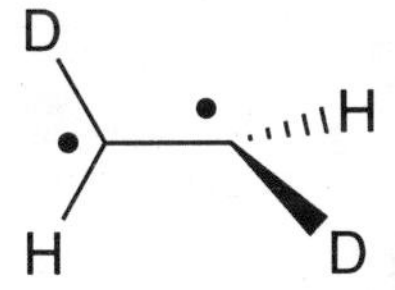

The barrier to thermal *cis-trans* isomerization in (dideutero)ethylene has been determined experimentally to be 65 kcal/mol; dismissing the small isotope effect, this corresponds to the π-bond energy in ethylene.

Note, however, that this simple measure of π-bond strength is not applicable in all cases. How, for example, would one measure the CO π-bond strength in formaldehyde or the π-bond energy in acetylene? In neither case does "rotation" lead

[1] For discussions on biradicals, see: W.T. Borden, **Diradicals**, Wiley, New York, 1982.

to bond fracture. An alternative measure, applicable in these and many other cases, proposed by Benson[2], relates π-bond strength to the difference in energies of hydrogen-atom addition to the unsaturated compound and to the resulting free radical, e.g., in ethylene,

$$E_\pi = \Delta E[H_2C{=}CH_2 + H^\bullet \rightarrow H_3C\text{-}CH_2^\bullet] - \Delta E[H_3C\text{-}CH_2^\bullet + H^\bullet \rightarrow H_3C\text{-}CH_3]$$
$$= 2E(CH_3\text{-}CH_2^\bullet) - E(H_2C{=}CH_2) - E(H_3C\text{-}CH_3) \quad (1)$$

In effect, addition of a hydrogen atom to ethylene leads to formation of a new CH bond, as well as to rupture of the π bond, while hydrogen-atom addition to the resulting ethyl free radical leads only to formation of a new CH bond. The difference in energy between the two steps thus corresponds approximately to the π-bond strength. We should be able to verify such an analysis in ethylene by direct comparison with the energetics of thermal isomerism.

The Benson analysis may also be applied to systems where experimental data may not be available or is subject to considerable uncertainty. For example, it may be used to examine the strength of multiple bonds between carbon and its group IVa analogues, i.e., silicon, germanium, tin and lead. Very few compounds of this type are stable enough to have been characterized. In fact, only for silicon have stable, isolable compounds with double bonds to carbon been prepared. Among the simplest of these are 1,1-dimethylsilaethylene and the parent silaethylene, both of which have now been detected.

$$(Me)_2Si{=}CH_2 \qquad H_2Si{=}CH_2$$

Crystal structures of more complicated systems of this type have been reported, but all in all, molecules with multiple bonds to silicon are rare. The fact that multiply-bonded (to carbon) silicon systems are not common (and the almost complete absence of molecules incorporating double bonds to heavier main-group elements), suggests that π bonds involving heavier elements may be significantly weaker than those between

---

[2] S.W. Benson, **Thermochemical Kinetics**, 2nd Ed., Wiley, New York, 1976, p. 63.

two carbons.[3] The best experimental estimate for the π bond strength in 1,1-dimethylsilaethylene is 37 kcal/mol.

The Benson analysis needs to be generalized because two different (intermediate) free radicals can be formed. This results in the following definition of π-bond strength (illustrated here for the π bond strength in silaethylene).

$$E_\pi = \Delta E[H_2Si{=}CH_2 + H^\bullet \rightarrow H_3Si\text{-}CH_2^\bullet] - \Delta E[H_2Si^\bullet\text{-}CH_3 + H^\bullet \rightarrow H_3Si\text{-}CH_3]$$
$$= E(H_2Si^\bullet\text{-}CH_3) + E(H_3Si\text{-}CH_2^\bullet) - E(H_2Si{=}CH_2) - E(H_3Si\text{-}CH_3) \quad (2)$$

It's easy to construct the appropriate reaction if you remember that hydrogen-atom addition occurs at the same position in both steps. The alternative definition of π-bond strength in this system, i.e.,

$$E_\pi = \Delta E[H_2Si{=}CH_2 + H^\bullet \rightarrow H_2Si^\bullet\text{-}CH_3] - \Delta E[H_3Si\text{-}CH_2^\bullet + H^\bullet \rightarrow H_3Si\text{-}CH_3] \quad (3)$$

leads to exactly the same result as equation 2. What principle does this illustrate?

In this experiment, we first apply the Benson analysis to determine the π-bond strength in ethylene (a known quantity), and then use the same computational methods to extend our treatment to silaethylene where experimental data is less certain. Optionally, we examine the π-bond energy in acetylene.

Procedure

Build and minimize at the 3-21G *ab initio* level ethylene, ethane and ethyl free radical (The UHF method must be employed for the ethyl free radical.) Don't worry about the conformation of ethyl radical as rotation about the CC bond occurs without significant barrier. Perform single-point correlated calculations at the MP2/6-31G* (UMP2/6-31G*) level on each of these molecules.

Correlated level calculations are required for the accurate description of the energetics of reactions such as (1) which involve different numbers of electron pairs for reactant and product.

[3] For reviews of the experimental and theoretical literature, see: W.J. Pietro and W.J. Hehre, J. Am. Chem. Soc., **104**, 4329 (1982); K.D. Dobbs and W.J. Hehre, Organometallics, **5**, 2057 (1986).

Record the total energies in the table below.

MP2/6-31G* (UMP2/6-31G*) energies (hartrees)
ethylene
ethyl radical
ethane

Evaluate the energy of equation (1) using the MP2/6-31G* energies and enter it in the table below.

MP2/6-31G* π-bond strengths (kcal/mol)
ethylene
silaethylene
acetylene

Is your result in reasonable agreement with the accepted π-bond strength in ethylene?

Build and minimize first using the AM1 semi-empirical method and then at the *ab initio* 3-21G$^{(*)}$ level, silaethylene, the intermediate silicon and carbon-centered free radicals and silaethane. Again the UHF method must be used for the free radicals.

Except for very simple molecules, it is almost always advantageous to precede geometry optimization at an *ab initio* level with optimization using a semi-empirical method. This generally provides a better starting geometry and Hessian (matrix of second derivatives) than available from molecular mechanics.

Assume that the radical centers are planar trigonal to start, and again don't worry about conformation. As with ethyl free radical, rotation in these species is essentially without barrier. After the optimizations have completed, perform single-energy calculations at the MP2/6-31G* level using the 3-21G(*) equilibrium geometries. Record your data in the table below.

MP2/6-31G* (UMP2/6-31G*) energies (hartrees)
silaethylene
methylsilyl radical
silylmethyl radical
silaethane

Evaluate the π-bond energy for silaethylene using (2) and MP2/6-31G* data. Enter it in the table next to the value for ethylene. How does this value compare with that earlier calculated for ethylene? Rationalize the difference in magnitudes. How does it compare with the experimental value of 37 kcal/mol in 1,1-dimethylsilaethylene?

To learn more about the properties and reactivity of silaethylene, display its highest-occupied molecular orbital. This corresponds to the silicon-carbon π bond. Is it more heavily localized on carbon or on silicon? What does this tell you about the likely site of electrophilic attack on silaethylene? You might consider displaying the corresponding molecular orbital in ethylene as a standard. Also, construct and display the total electron density surface for silaethylene onto which the electrostatic potential has been superimposed. This indicates the distribution of charge in this system. Is the information provided consistent with that from the orbital display? What does it tell you about the reactivity of silaethylene? Relative to ethylene, would you expect this system
to be more or less susceptible to attack by electrophiles? By nucleophiles? For each, what is the likely position of attack (carbon or silicon)? [**3**]

Optional

It is more difficult to remove an electron from the π bond in acetylene than it is from the π bond in ethylene.

$$HC{\equiv}CH \rightarrow HC{\equiv}CH^{+\bullet} + e^- \qquad \Delta E = 263 \text{ kcal/mol}$$

$$H_2C{=}CH_2 \rightarrow H_2C{=}CH_2^{+\bullet} + e^- \qquad \Delta E = 242 \text{ kcal/mol}$$

This has significant chemical consequences. For example, electrophilic additions involving alkynes are generally less facile than the corresponding processes with alkenes.

Apply the Benson analysis to the calculation of the π-bond strength in acetylene and compare it with that for ethylene.[4] The π-bond strength is related to the difference in energies of hydrogen atom addition to acetylene and to the vinyl free radical which results, i.e.,

$$E_{\pi} = \Delta E[HC{\equiv}CH + H^{\bullet} \rightarrow H_2C{=}\dot{C}H] - \Delta E[H_2C{=}\dot{C}H + H^{\bullet} \rightarrow H_2C{=}CH_2]$$

$$\doteq 2E(H_2C{=}\dot{C}H) - E(HC{\equiv}CH) - E(H_2C{=}CH_2) \qquad (4)$$

You already have the needed data for ethylene and only require 3-21G structures and MP2/6-31G* energies for acetylene and for vinyl radical. When you have collected the data, record it in the table below.

MP2/6-31G* (UMP2/6-31G*) energies (hartrees)	
acetylene	
vinyl radical	
ethylene	

Work out the energy for (4) using MP2/6-31G* data and enter it into the table containing the π-bond strength for ethylene. How does it compare with your previous result for ethylene?

[4] For recent theoretical work, see: A. Nicolaides and W.T. Borden, J. Am. Chem. Soc., **113**, 6750 (1991).

Experiment 6: Substituent and Solvent Effects on Tautomeric Equilibria

We use AM1 and AM1-SM2 semi-empirical calculations to investigate the tautomeric equilibria involving nitrogen heterocycles, and examine the role of substituents and the choice of solvent on the relative stabilities of tautomers.

Many molecules, especially heterocyclic systems, exist as equilibrium mixtures of tautomers.[1] The possibility of aromatic stabilization, substituents and solvent, among other factors, can influence which tautomer is favored thermodynamically. In this experiment, we use AM1 semi-empirical calculations to investigate tautomeric equilibria involving two different sets of nitrogen heterocycles, derivatives of pyrrole, **1a**, and its azadiene tautomers, **1b** and **1c**,[2] and 2-hydroxypyridine, **2a**, and its tautomer, pyridone, **2b**.[3]

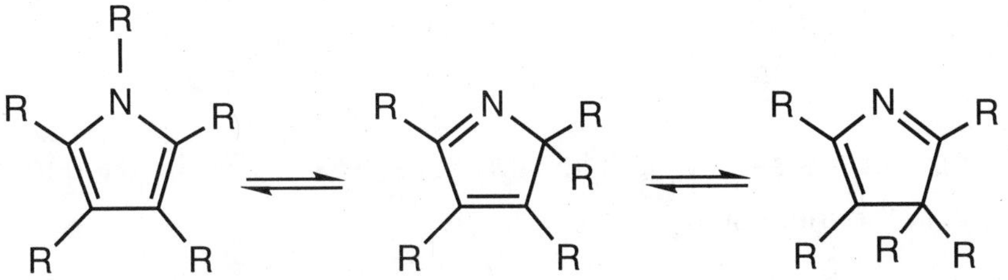

R=H, Cl

1a **1b** **1c**

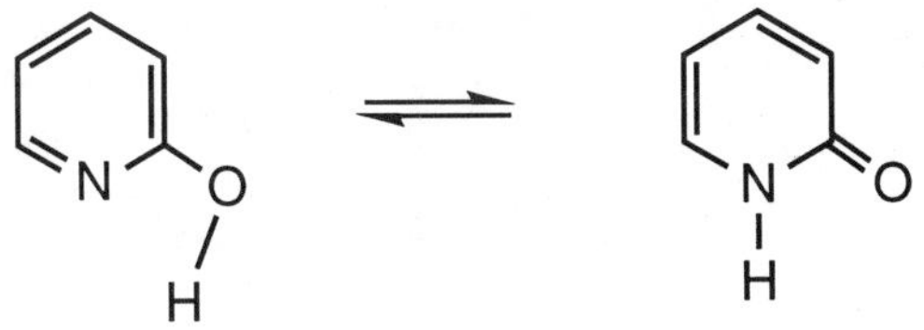

2a **2b**

The tautomeric equilibrium in the pyrrole system depends on the substituent, R=H, Cl. Since pyrrole is aromatic and the azadienes are not, it comes as no surprise

[1] March, p. 66.
[2] R.H. Daniels, J.L. Wong, J.L. Atwood, L.G. Canada and R.D. Rogers, J. Org. Chem., **45**, 435 (1980).
[3] N.S. Isaacs, **Physical Organic Chemistry**, Wiley, New York, 1987, p. 182; M.W. Wong, K.B. Wiberg and M.J. Frisch, J. Am. Chem. Soc., **114**, 1645 (1992).

that pyrrole is favored thermodynamically. However, even an experienced organic chemist might have trouble predicting the favored tautomer of the perchloro derivative.

The tautomeric equilibrium for 2-hydroxypyridine/2-pyridone depends on the medium. 2-Hydroxypyridine is slightly more stable in the gas phase ($\Delta E < 0.5$ kcal/mol). We expect this compound to be stable because it is aromatic and because it might contain a (weak) intramolecular hydrogen bond. 2-Pyridone is nearly as stable, however; note that this ring system also has some aromatic character.

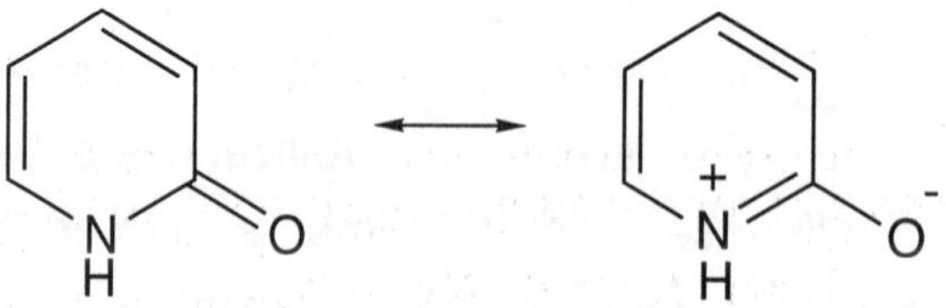

2-Pyridone is the favored form in polar solvents such as acetonitrile. This observation could be rationalized if it turned out that 2-pyridone were more polar than 2-hydroxypyridine, a prediction that is easily tested using calculations.

Procedure

Build and optimize at the semi-empirical AM1 level **1a-1c** (R=H). Record the AM1 heats of formation in the table below.

AM1 heats of formation and relative energies (kcal/mol)		
	ΔH_f°	rel. energy
1a (R=H)		
1b (R=H)		
1c (R=H)		
1a (R=Cl)		
1b (R=Cl)		
1c (R=Cl)		

Identify the most stable tautomer and calculate and record relative energies of the remaining tautomers. Do the calculations show pyrrole, **1a**, to be the most stable tautomer in accord with what is known experimentally? Can you rationalize your results?

Build and optimize at the AM1 level the corresponding structures for the perchloro system (R=Cl) and record your data in the table above. Do the calculations reproduce the observed shift in equilibrium toward the azadiene tautomers as suggested by experiment? What would you speculate is the reason that perchloropyrrole is less stable relative to its azadiene tautomers than is the parent compound?

Build and optimize at the AM1 level 2-hydroxypyridine, **2a**, and pyridone, **2b**. Also calculate the electric dipole moment for each tautomer. Record your data in the table below.

AM1 and AM1-SM2 heats of formation and relative energies (kcal/mol) and AM1 dipole moments (debye)					
	AM1			AM1-SM2	
	ΔH_f°	rel. energy	μ	ΔH_f°	rel. energy
2a					
2b					

Identify the more stable tautomer and calculate the energy of the higher-energy tautomer relative to this one. Do the calculations reproduce the fact that 2-hydroxypyridine and pyridine are very close in energy? Which of the two is indicated to be the more stable? Can you rationalize your result? Hint: which of the two has the larger electric dipole moment?

Perform single-point calculations on 2-hydroxypyridine and on pyridone using the AM1-SM2 solvation model developed by Cramer and Truhlar[4]. Record your data in the table above. What is the effect of the solvent on the relative stabilities of the two tautomers? Are your results in line with the experimental evidence?

Optional

The hydroxy group in 2-hydroxypyridine can adopt an alternative conformation in which the OH bond is *trans* rather than *cis* to nitrogen. AM1 calculations suggest that this is significantly higher in energy, to an extent which cannot be justified solely on the loss of a "poor" hydrogen bond. Offer an explanation for the large energy difference between the two conformers.

---

[4] C.J. Cramer and D.G. Truhlar, Science, **256**, 213 (1992).

5. Build and optimize at the AM1 level [illegible] for the [illegible] system [illegible] (C=O) and record your data in the table above. Do the calculations reproduce the observed shift in equilibrium toward the [illegible] suggested by experiment? What would you speculate is the [illegible] is less stable relative to [illegible] compound?

[illegible] and optimize at the AM1 level 2 [illegible]. Also calculate the [illegible] dipole moment for each [illegible] in the table below.

AM1 and AM1 [illegible] heats of formation and relative energies [illegible] dipole moments (debye)		
	AM1	
	[illegible]	
2 a		
2 b		

[illegible] the more stable [illegible] relative [illegible] the [illegible] why [illegible] electric dipole moment.)

[illegible]

Questions

Experiment 7: Glycine in the Gas Phase and In Water

We use both 3-21+G *ab initio* calculations and the semi-empirical AM1-SM2 solvation model to examine the role of solvent in altering the relative stabilities of "neutral" and "zwitterionic" forms of glycine in the gas phase. We also compare charges in zwitterionic glycine to those of separated ions containing the same basic and acidic groups to ascertain the extent to which charge is actually localized.

What is the structure of the simplest amino acid, glycine? Is it a molecule with no formal charge separation, **1**, or is it a zwitterion, **2**, obtained from **1** by deprotonation at oxygen followed by protonation at nitrogen?

$H_2NCH_2CO_2H$ — **1**

$H_3\overset{+}{N}CH_2CO_2^-$ — **2**

The answer is "it is both". While in the gas phase, structure **1** is favored, strong interactions between the solvent and the charged groups in **2**, lead to a reversal in water. Here, we employ *ab initio* calculations to obtain an estimate of the energy difference between **1** and **2** in the gas phase, and then apply the semi-empirical AM1-SM2 solvation model to estimate this same difference in water. We also compare both the geometry and charge distribution in **2** to those in isolated ions with similar structure. The question of interest will be to what extent zwitterionic forms such as **2** incorporate fully-developed charge centers.

Procedure

Build **1** and **2**, and optimize at the AM1 level.

Even molecules as simple as glycine have more than one available conformer. While it is unlikely that you will choose the lowest energy form, this is not so important in this experiment where we wish only to demonstrate the large difference in solvation energies between neutral and zwitterionic structures.

Enter the heats of formation for both structures and the difference in energy between neutral and zwitterionic forms of glycine in the table below.

AM1 and AM1-SM2 heats of formation (kcal/mol), solvation energies (kcal/mol) and gas and "aqueous" 3-21+G energies (hartrees)				
	heat of formation		solvation energy	3-21+G energy	
	AM1	AM1-SM2		gas	"aqueous"
1					
2					
ΔE					

Be certain to identify which form is the more stable.

Make two copies of the final structures for each. Use one copy to perform single-point energy calculations using the 3-21+G *ab initio* model.

> Basis sets such as 3-21+G incorporating diffuse "+" functions are required for accurate descriptions of the energetics of anionic systems, and presumably zwitterions as well. They are generally not as important for descriptions of equilibrium geometry.

[1] Make certain that you specify use of direct methods. Enter the total energies in the table. Calculate the difference in energy between the two and also enter this in the table. Which structure, **1** or **2**, do the *ab initio* calculations assign for glycine in the gas phase? Is the energy difference you calculate larger or smaller than you might expect based simply on the difference between the enthalpy of deprotonation of acetic acid,

$$CH_3CO_2H \rightarrow CH_3COO^- + H^+ \quad \Delta H_{expt} = 345 \text{ kcal/mol}$$

and the enthalpy of protonation of methylamine?

$$CH_3NH_2 + H^+ \rightarrow CH_3NH_3^+ \quad \Delta H_{expt} = -214 \text{ kcal/mol}$$

Explain.

Use the second set of copies to perform single-point energy calculations using the AM1-SM2 solvation model[1]. Enter the heats of formation into the table, and compute solvation energies (difference between AM1-SM2 and AM1 heats of formation). Add these to the gas phase 3-21+G energies. Watch out for units; the AM1 heats of formation are in kcal/mol, and the 3-21+G total energies are in hartrees (1 hartree=627.5 kcal/mol).

[1] C.J. Cramer and D.G. Truhlar, Science, **256**, 213 (1992).

We use the semi-empirical calculations only to calculate the difference in solvation energies between neutral and zwitterionic forms of glycine, and then add this to the difference in gas-phase energies obtained from *ab initio* methods. This bypasses any problems that the semi-empirical methods might have in dealing with the description of relative thermochemical stabilities (of isomers), and illustrates an important general strategy for practical calculations.

Calculate the difference in energy between the two glycine structures and enter this value in the table. According to your calculations, which structure for glycine is preferred in water?

To learn more about the zwitterionic form of glycine, compare its geometry and charge distribution to those in isolated ions containing $-NH_3^+$ and $-CO_2^-$ functionalities, respectively. Build methylammonium cation, **3**, and acetate anion, **4**,

$H_3\overset{+}{N}\text{-}CH_3$ $CH_3CO_2^-$

3   **4**

and optimize at the AM1 level. How do the calculated geometries compare with that for the zwitterionic form of glycine? Pay particular attention to the NH bond lengths and the CO bond lengths. Setup **3** and **4** for single-point energy calculations at the 3-21+G level. Also request charges based on fits to electrostatic potentials for **3** and **4** as well as for the zwitterionic form of glycine, **2** [for a discussion of different charge analysis methods, see **Experiment 22**]. Convert these atomic charges into "functional group" charges by adding together the three charges for CO_2 group and the four charges for the NH_3 group. Compare the "functional group" charges in **3** and **4** to the analogous charged groups in "zwitterionic" glycine, **2**. Is the conventional representation of **2** as fully charge separated supported by your results?

Optional

Repeat your calculations on neutral and zwitterionic forms of glycine following a full conformational search on it using the semi-empirical AM1 model. Have your basic conclusions regarding the structure of glycine in the gas phase and in water changed?

Experiment 8: Site of Protonation in Amides

We use semi-empirical AM1 and *ab initio* 3-21G calculations to assign the site of protonation in formamide, acetamide and N,N-dimethylformamide in the gas phase. We assess the effect of substituents in altering the site of protonation. We illustrate a general strategy for obtaining accurate energy differences of isomers from low-level *ab initio* calculations.

Many reactions involving the amide functionality are assumed to initiate via protonation. Thus, it is important to be able to identify the favored site of protonation in simple amides. In this experiment, we look first at the simplest amide, formamide, and consider the difference in calculated energies between N-protonated and O-protonated forms, i.e.,

$H_3\overset{+}{N}-C(=O)H$ N-protonated

$H_2N-C^{+}(OH)H$ O-protonated

as a measure of which is the more stable. We will then use experimental proton affinities for two closely related molecules to calculate absolute "nitrogen" and "oxygen" proton affinities of formamide. The difference in these proton affinities will provide a more reliable estimate of the difference between N- and O-protonation. Finally, we'll examine the effects of substituents in altering the favored site of protonation.

Procedure

Build N-protonated and O-protonated formamide. First optimize at the AM1 level and then perform single-point calculations using the 3-21G *ab initio* method. Enter both AM1 heats of formation and 3-21G energies in the table below.

AM1 heats of formation (kcal/mol) and 3-21G energies (hartrees)		
	AM1	3-21G
N-protonated formamide		
O-protonated formamide		
ammonia		
ammonium ion		
formaldehyde		
protonated formaldehyde		
formamide		
N-protonated N,N-dimethylformamide		
O-protonated N,N-dimethylformamide		
N-protonated acetamide		
O-protonated acetamide		

Which site, N or O, do the 3-21G calculations suggest as the preferred position of protonation? Is the calculated energy difference small enough that both protonated forms are likely to be observed?

Direct energy comparisons between molecules as different as N- and O-protonated formamide are not reliable unless high levels of (*ab initio*) theory are employed [see **Appendix B**]. Semi-empirical and low-level *ab initio* calculations (including 3-21G) are not suitable (not reliable) for this purpose. One way to obtain the same information reliably even from low-level calculations is to compare the proton affinity of N-protonated formamide with that of a closely related (nitrogen) base for which the proton affinity is experimentally known, and the proton affinity of O-protonated formamide with that of a closely related (oxygen) base (leading to an oxygen substituted carbocation) for which the proton affiinty is known. Let's do this using ammonia (experimental gas phase proton affinity = 207 kcal/mol) and formaldehyde (experimental gas phase proton affinity =183 kcal/mol) as "standards".

Build and optimize at the AM1 level all the molecules in the two comparison reactions below:

$$H_3\overset{+}{N}\text{-}CHO + NH_3 \rightarrow H_2N\text{-}CHO + \overset{+}{N}H_4 \qquad (1)$$

$$H_2N\text{-}\overset{+}{C}HOH + H_2CO \rightarrow H_2N\text{-}CHO + H_2\overset{+}{C}OH \qquad (2)$$

Perform single-point 3-21G calculations using the optimum AM1 geometries and enter the data in the table above. Evaluate the energies of (1) and (2), and given absolute proton affinities for ammonia and formaldehyde (above), compute the absolute N- and O-proton affinities for formamide. Enter these in the table below.

AM1 and 3-21G proton affinities and differences in N- and O-proton affinities (kcal/mol)			
		AM1	3-21G
formamide	N		
	O		
	ΔE(O-N)		
N,N-dimethylformamide	ΔE(O-N)		
acetamide	ΔE(O-N)		

Identify the favored form and compute the energy of the alternative relative to this form. Is this the same as you identified earlier? Has the predicted energy separation between the two forms altered appreciably?

This same strategy, using calculations to provide differences in proton affinities between closely-related systems rather than differences involving dissimilar molecules, may also be applied to the calculation of substituent effects. Obtain equilibrium geometries at the AM1 level for both N- and O-protonated structures for both N,N-dimethylformamide and for acetamide, and then perform single-point calculations at the 3-21G level on each. You will probably need to use direct methods. **[1]** Enter the AM1 heats of formation and 3-21G total energies into the first table (above) and then evaluate energies of reactions,

$$\mathrm{Me_2\overset{+}{N}H\text{-}CHO + H_2\overset{+}{N}\text{-}CHOH \rightarrow Me_2N\text{-}CHO\overset{+}{H} + H_3\overset{+}{N}\text{-}CHO} \qquad (3)$$

$$\mathrm{H_3\overset{+}{N}\text{-}C(Me)O + H_2\overset{+}{N}\text{-}CHOH \rightarrow H_2\overset{+}{N}\text{-}C(Me)OH + H_3\overset{+}{N}\text{-}CHO} \qquad (4)$$

Combine these reaction energies with the respective (AM1 or 3-21G) differences in N- and O-proton affinities for formamide obtained earlier to provide values for the differences in N- and O-proton affinities in N,N-dimethylformamide and in acetamide. Record these differences in the table. What do you conclude is the favored site of protonation in the gas phase in each of these systems? Rationalize your observations in view of what you already know about the ability of methyl to stabilize nitrogen bases and carbocations [see also **Experiment 37**].

Experiment 9: Atomic Hybridization and Bond Lengths

We use semi-empirical AM1 calculations to investigate the relationship between formal atomic hybridization and CH and CC bond lengths in hydrocarbons.

Acetylene is a linear molecule. The 1*s* atomic orbital on hydrogen overlaps with both 2*s* and $2p_Z$ atomic orbitals on the adjacent carbon (assuming the interatomic axis is the Z axis). We usually think of these two orbitals as forming an *atomic hybrid*, and the relative *s* and *p* contributions to the hybrid in terms of percentages. There is also a carbon hybrid orbital directed toward the other carbon; the s- and p-contributions of this hybrid will be exactly the reverse proportions found in the hybrid involved in the CH bond. The overall bonding picture for acetylene is very simple. The 2*s* atomic orbital on carbon hybridizes with only one of the three 2*p* atomic orbitals leading to a pair of "sp hybrids" pointing directly away from each other. The remaining 2*p* atomic orbitals on carbon are unhybridized and go on to form acetylene's two π bonds.

The situation in ethylene and ethane is subject to the same kind of analysis. In ethylene, the 1*s* atomic orbital on each hydrogen overlaps with the 2*s* on carbon, and also with both $2p_X$ and $2p_Y$ orbitals (assuming the molecule lies in the XY plane). Hybrids forming the four equivalent carbon-hydrogen bonds and one carbon-carbon bond in ethylene are therefore composed of the carbon 2*s*, $2p_X$, and $2p_Y$ atomic orbitals, and are termed "sp^2 hybrids". (The $2p_Z$ orbital remains unhybridized, and is used to form the π bond.) Again, we describe each hybrid's composition in terms of relative *s* and *p* percentages. In ethane, the 1*s* atomic orbital on each hydrogen can overlap with the 2*s* atomic orbital on carbon as well as all three 2*p* atomic orbitals. The resulting "sp^3 hybrids" give rise to six equivalent CH bonds.

Different sp^n hybrids lead to subtle but detectable structural changes.[1] For example, because *p*-type atomic orbitals are higher in energy and more diffuse than *s*-type atomic orbitals of the same principal quantum number, it is expected that the CH bonds in ethane (made from sp^3 hybrids) will be longer than those in ethylene (made from sp^2 hybrids), which in turn will be longer than the CH bonds in acetylene (made from sp hybrids). This is indeed observed. As seen by the experimental bond length data tabulated below, the anticipated trend applies to carbon bonded to other elements as well as to simple chemical groups.

---

[1] Carey and Sundberg A, p. 3; March, p. 18; J.E. Huheey, **Inorganic Chemistry**, Harper and Row, 1983, p. 239.

Experimental CX bond lengths involving sp^3, sp^2 and sp hybridized carbons (Å)			
X	H_3C-CH_2-X	$H_2C{=}CH-X$	$HC{\equiv}C-X$
H	1.102	1.085	1.061
CH_3	1.526	1.501	1.459
F	1.398	1.347	1.279
Cl	1.788	1.726	1.637

In this experiment, we first examine the extent to which calculated hybridizations approach ideal values (sp^3, sp^2, and sp for ethane, ethylene and acetylene, respectively). Then we will try to establish a correlation between atomic hybridization at carbon and CC bond lengths in a number of simple hydrocarbons. We explore and interpret deviations from correlations.

Procedure

Build and optimize at the semi-empirical AM1 level, ethane, ethylene and [**5**] acetylene. Request generation and printing of orbital hybrids.[2] As the jobs complete, record the calculated equilibrium CH bond lengths in the table below, along with calculated hybridizations at carbon.

AM1 CH bond lengths (Å) and hybridizations		
	r_{CH}	n in sp^n
ethane		
ethylene		
acetylene		
methylene		
cyclopropane		
cyclobutane		

Are the calculated AM1 bond lengths in accord with the experimental structural data (see table above)? Plot hybridization at carbon (n in sp^n) vs. CH bond distance.

[2] Use the Natural Bond Orbital procedure for hybrid orbital analysis: A.E. Reed, R.B. Weinstock and F. Weinhold, J. Chem. Phys., **83**, 735 (1985).

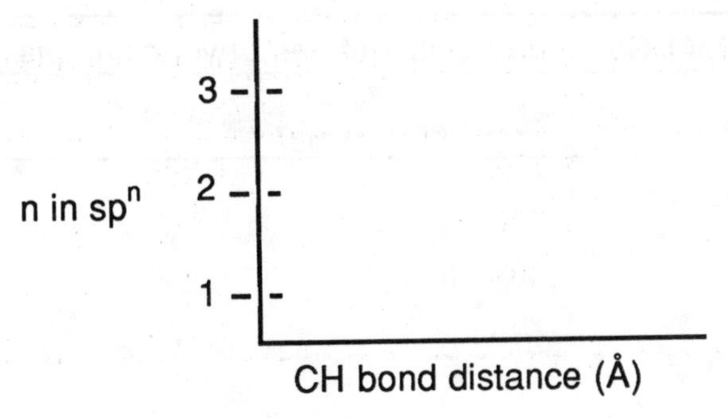

Do you observe a straight-line correlation?

Perform AM1 structure optimizations on singlet methylene (CH_2), cyclopropane and cyclobutane. Record the data (bond lengths and atomic hybridizations) in the table above. Explain why it is that carbon hybrids used in the construction of CH bonds in the small-ring compounds differ substantially from idealized sp^3 values. Do these data (CH bond lengths and hybridizations at carbon) fit on the previously established correlation line? If not, why not?

Build and minimize using the semi-empirical AM1 model hydrocarbons **1-10** below

$HC{\equiv}C{-}C{\equiv}CH$ (**1**) $HC{\equiv}C{-}CH{=}CH_2$ (**2**) $HC{\equiv}C{-}CH_2CH_3$ (**3**)

$H_2C{=}CH{-}CH{=}CH_2$ (**4**) $H_2C{=}CH{-}CH_2CH_3$ (**5**) $CH_3CH_2{-}CH_2CH_3$ (**6**)

7: three-membered ring CH_2 / H_2C—CH_2

8: four-membered ring H_2C—CH_2 / H_2C—CH_2

9: three-membered ring CH_2 / $HC{=}CH$

10: four-membered ring H_2C—CH_2 / $HC{=}CH$

Make sure all single bonds in acyclic systems are staggered, and where appropriate assume *trans* arrangements of CC bonds. Calculate atomic hybridizations and record both these and the CC bond distances indicated by thick lines in the table below.

AM1 CC bond lengths (Å) and hybridizations		
	CC single bond length	m, n in sp^m, sp^n
butadiyne		
but-1-yne-3-ene		
1-butyne		
1,3-butadiene		
1-butene		
n-butane		
cyclopropane		
cyclobutane		
cyclopropene		
cyclobutene (C_3C_4)		
(C_2C_3)		

Plot calculated CC single bond lengths in these systems versus the sum of the atomic hybridizations for the two carbon atoms involved.

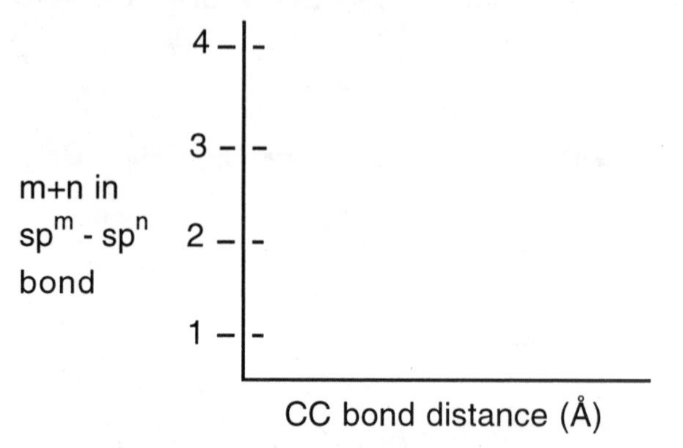

Which, if any, of the molecules do not closely fit on the correlation line? For each of any molecules which do not fit, is it the calculated hybridization or the calculated CC bond length which seems out of place? Rationalize your choice and provide an explanation.

Optional

Metal-ligand bonding molecular orbitals in organometallic compounds are made up primarily of (n)d- and (n+1) *s*-type functions, where *n* is the principal quantum number. We will assume that valence (n+1) *p*-type functions do not play a significant role in bonding. The *d* functions are less diffuse than the higher-energy *s* or *p* type orbitals, and hybridization changes which lead to reduced *d* character should also result in an increase in metal-ligand σ-bond lengths, assuming that contributions due to valence *p*-type functions are small. Discounting *p* orbital contributions entirely, changing from a tetrahedral, four-coordinate, to a planar-trigonal, three-coordinate, to a linear, two-coordinate geometry about a transition metal center, effects a (formal) change in hybridization from sd^3 to sd^2 to *sd*. This should lead to increased metal-ligand separation, the opposite trend as noted in analogous main-group compounds, that is, bonds to tetracoordinate transition metal centers should be shorter than bonds to tricoordinate centers which in turn should be shorter than bonds to dicoordinate centers. Stated another way, whereas the same "rules" apply, because the valence hybrids involve *d* type atomic orbitals instead of *p* orbitals, the result is different.[3] A single example should be sufficient to test this simple hypothesis.

Build and minimize at the STO-3G *ab initio* level, titanaethane ($H_3Ti\text{-}CH_3$), titanaethylene ($H_2Ti{=}CH_2$) and titanaethyne ($HTi{\equiv}CH$).

What we seek here is qualitative evidence for bonding changes with changes in formal hybridization. STO-3G should be as successful as 3-21G for this purpose.

Assume that H_3TiCH_3 looks like ethane, $H_2Ti{=}CH_2$ looks like ethylene and $HTi{\equiv}CH$ looks like acetylene. Be certain to specify calculation and printing of atomic hybridizations.

Record TiH bond lengths and hybridizations at titanium in the table below.

STO-3G TiH bond lengths (Å) and hybridization at titanium		
	r_{TiH}	n in sd^n
titanaethane		
titanaethylene		
titanaethyne		

Are the calculated hybrids at titanium in accord with the qualitative model? Do you see any significant contributions for valence p type (4p) orbitals? Do the calculations

[3] K.D. Dobbs and W.J. Hehre, J. Am. Chem. Soc., **108**, 4663 (1986).

show the expected lengthening of the TiH bond distance in going from the tetracoordinate, to the tricoordinate, to the dicoordinate titanium compounds?

Experiment 10: Molecular Recognition. Hydrogen-Bonded Base Pairs

We use electrostatic potentials obtained from PM3 semi-empirical calculations to anticipate the geometries of hydrogen-bonded complexes. We then use the PM3 method to evaluate binding energies of selected complexes and to relate these to experimental association constants.

Hydrogen bonding is one means by which biological molecules associate. Not only are hydrogen bonds responsible for the double-stranded structure of DNA, they also greatly influence the detailed three-dimensional geometries of proteins. In addition, artificial receptors which have been designed to mimic biological systems often employ hydrogen bonding to "recognize" and then selectively "capture" small molecules. Molecular recognition is a new and rapidly-developing branch of chemistry directed toward exploring the structures of intermolecular complexes, hydrogen-bonded complexes among them.

In this experiment, we examine a number of hydrogen-bonded complexes involving heterocyclic bases. We will start by obtaining structures for heterocyclic bases using the PM3 semi-empirical model, and then examine electrostatic potentials for these bases to identify regions that can act as hydrogen-bond donors and hydrogen-bond acceptors. This allows us to anticipate the geometries of hydrogen-bonded complexes.

We choose PM3 over AM1 in this experiment because it has been shown to be the more reliable of the two in dealing with hydrogen-bonded systems.

We will then examine the geometries and binding strengths in a variety of hydrogen-bonded complexes involving these or closely-related acceptors and donors which are known experimentally. We'll not only see to what extent our qualitative rationale, based on the donor/acceptor properties of the individual components, is valid but also assess the ability of the semi-empirical calculations to quantitatively evaluate trends in binding energies.

Procedure

Build and minimize at the PM3 semi-empirical level, each of the heterocyclic bases below.

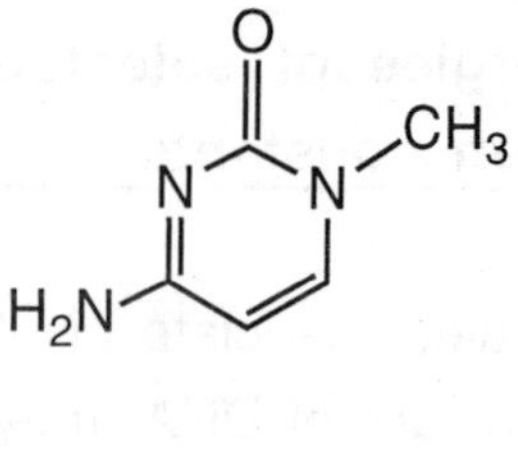

1-methylcytosine 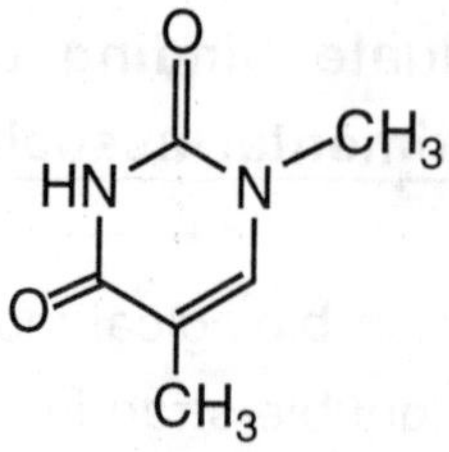 1-methylthymine 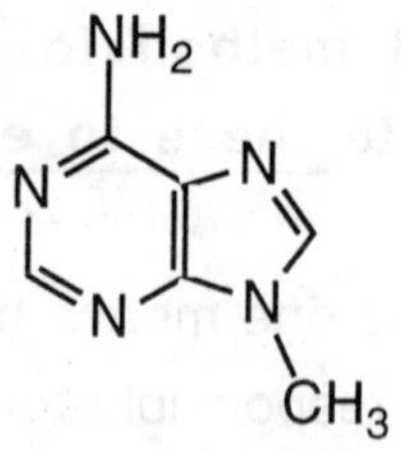 9-methyladenine 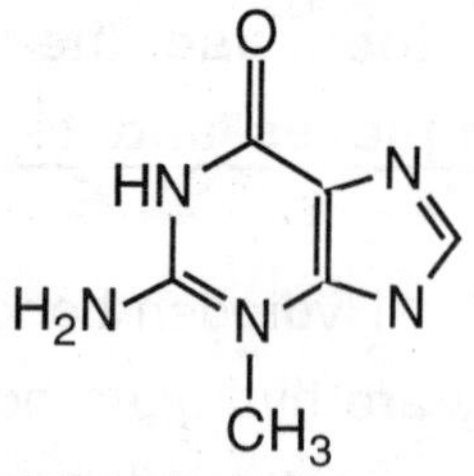 9-methylguanine

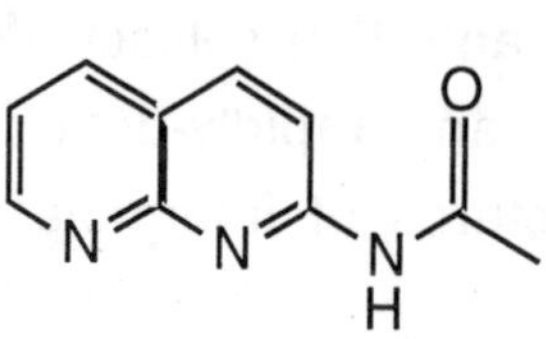

N-naphthridinylacetamide 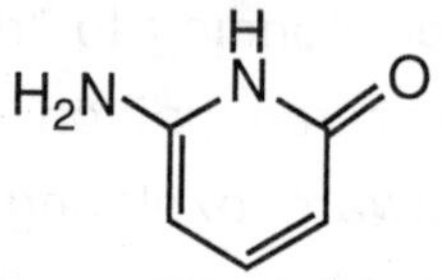 6-amino-2-pyridone

For each, request generation of the electrostatic potential encoded onto the total electron density surface. Record the heats of formation in the table below.

	PM3 heats of formation (kcal/mol)
1-methylcytosine	
1-methylthymine	
9-methyladenine	
9-methylguanine	
N-naphthridinylacetamide	
6-amino-2-pyridone	

[3] Display the electrostatic maps and identify regions (in the σ system) which are strongly positively charged, and those which are strongly negatively charged. Identify which of these correspond to hydrogen-bond donors and to hydrogen-bond receptors. Based on this analysis, suggest likely hydrogen-bonding arrangements, and put possible hydrogen bonded pairs on the screen at the same time. By aligning

complementary regions you should be able to anticipate the geometries of hydrogen-bonded complexes involving these bases.

PM3 level structures for complexes **1-6**,

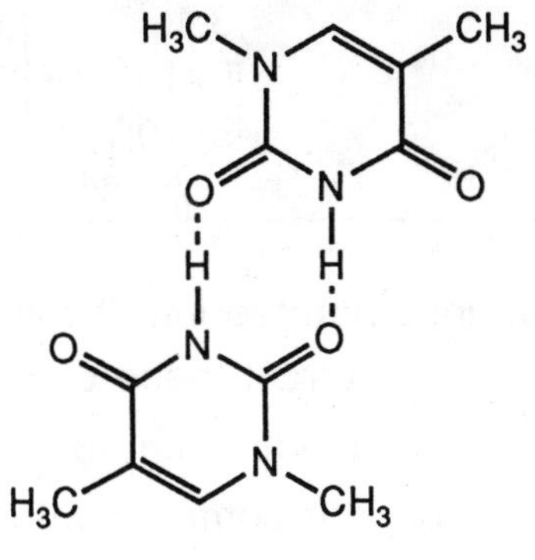

1 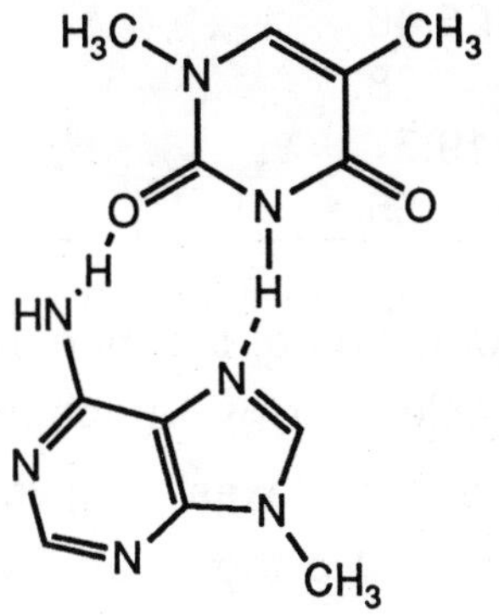 **2** 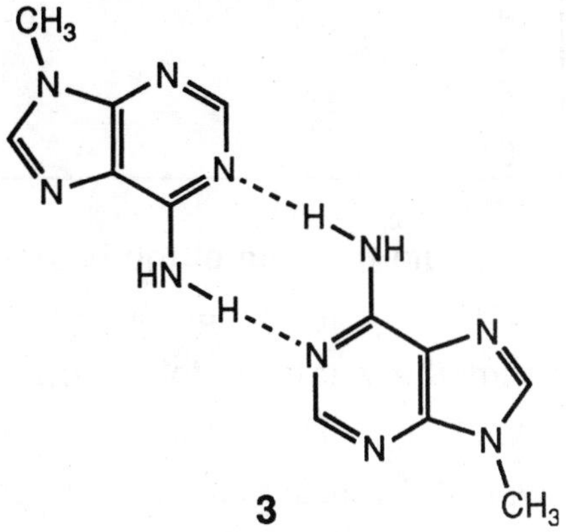 **3**

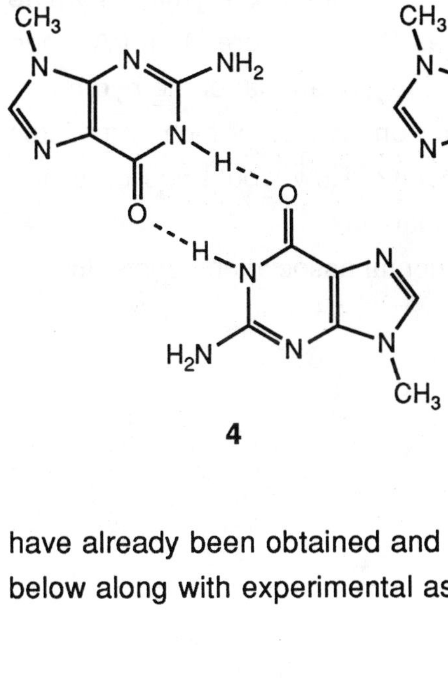

4 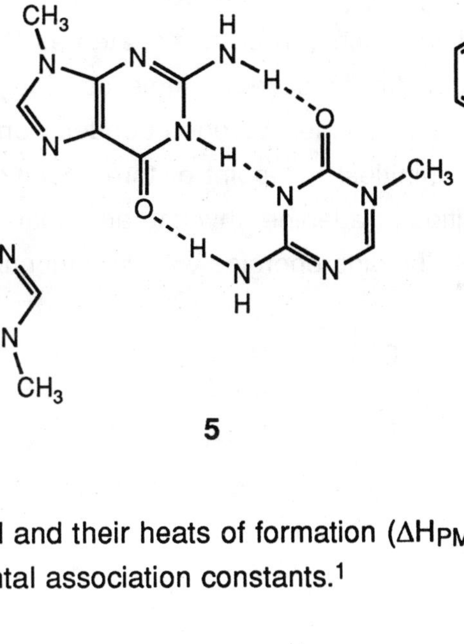 **5** 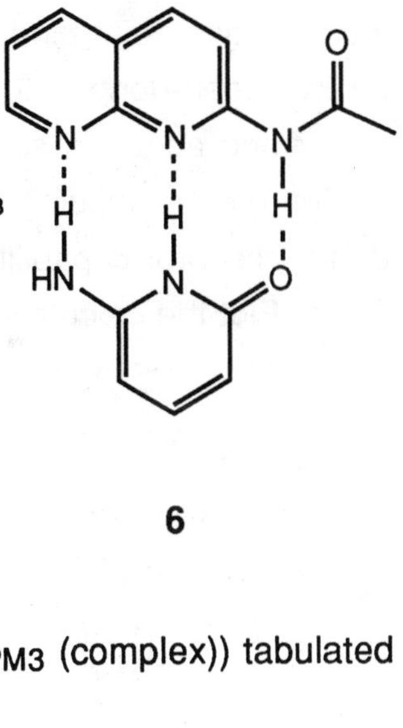 **6**

have already been obtained and their heats of formation (ΔH_{PM3} (complex)) tabulated below along with experimental association constants.[1]

[1] J. Pranata, S.G. Wierschke and W.L. Jorgensen, J. Am. Chem. Soc., **113**, 2810 (1991); T.J. Murry and S.C. Zimmerman, *ibid.*, **114**, 4010 (1992).

PM3 complex energies (kcal/mol) and experimental association constants				
	$\Sigma\Delta H_{PM3}$ (monomers)	ΔH_{PM3} (complex)	$\Delta\Delta H_{PM3}$	$K_{association}$
1		-157.81		3.2
2		-28.81		1.3×10^2
3		105.46		3.1
4		1.88		5×10^3
5		-19.77		5×10^4
6		-18.55		1.7×10^4

Compute the sum of the heats of formation of the monomers incorporated into these complexes and enter these in the table ($\Sigma\Delta H_{PM3}$ (monomers)). Subtract these data from the heats of formation of the complexes to give you the binding energies ($\Delta\Delta H_{PM3}$). Record these in the table. Do the values which you find compare with typical hydrogen-bond energies?

The number of hydrogen bonds holding a complex together is referred to as the number of point bindings, e.g., the hydrogen-bonded complex thymine:thymine involves two-point binding which can be designated as DA:AD where D and A stand for hydrogen-donor and hydrogen-acceptor moieties. Identify and label the hydrogen-donor and acceptor sites in all the hydrogen-bonded complexes. Which complexes exhibit greater binding affinities; two-point or three-point? How would you order the donor-acceptor capabilities of adenine, thymine and guanine?

Plot the calculated binding energies vs. experimental association constants.

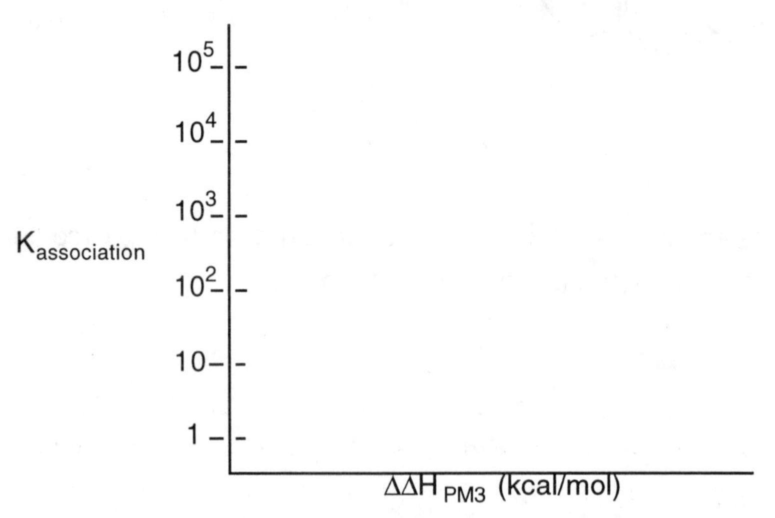

Are the calculations qualitatively successful in reproducing the range of binding energies?

Chapter 2. Conformation

Computational methods may be applied not only to rigid molecules, but also to flexible molecules capable of adopting a variety of different spacial arrangements.

Flexible Molecules

Molecules containing CC single bonds are unusually mobile. The groups attached to one carbon can rotate relatively freely about the CC bond axis without disrupting the CC bond. As a result, the molecule is able to experience a range of structures or *conformations* each which may have very unique chemical, physical, and biological properties.

For example, the *meso* isomer of stilbene dibromide, **1**, rapidly interconverts between three different staggered conformations. Treatment of **1** with potassium ethoxide causes loss of HBr and exclusive formation of *cis*-bromostilbene, **2**[1]. The selectivity of this reaction is best explained by proposing that loss of HBr only occurs when both atoms occupy an *anti* relationship, i.e., the H-C-C-Br dihedral angle = 180°, as in **1a** or **1b**.

Br
Ph H
Ph Br
H
1a

Ph
H Br
Ph Br
H
1b

H
Br Ph
Ph Br
H
1c

EtO^-K^+ EtO^-K^+

Ph Ph
C=C
Br H
2

The same type of reasoning explains why the *dl* isomer of stilbene dibromide, **3**, yields exclusively *trans*-bromostilbene, **4**. In this case, only one conformation, **3a**, possesses the necessary *anti* relationships between H and Br.

---

[1] P. Pfeiffer, Z. Phys. Chem. (Leipzig), **48**, 40 (1904).

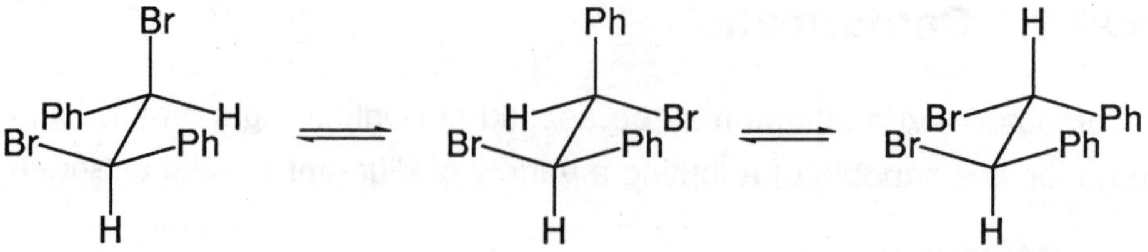

3a ⇌ 3b ⇌ 3c

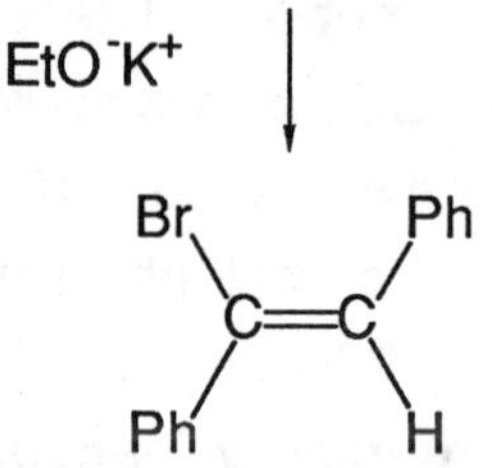

EtO^-K^+

4

The effect of conformation on physical properties is readily observed, particularly in cases where steric demands prevents rapid interconversion of *conformers*.

The terms "conformation" and "conformer" are often used interchangeably. However, to avoid (or perhaps promote) confusion we shall refer to the actual molecule as a "conformer" and to its structure as its "conformation".

For example, binaphthol, **5**, exists in one of two conformations differing only in the relative orientation of the naphthalene rings. Rotation about the C-C bond connecting the two rings is prevented at room temperature because it forces collisions between ring hydrogens and/or OH groups. The two conformers are *enantiomers* (non-superimposable mirror images) and each conformer interacts differently with plane-polarized light.

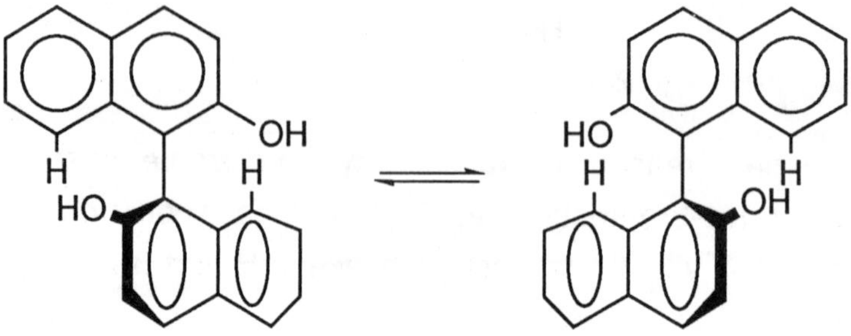

5a ⇌ 5b

Perhaps the most dramatic examples of how conformation can influence molecular properties are provided by enzymes. Enzymes, chemical catalysts, are proteins composed of long chains of amino acids connected by peptide bonds. With the exception of the peptide bond itself [NH-CO], every bond along the protein chain is flexible at room temperature, and the enzyme is able to fold itself into a staggering array of conformations. Typically, only one (or a very few) of these conformations yields an "active" enzyme, and the experimental determination and theoretical prediction of these active conformations is an exciting area of current research

The Global Minimum Problem

Application of computational methods to the description of the structures, relative energies and other properties of conformationally-flexible molecules is inherently much more difficult than to the description of rigid systems. It presents the computational chemist with both an opportunity and a challenge. On the one hand, computer modeling provides an indispensable tool for investigating the energies and properties of conformers, whose short lifetime makes them very difficult to study in the laboratory. On the other hand, even a molecule of modest proportions can access a large number of conformations and the problem of identifying and characterizing each conformation can quickly become overwhelming.

Typically, a set of four bonded atoms will give rise to 3 distinct staggered conformers. If a molecule contains N bonds that are susceptible to internal rotation, the total number of potential conformers may be as large as 3^N. Thus, chlorobutane ($N = 2$) and chlorooctane ($N = 6$) have 9 and 729 staggered conformers, respectively. Each of these conformations represents a *local* minimum on the potential energy surface and geometry optimization may locate any one of these conformers without alerting the chemist to the existence of other, potentially more stable, conformers.

The computational chemist needs to approach such compounds with several goals in mind. First, it will usually be necessary to locate the conformer of lowest energy, the so-called *global* minimum. The majority of the molecules will usually have this structure, and it can provide important clues about molecular behavior. Second, all "important" (depending on the property of interest) conformers of higher energy should be located. Chemical reactions often require a particular orientation of reactants in order to proceed, and it is frequently the case that this orientation can only be achieved when one of the reactants adopts a "high-energy" conformation. For example, whereas the *s-trans* conformer of a simple acyclic diene, e.g., 1,3-butadiene, is thermodynamically more stable than the *cis* structure, i.e., it is the global minimum, it cannot be the reactive species in Diels-Alder cycloaddition. Rather, it must first rotate into an *s-cis* geometry,

Diels Alder adduct

EWG

s-trans *s-cis*

in order for reaction to occur. Clearly in this case one needs to identify not the low-energy structure but rather the one which is "poised" to react. Unfortunately, in many situations (such as the design of drugs) it is impossible to predict the structure of "important" conformers without first performing a complete "conformer search". The chemist also needs to consider what effects temperature, medium, and so on, might have on conformer distribution and/or ease of conformer interconversion.

All of the experiments in this chapter relate to assigning and rationalizing molecular conformation. Most deal only with very simple systems, where the objective is to understand the origin of the conformational preference. The first several experiments concern acyclic systems incorporating only a single rotatable bond. Here complete conformational searches are practical, and the results of these searches may be easily interpreted. The hope here is that the calculations will not only serve to identify favored conformations but also to provide some idea of the magnitudes of conformational energy differences. The next two experiments focus on the conformational preferences of substituents attached to six-membered rings, in particular, cyclohexane and tetrahydropyran. Parallels with acyclic systems are discussed and an interesting and important effect, the anomeric effect, is introduced. "Conformers" arising from inversion at nitrogen are discussed next, and the competition between inversion and rotation analyzed. The last experiment provides an example of conformational searching in a complex system, where the emphasis is not on conformation itself, but rather on the calculation of properties of a conformationally-flexible molecule.

Experiment 11: Conformational Isomerism in n-Butane

We use the semi-empirical AM1 method to examine the potential energy of rotation in n-butane, establish relative energies of local minima on this potential and predict the energy barriers separating these minima. We compare the results of the semi-empirical calculations with previously obtained results from *ab initio* calculations.

There are two stable forms for n-butane, *anti* and *gauche*.[1]

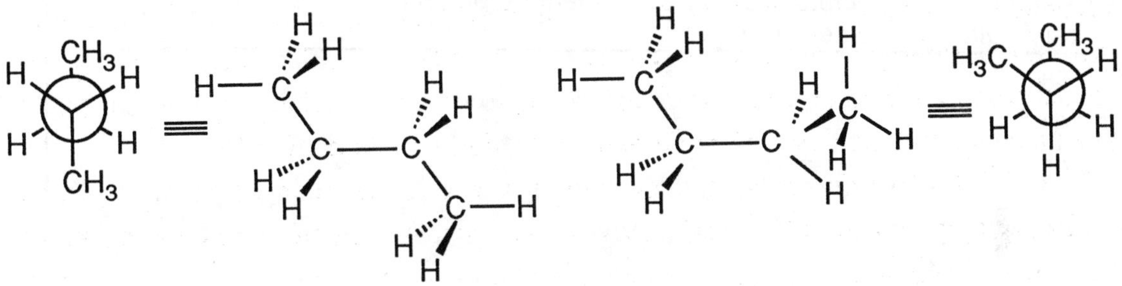

anti *gauche*

This suggests a preference for staggering of CC single bonds (analogous to the preference for staggering of CH bonds in ethane). The observed ordering of conformer stabilities (*trans* n-butane is known experimentally to be 0.8 kcal/mol more stable than *gauche* n-butane) further suggests that avoiding (non-bonded) interactions between methyl groups is more important than avoiding interactions between hydrogens or between hydrogens and methyl groups.

In this experiment, we apply the semi-empirical AM1 method first to the assignment of the stable conformer of n-butane, then to calculation of the relative energies of any additional conformers, and finally to the description of the energy barriers separating conformers. We also compare our results with calculations on rotation in n-butane performed using the 3-21G *ab initio* method. Optionally, we also examine the performance of common molecular mechanics force fields to reproduce known conformational energy differences and rotational barriers.

---

[1] Carey and Sundberg A, p. 121; March, p. 122.

Procedure

Build conformers of n-butane in which the CCCC dihedral angle is fixed at approximately 0°, 30°, 60°, 90°, 120°, 150° and 180° (hydrogens in all conformers should be staggered). Perform AM1 geometry optimizations on each (you will need to [6] constrain the dihedral angle). Record the final heat of formation for each conformer, as well as the actual dihedral angle resulting from the constrained optimization in the table below.

AM1 heats of formation and relative conformer energies (kcal/mol) of n-butane			
ideal CCCC dihedral angle	actual CCCC dihedral angle	heat of formation	rel. energy
0°			
30°			
60°			
90°			
120°			
150°			
180°			

Calculate energies relative to that of the most stable conformer, and record these in the table. Plot relative energy vs. dihedral angle.

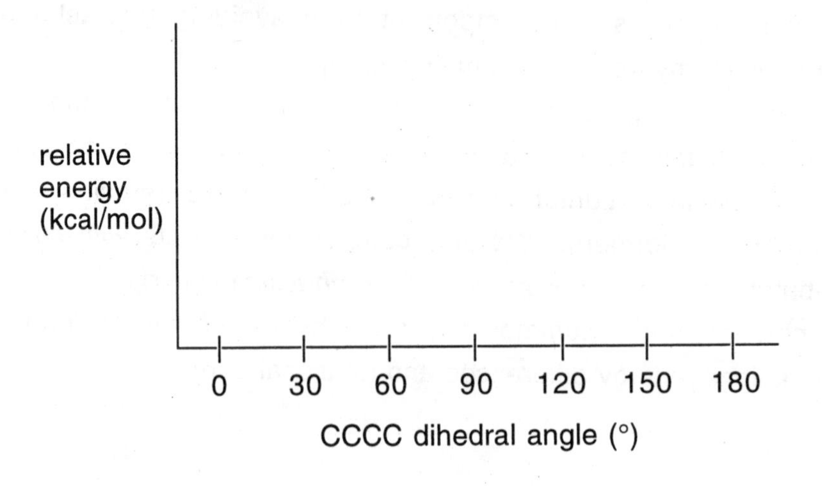

Pick out the local minima (stable conformers) and maxima (transition states connecting stable conformers) from this plot. What do you conclude is the most favorable conformation (global minimum) for n-butane? What does this tell you about the relative importance of CH and CC non-bonded interactions?

For one of the maximum energy conformers perform a normal-mode analysis at the AM1 level. When completed, display the vibration corresponding to the imaginary frequency. This provides a "movie" of the molecule moving from one stable conformer to another. [7]

Compare your results with those already obtained using the 3-21G *ab initio* method which are tabulated below.

3-21G total energies (hartrees) and relative conformer energies (kcal/mol) of n-butane		
CCCC dihedral angle	total energies	rel. energy
0°	-156.41638	
30°	-156.42670	
60°	-156.43106	
90°	-156.42958	
120°	-156.42673	
150°	-156.42963	
180°	-156.43247	

You will need to work out relative conformer energies (recall that 1 hartree=627.5 kcal/mol). Plot these data as well (in the graph above). Point out any significant differences between the two sets of data.

Optional

How well do molecular mechanics force fields handle conformational equilibria in n-butane? Repeat your AM1 calculations using the SYBYL, MM2 and/or MM3 force fields. Do the mechanics methods properly assign the ground-state conformer? Do they properly account for the energy of the alternative form and provide a reasonable description of the energy isomer separating the two?

Experiment 12: Conformational Preferences Involving Multiple Bonds

We use 3-21G *ab initio* calculations to establish the equilibrium conformations of acetaldehyde and propene and confirm the known preference for single bonds to eclipse double bonds. We examine the potential for rotation about carbon-carbon single bonds in 1-butene and propanal.

Just as single bonds prefer to stagger rather than to eclipse other single bonds, e.g., in ethane and n-butane [see **Experiment 11**], strong conformational preferences exist for rotors adjacent to multiple bonds.[1] Specifically, single bonds prefer to eclipse double bonds, with the magnitude of the conformational preference dependent on the polarity of the double bond, e.g., the energy barrier in propene is 1.98 kcal/mol while that in acetaldehyde is 1.16 kcal/mol.[2] In the first part of this experiment, we establish conformational preferences of methyl rotors attached to CC and CO double bonds, in propene and acetaldehyde, respectively. We seek to confirm the experimental preference (for eclipsing), to establish the relative magnitudes of the preference and finally to provide qualitative rationale for these observations. In the second part, we examine conformational preferences in 1-butene and propanal. These exemplify situations in which CC single bonds are disposed about unsaturated linkages. Our principle objective, as in the first part, is to confirm using calculations the experimentally established conformational preferences.

Procedure

Build and minimize using the 3-21G *ab initio* model, two conformers for propene, one in which a methyl CH bond eclipses and the other in which it staggers the CC double bond. Also perform 3-21G optimizations for "eclipsed" and "staggered" conformers of acetaldehyde. Make certain that you maintain a plane of symmetry (C_s symmetry) for all molecules. Record the total energies in the table below.

---

[1] Carey and Sundberg A, p. 126.

[2] For a discussion of the origin, see: W.J. Hehre, A.J.P. Devaquet and J.A. Pople, J. Am. Chem. Soc., **98**, 664 (1976).

3-21G energies (hartrees) and rotational barriers (kcal/mol)			
	eclipsed	staggered	barrier
propene			
acetaldehyde			

Identify the conformation ("eclipsed" or "staggered") which is preferred for each of these systems and calculate and record the rotational barrier. What is the ordering of barrier heights in the two systems? How do the results of your calculations compare with what is known experimentally about equilibrium conformations and barrier heights in propene and acetaldehyde?

Why is the eclipsed conformer more stable? Hint: calculate and display the highest-occupied molecular orbital in the eclipsed conformer of propene. It will correspond to the CC π bond. Note from the graphic that the eclipsing methyl hydrogen lies in the nodal plane of the π bond. Hence, single bonds eclipse double bonds to reduce electron repulsion between the C=C π electrons and the electrons involved with the C-H σ bond. You can also think about the conformational preference in these systems in terms of the CH single bonds on the methyl group staggering the CH single bond in the vinyl fragment.

Build conformers for 1-butene in which the CCCC dihedral angle is fixed approximately at 0°, 30°, 60°, 90°, 120°, 150° and 180°. Make certain that the ethyl group maintains its normal staggered conformation. Optimize each conformer at the **[6]** 3-21G level. You will need to constrain the dihedral angle. When each calculation has completed, record the actual dihedral angle and the total energy in the table below.

3-21G energies (hartrees) and relative conformer energies (kcal/mol) of 1-butene			
ideal CCCC dihedral angle	actual CCCC dihedral angle	energy	rel. energy
0°			
30°			
60°			
90°			
120°			
150°			
180°			

Identify the most-stable conformer, and work out energy differences relative to this conformer and record these differences in the table.

In a similar manner, compute a rotational potential at the *ab initio* 3-21G level for propanal; this will again require calculations at several intermediate points, 0°, 30° ... . Identify the lowest-energy conformer and work out energy differences relative to this conformer. Record your data in the table below.

3-21G energies (hartrees) and relative conformer energies (kcal/mol) of propanal			
ideal CCCO dihedral angle	actual CCCO dihedral angle	energy	rel. energy
0°			
30°			
60°			
90°			
120°			
150°			
180°			

Plot the total energy of 1-butene as a function of CCCC dihedral angle

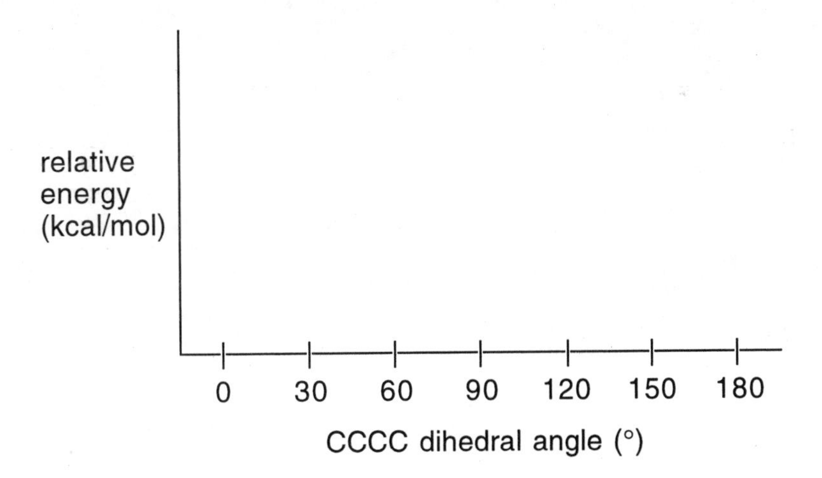

and the energy of propanal as a function of CCCO dihedral angle.

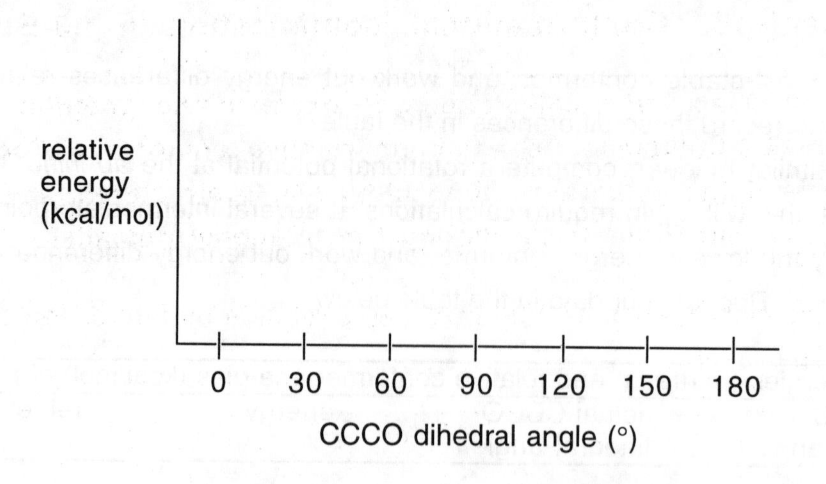

Calculate approximate barrier heights separating the stable conformers. Do the conclusions made for CH bond conformations earlier in this experiment hold up here for CC bond conformation? Are the relative barrier heights (for rotation involving CC and CO double bonds) carried over between the two sets of molecules?

Are there any significant differences between the conformational profiles you have obtained for 1-butene and propanal?

Experiment 13: Conformational Isomerization in 1,3-Butadiene

We use 3-21G *ab initio* calculations to examine the potential energy of rotation in 1,3-butadiene, to establish relative energies of local minima as well as heights of barriers connecting stable structures, and to assess the effects of substituents in altering the rotational potential.

Simple dienes, such as 1,3-butadiene, exist as a mixture of conformers. The *s-trans* arrangement,

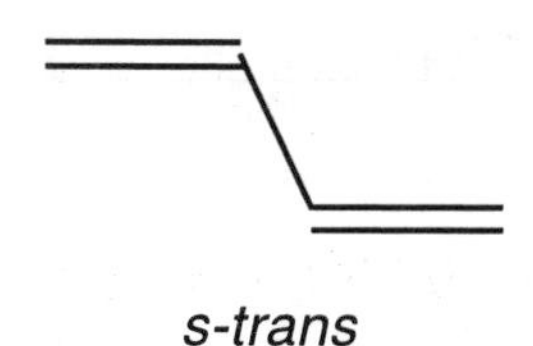

s-trans

seems to best satisfy both steric demands as well as the desire to keep the two π systems coplanar (conjugation).[1] It is the geometry of the second (and presumably higher energy) form which is questionable. Is it *s-cis* (planar), thereby maximizing conjugation, or is the carbon skeleton twisted in order to relieve the obvious steric congestion?

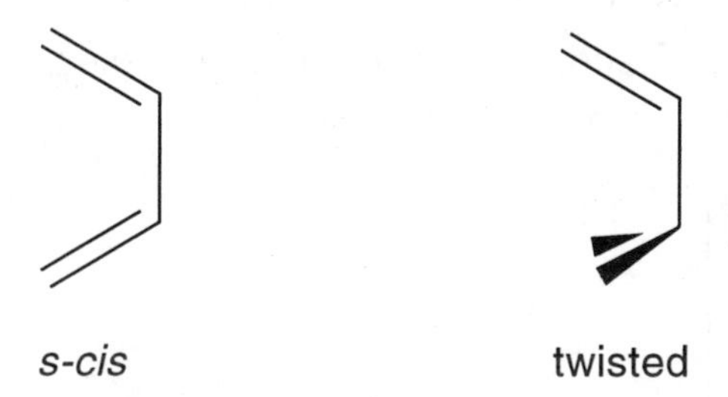

s-cis twisted

In this experiment, we first examine the rotation about the CC single bond in 1,3-butadiene, seeking to establish the geometry of the "*cis*" structure (planar or twisted). We then go on to compare the rotational potential for E-1-methyl-1,3-butadiene to that for butadiene in order to assess the effect of substitution on conformation. Optionally, we use the electrostatic potential to examine the reactivity of 1,3-butadiene as a function of conformation.

---

[1] Carey and Sundberg A, p. 128. For a review of experimental and theoretical work, see: A.J.P. Devaquet, R.E. Townshend and W.J. Hehre, J. Am. Chem. Soc., **98**, 4068 (1976).

Procedure

[6] Build conformers of 1,3-butadiene in which the CCCC dihedral angle is fixed at 0°, 30°, 60°, 90°, 120°, 150° and 180°. Optimize each at the 3-21G level. You will need to constrain the dihedral angle. Record the total energy in the table below, along with the actual CCCC dihedral angle.

3-21G energies (hartrees) and relative conformer energies (kcal/mol) of 1,3-butadiene			
ideal CCCC dihedral angle	actual CCCC dihedral angle	energy	rel. energy
0°			
30°			
60°			
90°			
120°			
150°			
180°			

Identify the most stable conformer and compute energies of all other conformers relative to this structure. Record these relative energies in the table. Plot relative energy vs. dihedral angle.

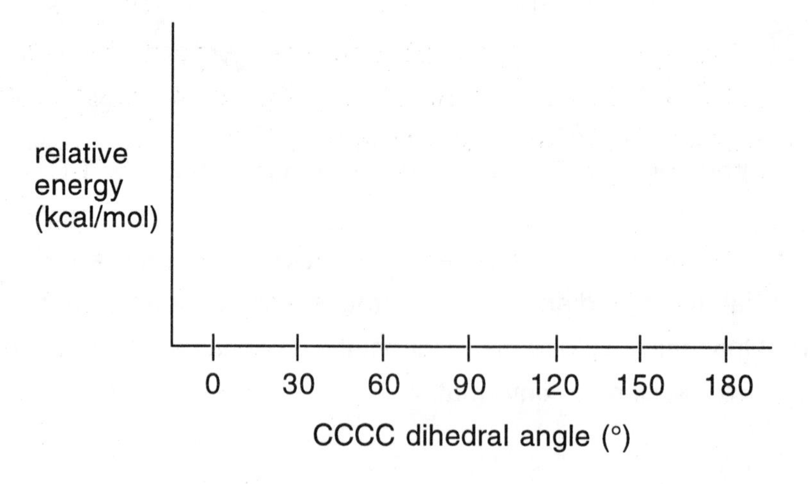

Pick out any local minima (stable conformers) and maxima (transition states connecting stable conformers) from this plot. What do you conclude is the most favorable conformation for 1,3-butadiene? Is this in accord with what is known experimentally? Can you identify a second minimum energy conformer? What is its structure? How many different energy barriers can you identify in your calculated rotational profile? Classify each with respect to which conformers they connect.

On the same plot as you made for rotation in 1,3-butadiene, plot the relative energies of E-1-methyl-1,3-butadiene as a function of conformation.

CH_3

E-1-methyl-1,3-butadiene

3-21G *ab initio* total energies are provided in the table below.

3-21G energies (hartrees) and relative conformer energies (kcal/mol) of E-1-methyl-1,3-butadiene		
CCCC dihedral angle	energy	rel. energy
0°	-192.87238	
30°	-192.87454	
60°	-192.87514	
90°	-192.87336	
120°	-192.87388	
150°	-192.87768	
180°	-192.88239	

What differences in rotational profile do you see between the substituted and unsubstituted molecules? Can you rationalize these on the basis of known steric and/or electronic effects of the methyl substituent?

Optional

For the 0°, 90° and 180° conformations of 1,3-butadiene, calculate electrostatic [3] potentials superimposed onto total electron density surfaces. This provides a measure of reactivity toward electrophiles.[2] In particular, the more negative the electrostatic potential the more attracted will be an electrophile to the π system. Display the maps [8] on the same scale, and also measure the minimum (most negative) values of the electrostatic potential. Do you see evidence for change in potential as a function of conformation? How would this translate into a change in reactivity? Is the ground-state conformer more or less reactive than any higher energy conformers according to this measure? Try to rationalize the directions of any changes which you observe.

---

[2] S.D. Kahn, C.F. Pau, L.E. Overman and W.J. Hehre, J. Am. Chem. Soc., **108**, 7381 (1986).

Experiment 14: Conformational Equilibria in Substituted Cyclohexanes

We use AM1 semi-empirical calculations to assign conformational preferences in mono- and disubstituted cyclohexanes, and to interpret these preferences in terms of steric and stereoelectronic effects. We assess the performance of the AM1 method with respect to both experiment and to the results of 3-21G *ab initio* calculations.

Alkyl groups prefer equatorial positions on cyclohexane.[1] The equatorial conformer of methylcyclohexane is 1.8 kcal/mol lower in energy than the axial conformer, and the difference increases to 5.4 kcal/mol in *tert*-butyl cyclohexane. The *tert*-butyl group is often used to "lock" the cyclohexane ring into a "single conformation". The usual preference for equatorial substitution in cyclohexane is consistent with the fact that the terminal methyl groups in the ground-state conformer of n-butane are *antiperiplanar* rather than *gauche* [see also **Experiment 11**]; this minimizes unfavorable (steric) interactions between them, i.e.,

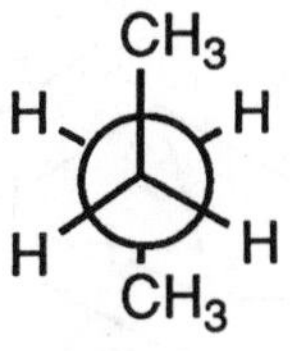

unfavorable steric interactions

antiperiplanar 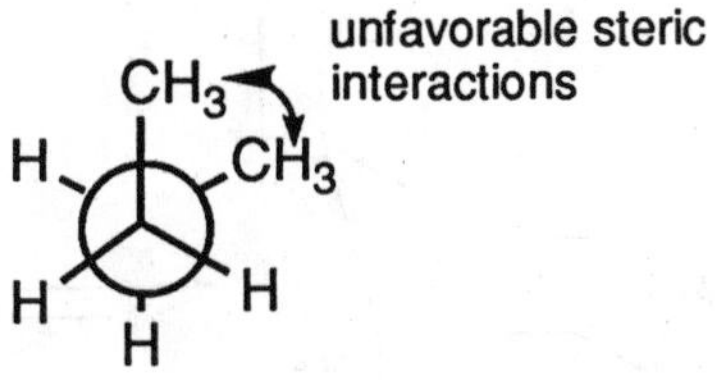 *gauche*

The corresponding Newman projections for substituted cyclohexanes reveal that equatorial substituents R are *antiperiplanar* to CC bonds C_2C_3 and C_5C_6, but that axial substituents R are *gauche* to these bonds.

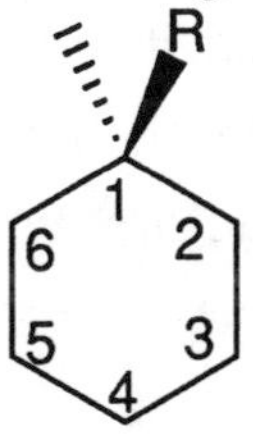

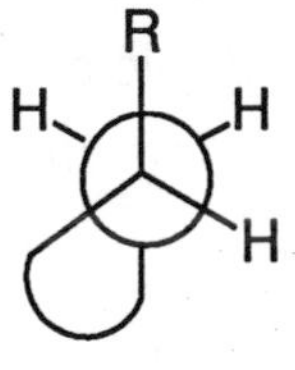

R equatorial 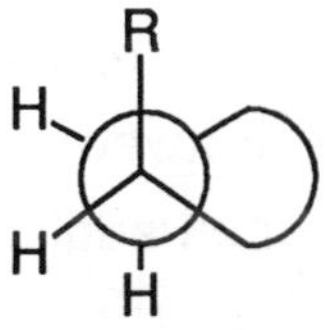 R axial

[1] Carey and Sundberg A, p. 130; Lowry and Richardson, p. 138; March, p. 124.

Identical substituents placed either 1,2 or 1,3 on cyclohexane lead to two distinct conformational arrangements, one with both groups equatorial (e/e) and the other with both groups axial (a/a). Deviations from additivity of substituent effects must be due to interactions of substituents. For example, alkyl groups placed 1,3-diaxially might be expected to give rise to large unfavorable "diaxial" steric interactions.

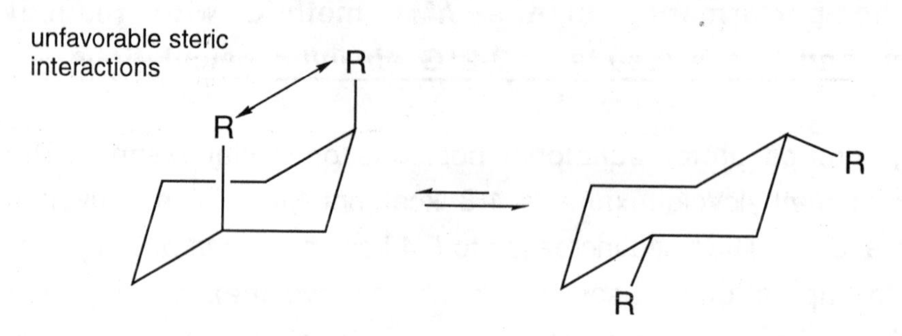

In contrast, a 1,2 diaxial arrangement of fluorine substituents might actually be favored over a diequatorial arrangement because of the possibility of minimizing the overall dipole moment, i.e.,

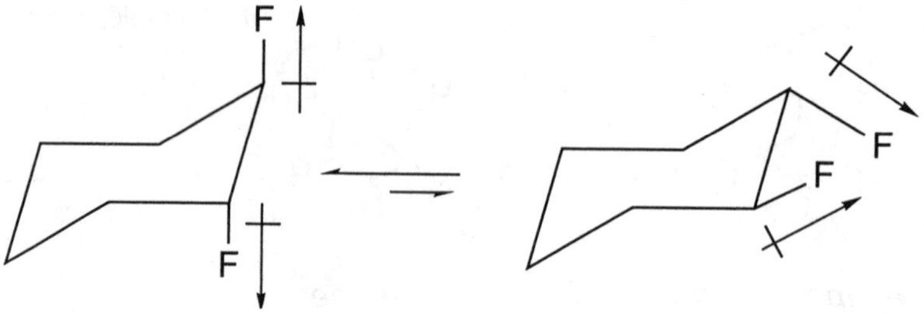

dipoles cancel

dipoles add

In this experiment, we first examine the conformational preferences in a variety of monosubstituted cyclohexanes, and then investigate the additivity of substituent effects in both 1,2- and 1,3-disubstituted cyclohexanes. We search both for steric interactions between substituents and for stereoelectronic factors which might contribute to non-additive behavior.

Procedure

Build and minimize at the semi-empirical AM1 level both equatorial and axial conformers of methylcyclohexane, *tert*-butylcyclohexane, fluorocyclohexane, chlorocyclohexane and cyanocyclohexane. Record the AM1 heats of formation in the table below, note which conformer (axial or equatorial) is the more stable, and work out the axial-equatorial energy difference.

AM1 heats of formation and axial-equatorial energy differences (kcal/mol) and steric parameters					
	heat of formation		relative energies		A
	axial	equatorial	axial	equatorial	
methylcyclohexane					1.8
tert-butylcyclohexane					> 4.5
fluorocyclohexane					0.25
chlorocyclohexane					0.5
cyanocyclohexane					0.2

How do your results compare with the measured energy differences for methylcyclohexane and *tert*-butylcyclohexane? Do calculated axial-equatorial energy differences correlate with the A values provided in the table?

Build and minimize at the semi-empirical AM1 level the two different conformers for each of *trans*-1,2-dimethylcyclohexane, *trans*-1,2-difluorocyclohexane, *cis*-1,3-dimethylcyclohexane and *cis*-1,3-difluorocyclohexane. Record the heats of formation in the table below, identify the lower energy conformer and work out the relative energy of the other conformer.

AM1 heats of formation and relative energies (kcal/mol)				
	heat of formation		relative energies	
	a/a	e/e	a/a	e/e
trans-1,2-dimethylcyclohexane				
trans-1,2-difluorocyclohexane				
cis-1,3-dimethylcyclohexane				
cis-1,3-difluorocyclohexane				

How do the calculated energy differences compare with those based on strict additivity of substituent effects? Do you see different behavior for alkyl groups and for fluorine substituents? Explain your observations. Hint: examine the electric dipole moments for systems with polar substituents.

Tabulated below are total energies previously obtained at the 3-21G *ab initio* level for the mono- and disubstituted cyclohexanes you have calculated at AM1.

3-21G energies (hartrees) and relative energies (kcal/mol)				
	energies		relative energies	
	axial	equatorial	axial	equatorial
methylcyclohexane	-271.72137	-271.72541		
tert-butylcyclohexane	-388.15860	-388.17186		
fluorocyclohexane	-331.22899	-331.23053		
chlorocyclohexane	-689.73222	-689.73386		
cyanocyclohexane	-324.12453	-324.12483		

3-21G energies (hartrees) and relative energies (kcal/mol)				
	total energies		relative energies	
	a/a	e/e	a/a	e/e
trans-1,2-dimethylcyclohexane	-310.53701	-310.54242		
trans-1,2-difluorocyclohexane	-429.54926	-429.54930		
cis-1,3-dimethylcyclohexane	-310.53223	-310.54524		
cis-1,3-difluorocyclohexane	-429.54753	-429.55267		

Assign the lower energy conformation for each system and work out conformational energy differences (in kcal/mol in order to compare with your previous AM1 results; you need to know that 1 hartree is 627.5 kcal/mol). Point out any significant differences between these data and those you obtained at the AM1 level.

Experiment 15: The Anomeric Effect

We use semi-empirical AM1 calculations to examine differences in conformational preferences between substituted cyclohexanes and substituted tetrahydropyrans, and to interpret these differences in terms of the anomeric effect.

Glucose normally exists as a mixture of two diastereomeric cyclic hemiacetals known as *anomers*.

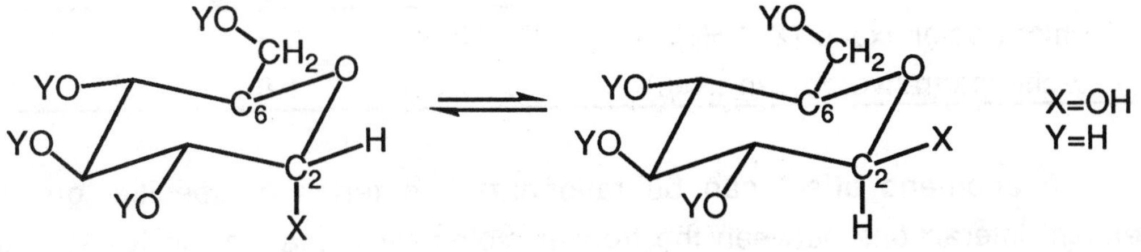

α-anomer β-anomer

X=OH
Y=H

The minor anomer, known as α-glucose, has an axial OH group at C_2, while the OH group at C_2 in the major anomer, β-glucose, is equatorial. The greater stability of β-glucose fits well with our expectation that bulky substituents on a six-membered ring prefer sterically less-hindered equatorial positions [see **Experiment 14**]. This expectation is misleading, however, since the α anomer is more stable for many glucose derivatives, e.g.,

Experimental α/β isomer ratios and free energy differences in glucose derivatives (kcal/mol)				
X	Y	%α anomer	%β anomer	ΔG (α-β)
OH	H	36	64	-0.33
OCH_3	H	67	33	0.42
$OC(=O)CH_3$	$C(=O)CH_3$	88	12	1.2
Cl	$C(=O)CH_3$	94	6	1.6

This unusual preference for axial substitution is called the ***anomeric effect***.[1] Although the anomeric effect was first discovered by studying the structures of

[1] Carey and Sundberg A, p. 146; March, p. 128.

carbohydrates, it influences the conformational equilibria of many other compounds, e.g., in chlorotetrahydropyrans.

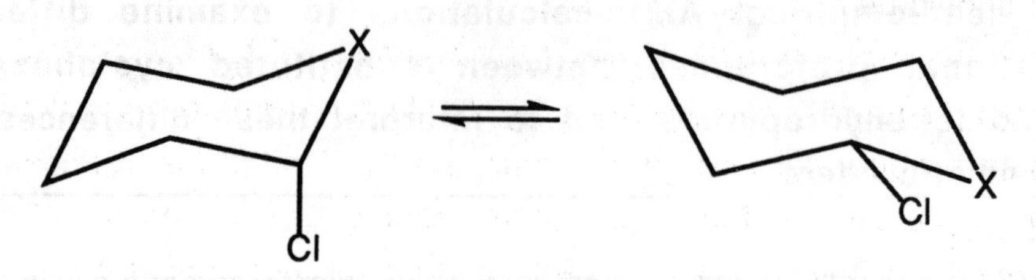

Experimental free energy differences (kcal/mol)	
	ΔG(eq-ax)
chlorocyclohexane (X=CH_2)	-0.5
2-chlorotetrahydropyran (X=0)	1.8

The anomeric effect can be rationalized in terms of specific, geometry-dependent interactions between the frontier molecular orbitals of an X-C-Y system, where C is a tetrahedral center and X and Y are electronegative atoms or groups. Here, the more stable anomer will be the one that provides the better overlap between a filled p lone pair on X and the empty C-Y σ* orbital. This orbital interaction creates a new, more stable, filled orbital.

X and Y in 2-chlorotetrahydropyran correspond to O and Cl, respectively. Oxygen has two lone-pair orbitals, a high-energy p-type orbital that is perpendicular to the C-O-C plane, and a lower-energy, sp^2-type orbital.

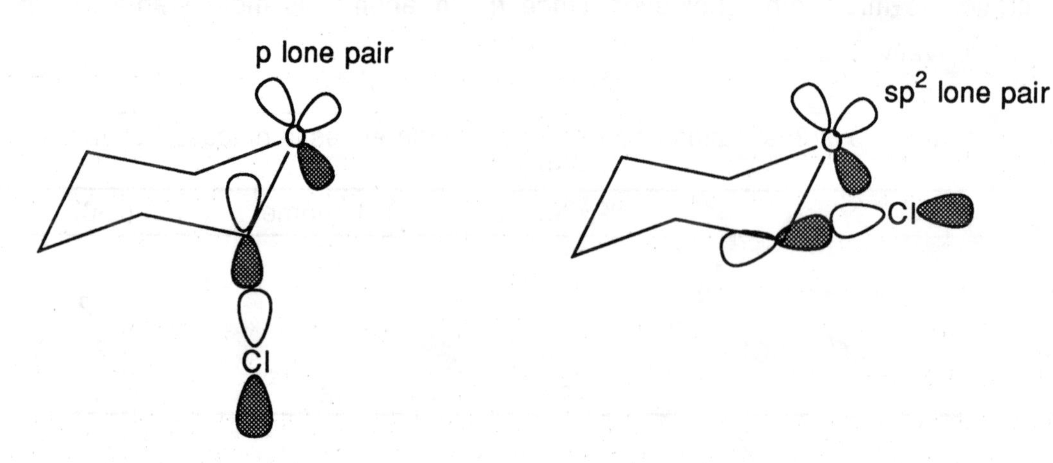

interaction involves p lone pair

interaction involves sp^2 lone pair

Favorable overlap between the high-energy filled p-type lone pair on oxygen and the unfilled C-Cl σ^* orbital is much more effective when Cl is axial, and so the axial conformer should be more stable.

Since the p-σ^* interaction affects the character of the C_2-O and C_2-Cl bonds, both their bond strengths and bond lengths should depend on conformation. The C_2-O bond should be stronger and shorter than the C_6-O bond (see previous figure for numbering) in the axial conformation, but not in the equatorial conformation. Likewise, the C_2-Cl bond should be weaker and longer in the axial conformation.

In this experiment, we use semi-empirical AM1 calculations to determine the conformational preferences of chlorocyclohexane and 2-chlorotetrahydropyran. In addition, we examine bond lengths in the axial and equatorial conformers of 2-chlorotetrahydropyran in light of the predictions made from the simple orbital model. Finally, the conformational preference of various substituted tetrahydropyrans are examined in order to discover substituents capable of producing an anomeric effect.

Procedure

Build and optimize at the AM1 level, axial and equatorial conformers of chlorocyclohexane. Record the heats of formation in the table below.

AM1 heats of formation and axial-equatorial energy differences (kcal/mol)			
	axial	equatorial	axial-equatorial
chlorocyclohexane			
2-chlorotetrahydropyran			

Identify the more stable conformer and work out the energy of the other conformer relative to this form. Which conformer (axial or equatorial) is the more stable? How well does the energy difference obtained from the AM1 calculations compare with the experimental value (0.5 kcal/mol in favor of the equatorial conformer)?

Build and optimize at the AM1 level, axial and equatorial forms of 2-chlorotetrahydropyran. Record your data in the table. Which conformer (axial or equatorial) is the more stable? How well does the energy difference obtained from the AM1 calculations compare with the experimental value (1.8 kcal/mol in favor of the axial conformer)?

Enter the calculated C-O and C-Cl bond lengths in axial and equatorial conformers of 2-chlorotetrahydropyran in the figure below.

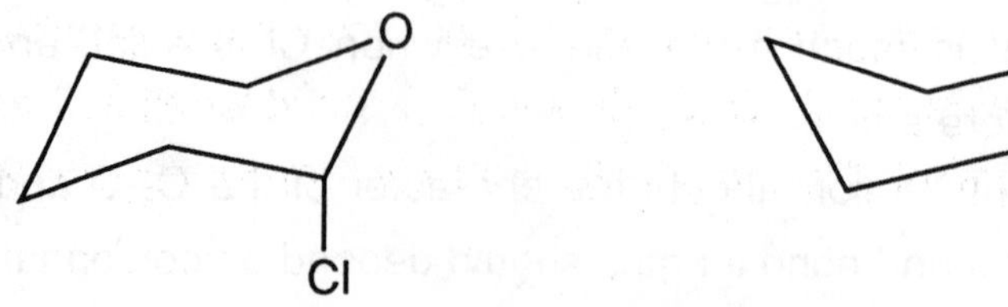

For reference, the AM1 C-O bond length in tetrahydropyran is 1.423Å and C-Cl bond lengths in axial and equatorial chlorocyclohexane are 1.776Å and 1.772Å, respectively. Assuming these bond lengths to be "normal", which C-O and C-Cl bond lengths in axial and equatorial 2-chlorotetrahydropyran seem to be "abnormal"? Are the directions of the noted deviations consistent with the predictions of the simple orbital model?

Select a substituent X from among the following: SiH_3, CF_3, NO_2, CN, F and Br, and perform AM1 calculations on axial and equatorial conformers of 2-X-tetrahydropyran. Record your data in the table below.

AM1 heats of formation and axial-equatorial energy differences in 2-X-tetrahydropyrans (kcal/mol)			
X	axial	equatorial	axial-equatorial
SiH_3			
CF_3			
NO_2			
CN			
F			
Br			

Compare the conformational preferences you find with the calculated and measured preferences in the corresponding substituted cyclohexanes.

AM1 and experimental axial-equatorial energy (free energy) differences in X-cyclohexanes (kcal/mol)		
X	AM1	Expt. ΔG
SiH_3	-2.7	--
CF_3	-2.1	--
NO_2	-0.6	-1.1
CN	-1.1	-0.2
F	-1.2	-0.3
Br	-0.9	-0.5

Based on this comparison, does the substituent you have selected produce an anomeric effect? Examine the C_2-O, C_6-O, and C_2-X bond lengths of each conformer. Are the results in agreement with the substituent's conformational preference?

Optional

1. AM1 calculations give equatorial preferences of 1.3 kcal/mol for methylcyclohexane and 0.3 kcal/mol for 2-methyltetrahydropyran. Assuming that the methyl group cannot produce an anomeric effect, explain why the equatorial preference is reduced in the tetrahydropyran ring.

2. AM1 calculations indicate that α-glucose is more stable than β-glucose, even though the β anomer is observed as the major component of the equilibrium mixture when glucose is dissolved in water. Reconcile these apparently contradictory results.

3. The anomeric effect has also been rationalized in terms of dipole-dipole interactions. Draw the bond dipole associated with a C-Cl bond on the diagrams of equatorial and axial 2-chlorotetrahydropyran. Draw the dipole associated with a COC group on each diagram as well. If the relative stability of the two conformers is determined by dipole-dipole interactions, the more stable conformer will be the one with the smaller *net* dipole moment. Based on your diagrams, which conformer do you predict to have the smaller dipole moment? Use AM1 calculations to obtain the dipole moment of each conformer. Do the calculated dipole moments agree with your predictions? Is this theory of the anomeric effect plausible?

Experiment 16: Conformational Isomerism in Hydrazine. Keeping Lone Pairs Out of Each Other's Way

We use 3-21G *ab initio* calculations to investigate the potential for rotation about the NN bond in hydrazine. We relate this potential to unfavorable non-bonded interactions of the nitrogen lone pairs as "measured" by orbital energy splittings.

The same guidelines which tell us that ethane prefers a staggered rather than an eclipsed geometry may also be applied to the conformations of molecules containing heteroatoms. What we first need to know is that a lone pair, like a CH bond, "takes up space". In fact, some evidence suggests that lone pairs generally take up more space than σ bonds. This said, the preferred geometry of methylamine will be one in which both NH bonds and the lone pair at nitrogen stagger the CH linkages, i.e.,

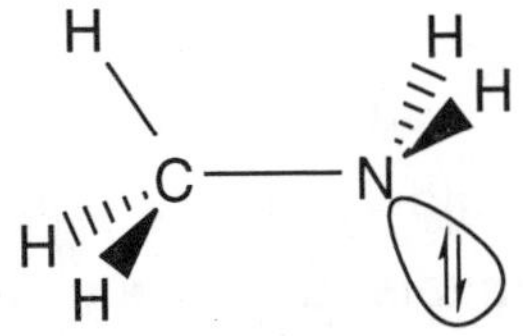

This also leads to staggering of CH and NH bonds.

The situation is more involved when both centers contain lone pairs. There are, for example, two "staggered" conformers for hydrazine, one in which the lone pairs are *anti* and the other in which they are *gauche*.[1]

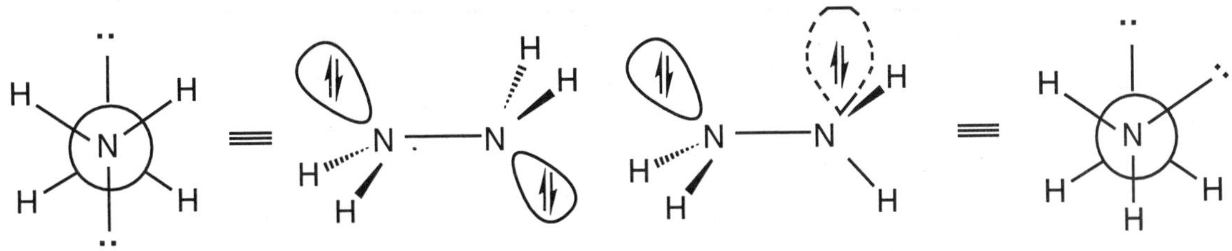

lone pairs *anti* lone pairs *gauche*

---

[1] S.F. Nelsen in **Molecular Structure and Energetics**, vol. 3, J.F. Liebman and A. Greenberg, eds., VCH Publishers, Deerfield Beach, Fl., 1986, p. 1.

In this experiment, we examine the energy of rotation about the NN bond in hydrazine, and rationalize why the "*anti*" conformer is observed to be significantly less stable than the "*gauche*" conformer. We will do this by "measuring" the interaction between the nitrogen lone pairs, and then relating this interaction to the energy of rotation about the NN bond.

Procedure

[9] Construct conformers of hydrazine with C_2 symmetry so that the twist angle between the lone pairs, ω(:NN:), is close to 0°, 30°, 60°, 90°, 120°, 150° and 180°. (ω(:N:) is equivalent to ω(HNNH) between the two hydrogens that are not symmetry-related.)

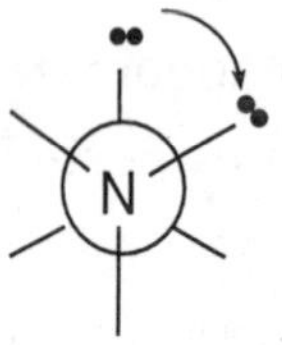

N

ω(:NN:) = 0°, 30°, 60°, 90°, 120°, 150°, 180°

Perform single-point energy 3-21G calculations for each of the conformers (**don't try to optimize**; the structures would revert to one of the minimum energy forms). Specify printing of molecular orbitals and associated orbital energies. Write down ω(:NN:), the total energy, and the energies of the two highest-energy filled molecular orbitals for each conformer in the table below.

3-21G energies (hartrees), relative energies (kcal/mol) and orbital energies (hartrees) in hydrazine					
ideal ω(:NN:)	actual ω(:NN:)	energy	relative energy	E_{HOMO}	E_{HOMO-1}
0°					
30°					
60°					
90°					
120°					
150°					
180°					

Identify the lowest-energy conformer and calculate the energy of each conformer relative to this structure.

Make three plots in the space provided below.

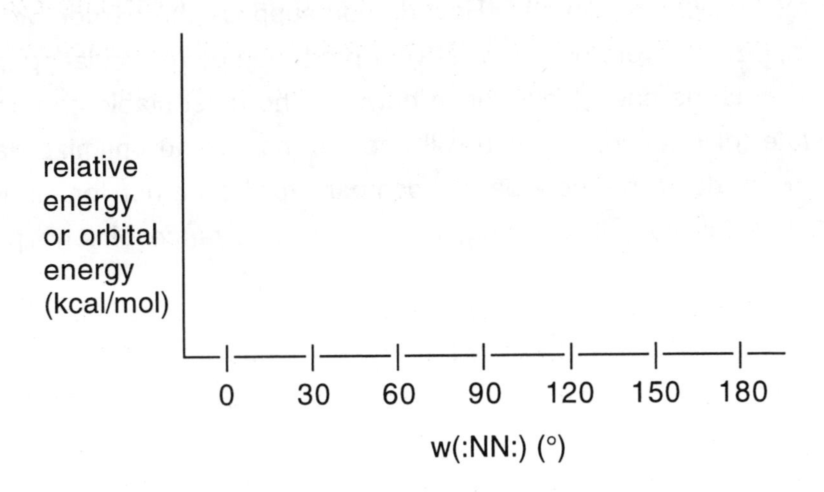

First, plot the relative energies of the different conformers relative to the lowest-energy conformer. Next, plot the variation in energy of each of the two highest-filled molecular orbitals of hydrazine as a function of ω(:NN:). It might be convenient to convert from hartrees to kcal/mol (1 hartree=627.5 kcal/mol). These two molecular orbitals are built from the nitrogen lone pairs. If the lone pairs interact weakly, the two orbitals will have roughly the same energy. If the lone pairs interact more strongly, they will combine to form a "bonding" orbital of lower energy and an "antibonding" orbital of higher energy. The energy separation or "splitting" between these two orbitals reflects the degree of lone pair-lone pair interaction. What is the relationship between ω(:NN:) and the degree of splitting? What is the source of this relationship? What is the relationship between conformer energy and the degree of splitting? Why should lone pair-lone pair interactions have this effect on the overall energy?

Generate and examine isosurfaces for the two highest-occupied molecular orbitals of hydrazine both for a conformer in which the splitting is large and for a conformer in which it is small. Describe the difference between the two sets of orbitals (for the two different conformers).

Optional

1. The preferred conformation of a simple molecule often corresponds to the conformer with the lowest HOMO energy. Check whether or not this rule-of-thumb holds for hydrazine. Why do you suppose this rule is so general?

2. How does your estimated barrier for hydrazine rotation compare to the barrier for ethane rotation (2.8 kcal/mol)? How do you suppose the barrier would change if geometry optimization were used? Test your prediction by recalculating the hydrazine rotation barrier as the energy difference between the most stable conformer and the transition state for rotation, i.e., you will need to locate and optimize each of these structures. How does this new barrier compare to the barrier for ethane rotation? What does this tell you, if anything, about the importance of lone pair-lone pair interactions?

Experiment 17: Configurational Stability in Amines

We use semi-empirical PM3 calculations to examine the configurational stability of compounds involving tricoordinate nitrogen centers, and to identify those factors which influence configurational stability, in particular, substitution and ring strain.

Stereoisomerism exists not only for tetracoordinate tetrahedral centers but also for tricoordinate nitrogen centers,[1] which also adopt approximate tetrahedral geometries, the remaining tetrahedral site being taken up by a non-bonded electron pair (lone pair) rather than a fourth group, e.g.,

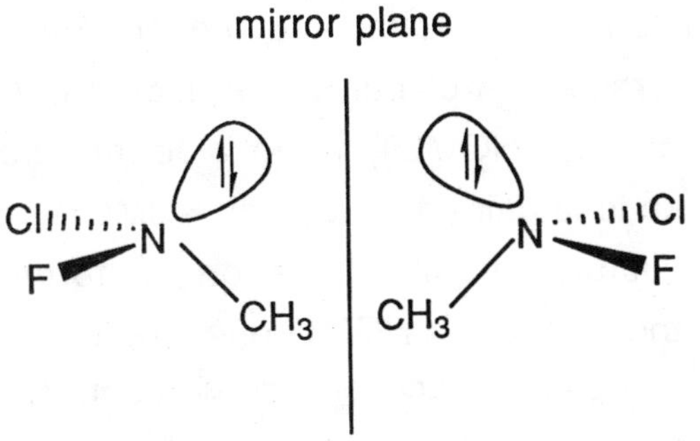

mirror plane

The requirement for stereoisomerism is that the attached "groups" (substituents and the lone pair) all be different. Enantiomer interconversion involves inversion at the tricoordinate center, e.g.,

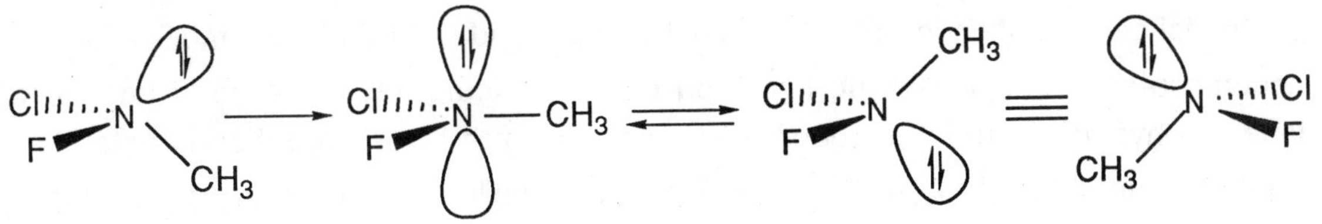

and, while the energy for inversion will certainly be smaller than that required for interconversion at tetracoordinate carbon, it can still be sizable. The point that is important, is that it is possible in some cases for the configurational stability to be high enough to lead to distinct isolable compounds.

In this experiment, we first investigate the effects of substituents on the barrier to inversion in ammonia. To rationalize these effects, we need to account for the

[1] March, p. 86.

observation that (most) tricoordinate nitrogen compounds prefer (approximate) tetrahedral geometries rather than planar structures. The simplest explanation is that the lone pair occupies space, and that the best way to position four electron pairs (three electron-pair bonds and one non-bonded electron pair) around a center is in a tetrahedron. It has already been pointed out [see **Experiment 16**] that a non-bonded pair is often actually larger than a bonding electron pair. Evidence for this is that bond angles involving the attached groups are often smaller than tetrahedral values in order to reduce overall "steric repulsion". For example, the experimental HNH bond angle in ammonia is 106.7°, which is less than the tetrahedral value (109.47°). This implies that "bond angles" involving the lone pair will be larger than the tetrahedral value.

Another explanation relies on the correlation that is often observed between HOMO energy and conformer energy [see **Experiment 16, Optional 1**]. The amine HOMO is the nitrogen lone pair orbital and the energy of this orbital is largely determined by its %s character. A planar amine (higher energy conformer) has a p-type lone pair (higher energy HOMO), while a tetrahedral amine (lower energy conformer) has an sp^3-like lone pair (lower energy HOMO).

The effect of structural modifications on conformer energy can also be understood in terms of their effect on HOMO energies for different conformers. For example, attachment of a π electron acceptor substituent, Z, to nitrogen stabilizes the HOMO by introducing an NZ π-bonding interaction into the HOMO. Since π bonding is enhanced (and the HOMO is most stabilized) when N and Z establish good π overlap, the conformation at nitrogen will become more planar. A π electron donor substituent, on the other hand, might destabilized the HOMO of a planar amine by introducing an NZ π-antibonding interaction into the HOMO. In this case, the amine will adopt a more pyramidal conformation in order to avoid π overlap and the HOMO destabilization that accompanies it. Logically, the inversion barriers should follow the bond angles (or lone pair hybridization) at nitrogen. π interactions which favor larger bond angles (and a p-type lone pair) will shrink the inversion barrier, while interactions that favor smaller bond angles (and higher %s character in the lone pair) will increase the barrier.

It might also be anticipated that bond angles and inversion barriers in cyclic amines will depend on ring size. The ideal bond angles around planar nitrogen (120°) are larger than the ideal bond angles around tetrahedral nitrogen (109.5°). If nitrogen is part of a small ring, ring strain will favor smaller bond angles at nitrogen and this will create a larger barrier to inversion.

In this experiment we examine both the electronic effects of substituents and the effect of ring size on inversion barriers.

Procedure

Build and optimize at the PM3 semi-empirical level pyramidal and planar forms of ammonia.

> We use the PM3 rather than the AM1 semi-empirical method in this experiment because it has been shown to be the more reliable of the two in accounting for nitrogen inversion barriers.

Be certain to request printing of the molecular orbitals (and associated orbital energies), and for graphical display of the four valence molecular orbitals. Record your data in the table below.

PM3 heats of formation (kcal/mol), HNH bond angles (°) and orbital energies (eV) for ammonia		
	pyramidal	planar
ΔH_f		
∠ (HNH)		120°
E (HOMO)		
E (HOMO-1)		
E (HOMO-2)		
E (HOMO-3)		

Compute the ammonia inversion barrier. How does it compare with the experimental value of 5.9 kcal/mol?

Construct a **Walsh diagram**,[2] connecting the energies of the four valence molecular orbitals of pyramidal and planar ammonia.

[2] A.D. Walsh, Prog. Stereochem., **1**, 1 (1954).

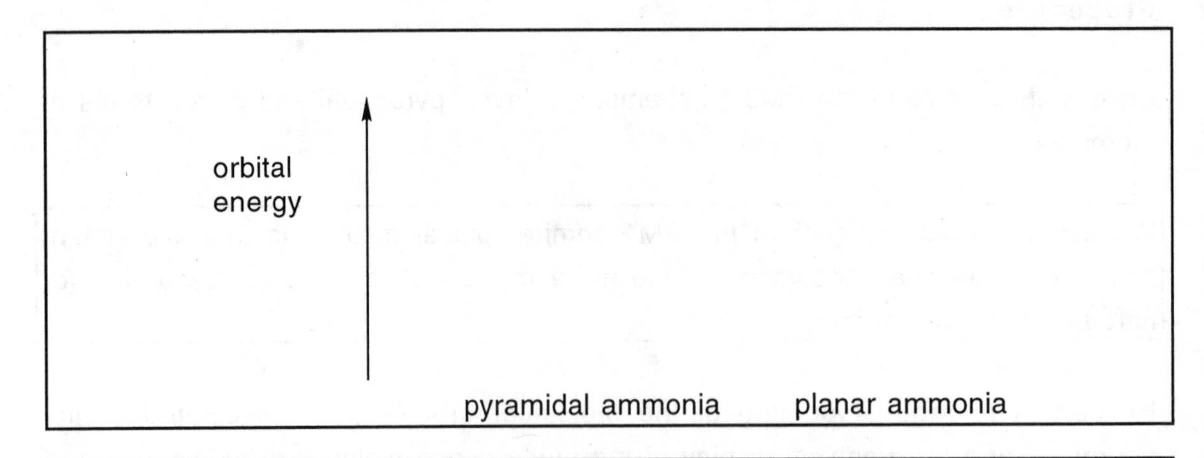

Walsh diagrams relate changes in valence orbital energies to changes in bond angles. They have been most commonly used to rationalize geometry changes as a function of number of valence electrons, for example in AH_2 and AH_3 molecules, where A is a main-group element.

Draw lines between analogous orbital energies (in this case, the ordering of energies will not change between the two structures). You will note that two of the valence orbitals of both planar and pyramidal ammonia have the same energy. They are said to be degenerate. Can you explain why? Which orbital energies are most (least) sensitive to conformation? Why? (It may help to examine the orbital shapes.) Are the trends in orbital energies consistent with the trends in conformer energy?

Build and optimize at the semi-empirical PM3 level, pyramidal and planar forms of trimethylamine, trifluoroamine and tricyanoamine. Record heats of formation and XNX bond angles in the table below.

PM3 heats of formation (kcal/mol), XNX bond angles (°) and pyramidal-planar energy differences (kcal/mol)

	pyramidal		planar	pyramidal-planar
	ΔH_f	$\angle$ (XNX)	ΔH_f	
ammonia				
trimethylamine				
trifluoroamine				
tricyanoamine				

Compute the inversion barriers in these compounds. Plot calculated bond angles about nitrogen in these compounds vs. calculated inversion barriers. Be sure to include the previous data for ammonia in your plot.

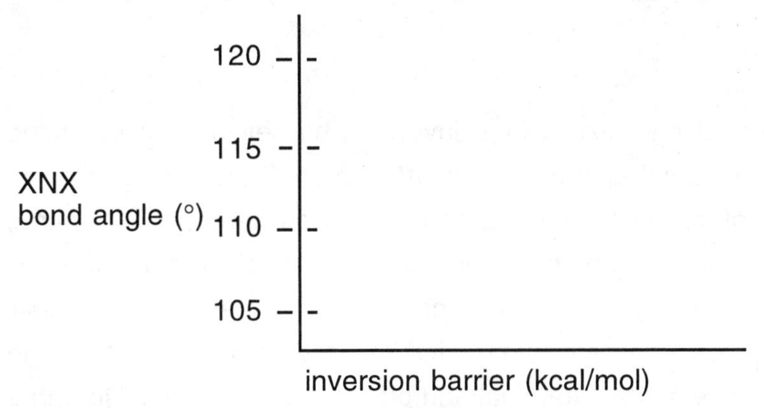

Do the PM3 calculations reproduce the experimental bond angle of 106.7° in ammonia? Do you find a reasonable correlation between bond angle and inversion barrier? Try to rationalize any significant deviations.

On the basis of calculated changes in nitrogen inversion barriers (relative to ammonia), classify the substituents as either π-electron donors or acceptors. How does your classification fit with "conventional wisdom"? Can you think of any other factors (other than π donor/acceptor substituent effects) which might contribute to changes in inversion barriers? Without doing any further calculations, predict whether the inversion barriers in formamide, trifluoromethylamine and hydrazine would be smaller or larger than that in ammonia? Comment on the configurational stability of each of the amines you have examined. For which (if any) might there be a good chance of actually isolating *enantiomers* (in suitable substituted systems)?

We next examine the barrier to inversion in aziridine (using dimethylamine as a reference) in order to assess the effect of ring strain on configurational stability. Build and minimize at the semi-empirical PM3 level, pyramidal and planar forms of aziridine and dimethylamine. Record your data in the table below.

PM3 heats of formation and pyramidal-planar energy differences (kcal/mol)			
	pyramidal	planar	pyramidal-planar
aziridine			
dimethylamine			

Compute barriers to inversion in both compounds. Rationalize the difference in barrier heights, and comment on the configurational stability of the two compounds. Would you expect optically active aziridines to maintain their optical purity at room temperature? What kinds of substituents at nitrogen in aziridine would you expect would act further to increase configurational stability?

Optional

1. The effect of ring size on the inversion barrier in a cyclic amine can also be understood by examining the factors affecting HOMO energies in cyclic amines. Smaller rings enforce smaller bond angles around nitrogen, i.e., nitrogen's bonding orbitals must contain more p character. As the p character of these orbitals increases, the p character of nitrogen's lone pair necessarily decreases. The resulting increase in s character in the lone pair orbital (HOMO) stabilizes this orbital. The difference in the HOMO energies of the pyramidal and planar conformers is also enhanced (and the inversion barrier too) because the lone pair of the planar conformer must always be a p-type orbital. To test this explanation, compare the HOMO energies and the HOMO shapes of the pyramidal and planar conformers of aziridine and dimethylamine. Do the HOMOs correspond to lone pair-type orbitals? How similar are the HOMO energies for the two pyramidal molecules? How similar are they for the two planar molecules? Do the expected correlations between ring size, lone pair hybridization,[3] HOMO energy, CNC angle, and inversion barrier exist?

---

[3] Use the Natural Bond Orbital procedure for hybrid orbital analysis: A.E. Reed, R.B. Weinstock, and F. Weinhold, J. Chem. Phys., **83**, 735 (1985).

Experiment 18: Stereodynamics of Dimethylisopropylamine

We use semi-empirical PM3 calculations to elucidate the mechanism of interconversion of conformers of dimethylisopropylamine, and to establish the difference in energy between isomerism via a single-bond-rotation and nitrogen-inversion pathways.

Three "reasonable" staggered conformers exist for dimethylisopropylamine, **1**.[1] These are **1a**, in which both methyls on the isopropyl group are *gauche* to the nitrogen lone pair, and **1b** and **1c**, in which one methyl is *gauche* and one is *anti*.

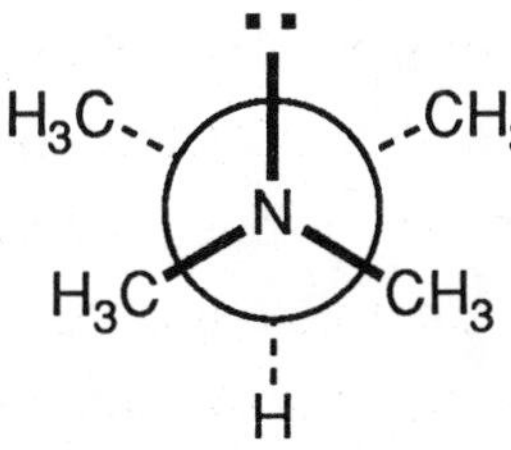

1a *gauche:gauche*

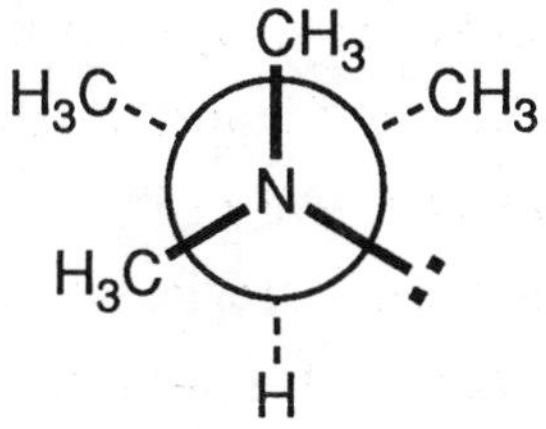

1b *anti:gauche*

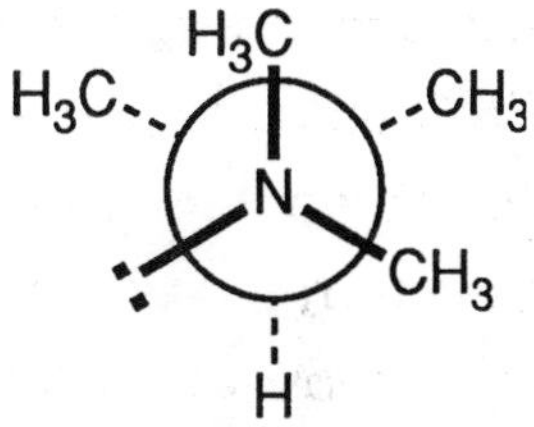

1c *gauche:anti*

Arrangements **1d** and **1e**, in which the methyl groups or the hydrogen associated with the isopropyl group *eclipse* the nitrogen lone pair, respectively, are presumably higher in energy, and correspond to transition states for rotation.

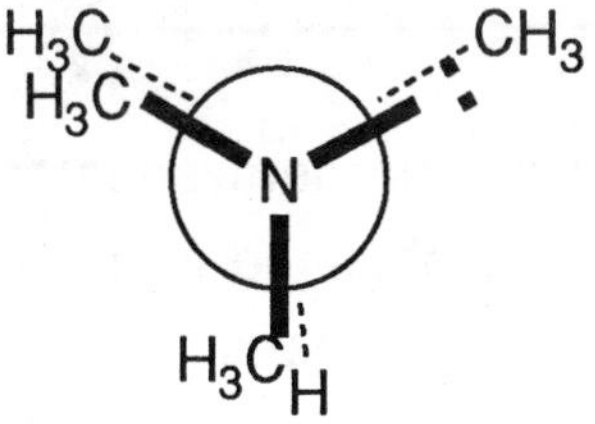

1d

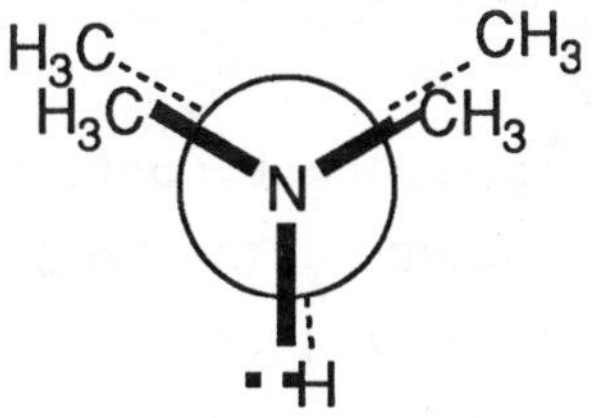

1e

Note that **1b** and **1c** are *enantiomers*; they can be interconverted by way of rotation about the CN single bond (via **1e**) or alternatively through inversion at nitrogen (via **1f**), i.e.,

[1] J.H. Brown and C.H. Bushweller, J. Am. Chem. Soc., **114**, 8153 (1992).

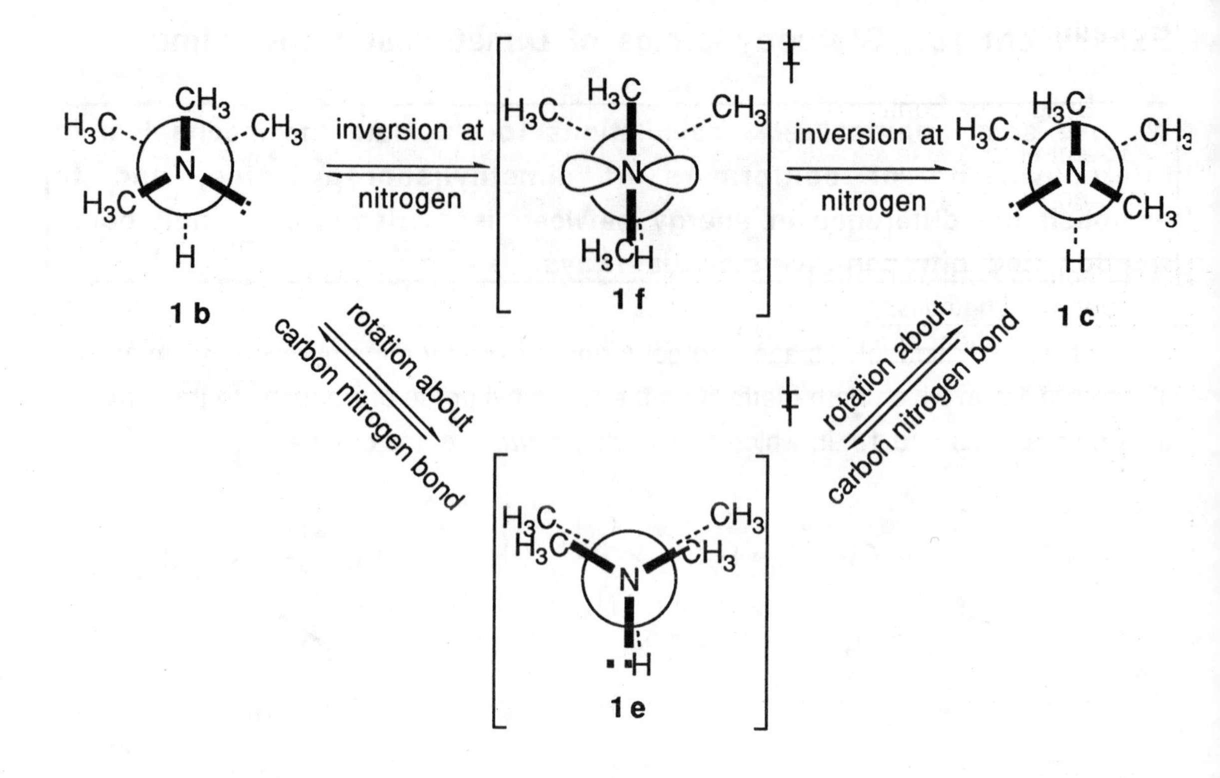

In this experiment, we model the stereodynamics of dimethylisopropylamine using the PM3 semi-empirical method.

> This experiment, like **Experiment 17**, involves calculations involving inversion at nitrogen. We use the PM3 method in lieu of AM1 because of its more reliable performance for this purpose.

The relative energies of the conformers and the barriers separating them will be computed and compared to the experimental data obtained from NMR spectroscopy. NMR measurements have produced two barriers for isomerism in this system: a lower energy barrier (4.5 kcal/mol) separating **1b/1c** from **1a**, and a higher energy barrier (5.2 kcal/mol) separating **1b** and **1c**. The NMR measurements do not, however, indicate whether the latter barrier results from bond rotation (transition state **1e**) or nitrogen inversion (transition state **1f**). Therefore, we wish to use models of the two transition states to determine which process, rotation or inversion, best accounts for the observed energy barrier separating **1b** and **1c**.

Procedure

Build three conformers of dimethylisopropylamine, **1a-1c**. Optimize each at the PM3 semi-empirical level, record the heats of formation for each conformer in the table below, and compute the energy of each relative to the most stable arrangement.

PM3 heats of formation and relative energies and experimental relative free energies of dimethylisopropylamine (kcal/mol)			
structure	heat of formation	relative energy	experimental relative free energy
1a			0.7
1b			0.0
1c			0.0
1d			4.5
1e			5.2 (?)
1f			5.2 (?)

Build the two rotational transition states, **1d** and **1e**. For each, perform a transition state optimization at the PM3 level and record the heats of formation in the table. Be certain to request normal mode analyses, so that you can confirm that you have indeed obtained reasonable transition structures. Finally, build the transition state **1f** for interconversion of **1b** and **1c** via inversion at nitrogen. Perform a transition state optimization at the PM3 level, together with a normal-mode analysis. Record the heat of formation in the table.

Compute relative energies (referenced to the most stable form) for structures **1a-1c**. How do your data compare with what is known experimentally from NMR spectroscopy (also given in the table)? Rationalize what you find to be the most stable conformation of dimethylisopropyl amine. Explain the calculated energy difference between **1b** and **1c**.

Compute interconversion barriers for rotation via structures **1d** and **1e**, and for inversion via structure **1f**. Which pathway, rotation or inversion, is energetically the most favorable?

Experiment 19: Hydrazine Conformations by Photoelectron Spectroscopy and Molecular Orbital Calculations[1]

We correlate orbital energy splittings in hydrazines obtained from semi-empirical PM3 calculations with differences in ionization potentials from photoelectron spectroscopy and with :NN: dihedral angles. We use calculated orbital splittings to assign conformations in hydrazines.

In **Experiment 16**, we examined the difference in energy between the two highest-occupied molecular orbitals in hydrazine as a function of :NN: dihedral angle. We observed that the conformation for which the energy splitting was at a minimum (corresponding to the lone pairs being approximately orthogonal) was also the lowest energy conformation. In this experiment, we examine a number of hydrazines in more detail, including systems in which the dihedral angle involving the nitrogen lone pairs is fixed. We attempt to correlate HOMO/HOMO-1 splittings with differences in experimental ionization potentials (IP_2-IP_1) obtained from photoelectron spectroscopy,

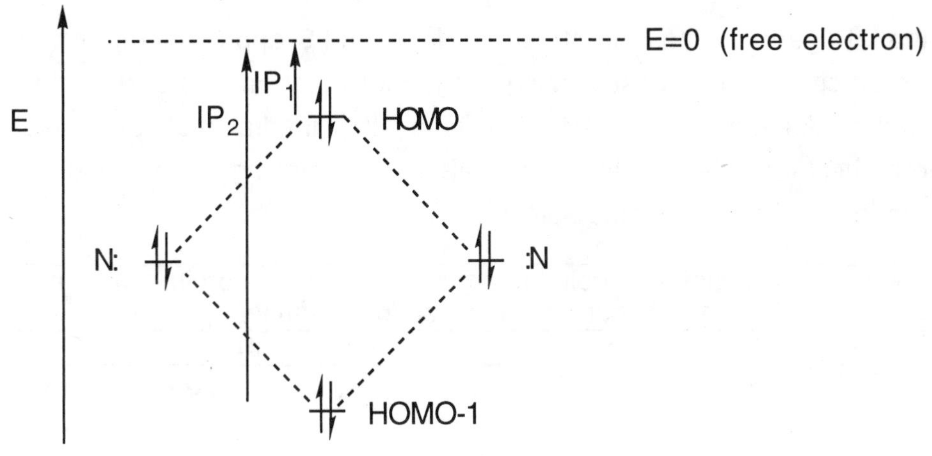

and, more importantly, with :NN: dihedral angles in stable compounds. The latter provides a possible method for assigning conformation in complex hydrazines on the basis of either experimental ionization potentials or orbital energies from quantum chemical calculations.

---

[1] S.F. Nelsen, in **Molecular Structure and Energetics**, vol. 3, J.F. Liebman and A. Greenberg, eds., VCH Publishers, Deerfield Beach, Fl., 1986, p. 1.

Procedure

Build and optimize at the PM3 level hydrazines **1-6**.

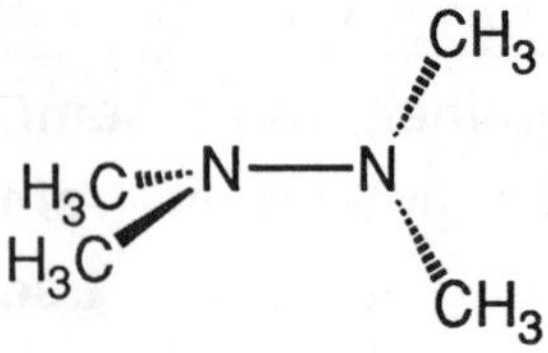

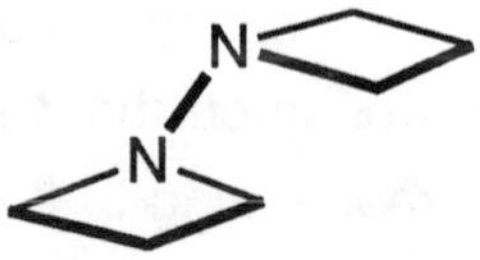

Position the nitrogen lone pairs in structures for **1** and **6** approximately orthogonally (90°). Also be certain to request printing of the molecular orbitals and corresponding orbital energies. As each job finishes, record the :NN: dihedral angle and the energies of the two highest-occupied molecular orbitals (corresponding to combinations of the two nitrogen lone pairs) in the table below. [9]

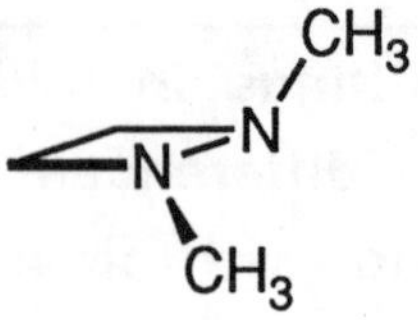

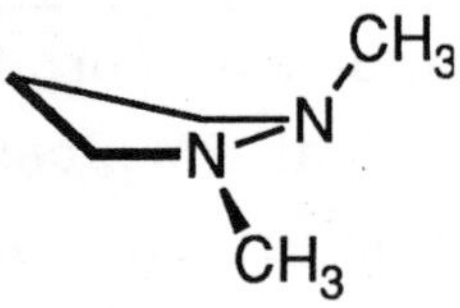

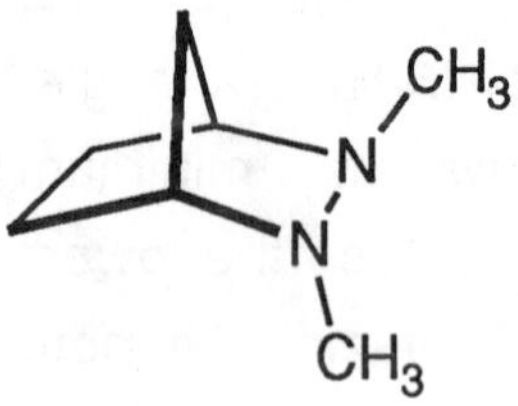

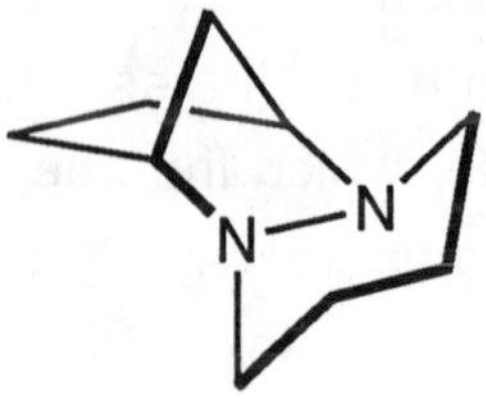

PM3 :NN: dihedral angles (°), orbital energies, difference in orbital energies and difference in experimental ionization potentials (eV)					
	:NN: dihedral angle	E_{HOMO}	E_{HOMO-1}	ΔE	IP_2-IP_1
1					0.55
2					2.04
3					2.30
4					1.78
5					2.11
6					0.73

Plot the difference in orbital energies vs. :NN: dihedral angle.

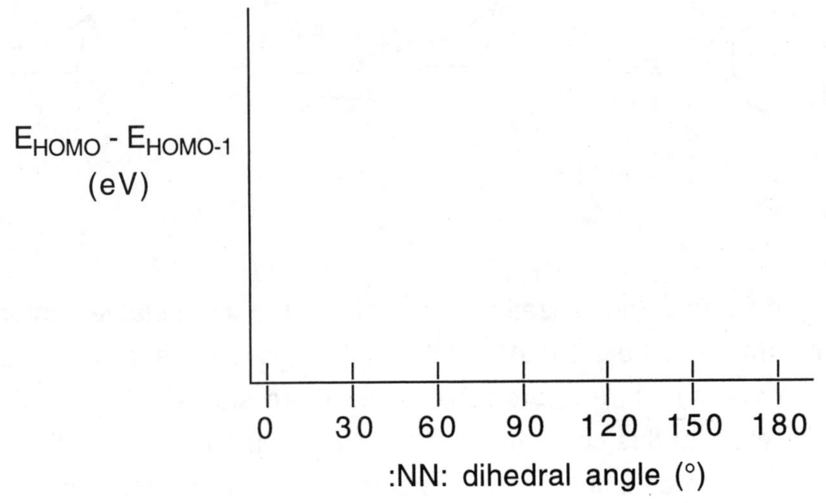

Plot the calculated difference in orbital energies vs. the difference in experimental 1st and 2nd ionization potentials.

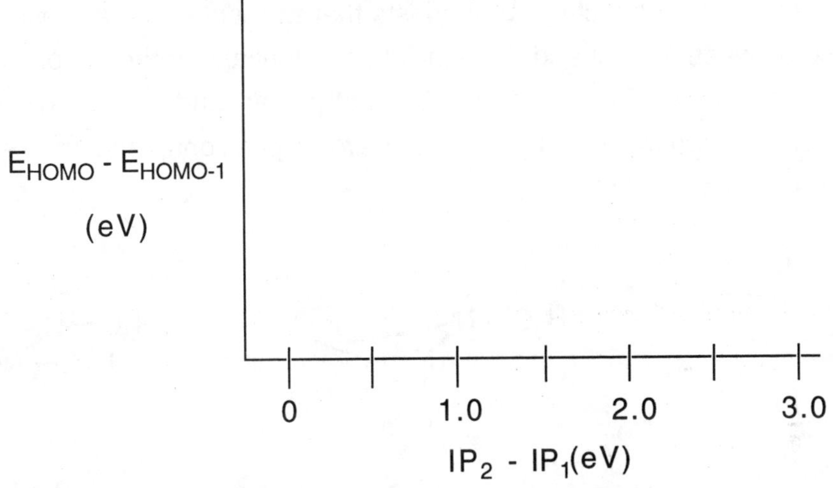

Are the semi-empirical calculations able to account qualitatively for the observed splitting? Could you use the relationship between orbital energies (or ionization potentials) and dihedral angle to predict hydrazine conformation? What information would you need to calculate (or measure) in order to make a prediction?

Optional

1. Among the stable conformers available to hydrazine **7** are structures **7a** and **7b**, in which the nitrogen lone pairs are approximately *anti* and *gauche*, respectively.

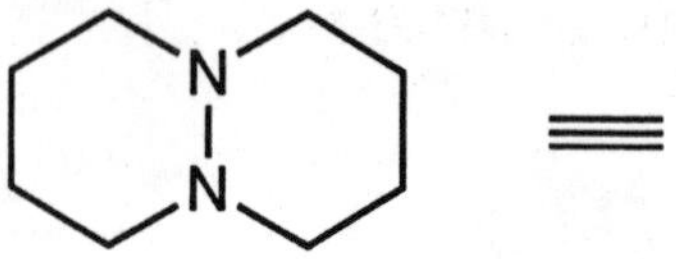

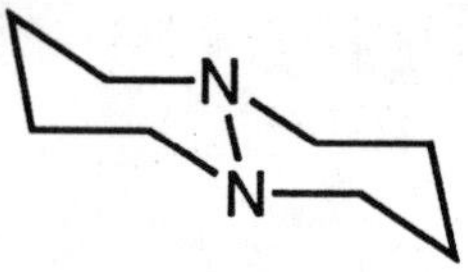

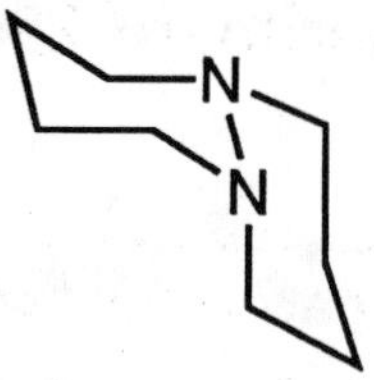

N—N (bicyclic structure) ≡ N—N (chair conformers)

7 7a 7b

The difference in 1st and 2nd ionization potentials for the more stable conformer of **7** is known experimentally to be 2.31 eV. Build both **7a** and **7b** and optimize using the PM3 model. Which structure is predicted to be more stable? Is the orbital energy difference calculated for this conformer consistent with the measured difference in 1st and 2nd ionization potentials? Is the calculated orbital energy difference for the alternative conformer inconsistent?

2. The photoelectron spectrum **3** suggests that two isomers are present, and that the difference between the 1st and 2nd ionization potentials for the minor isomer is 0.8 eV. Identify this isomer. Hint: the ring in **3** is not planar, and the methyl substituents may occupy either *pseudo axial* or *pseudo equatorial* positions, leading to a possibility of three different isomers.

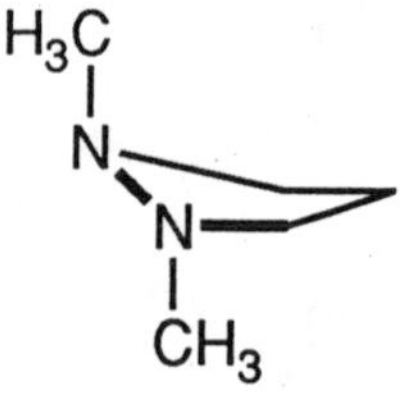

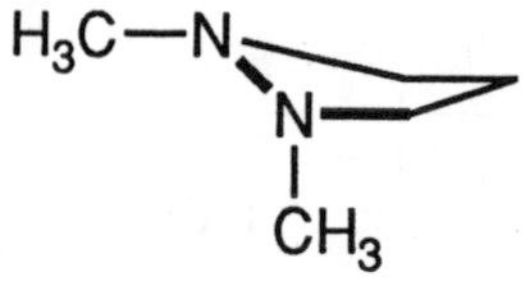

3a	3b	3c
axial-axial	equatorial-axial	equatorial-equatorial

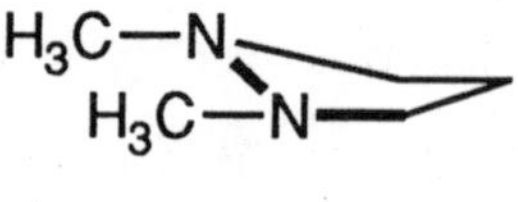

Build and optimize at the PM3 level all three conformers of **3** (you have already dealt with one of them). Compute the difference in energy between the two highest-occupied molecular orbitals for each. Are all three conformers minima at the PM3 level? Are you able to associate values for two of the conformers to the two experimental ionization potential differences of 0.8 and 2.31 eV?

Experiment 20: Structures and Stabilities of *meta*-Cyclophanes

We carry out conformational searches on *meta*-cyclophanes and their bridged cyclohexadiene precursors using the MM3 molecular mechanics model, and follow these by semi-empirical AM1 structure optimizations, in order to investigate the structures and stabilities of this class of strained aromatics.

meta-Cyclophanes, **2**, may be reached from the analogous bridged cyclohexadienes, **1**, via elimination of H_2.[1]

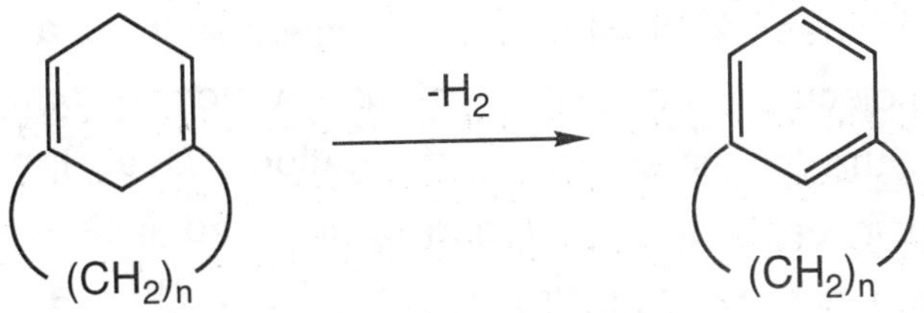

$$\mathbf{1}\ \xrightarrow{-H_2}\ \mathbf{2} \qquad (1)$$

$(CH_2)_n$ $(CH_2)_n$

1 **2**

While the hydrocarbon tether appears to predispose the hydrogens on cyclohexadiene for *syn* elimination, i.e.,

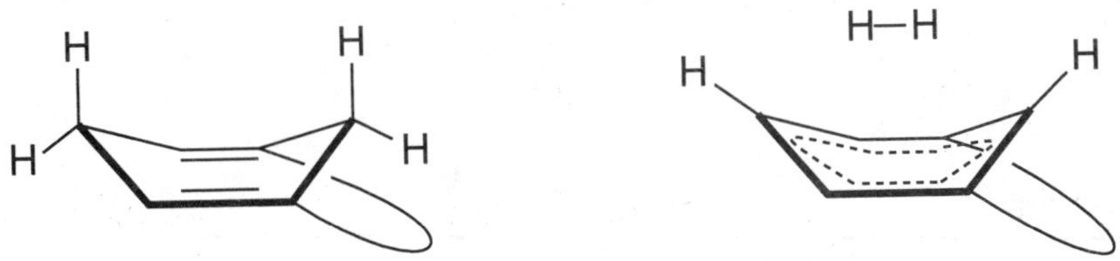

H H H H H—H H H

it also acts to severely distort the aromatic ring in the resulting *meta*-cyclophane. In this experiment, we employ semi-empirical AM1 calculations to examine the thermodynamics of hydrogenation reactions (1) for tether lengths (n) of ∞ (cyclohexadiene→benzene), 4, 5, 6 and 7. Except for cyclohexadiene itself (n=∞), both reactant, bridged cyclohexadienes, and product, *meta*-cyclophanes, are conformationally flexible, and we need to precede the AM1 quantum chemical

[1] K.J. Shea, L.D. Burke and R.J. Doedens, J. Am. Chem. Soc., **107**, 5306 (1985).

calculations with conformational searches in order to establish the proper geometry. In this experiment we will use molecular mechanics techniques for this purpose.

The strategy employed here, use of molecular mechanics to fully explore conformation space followed by use of electronic structure calculations to assign relative energies, is about the only practical strategy for systems of this size and conformational complexity.

Procedure

The heat of reaction (1) for n=∞ has already been established as 1 kcal/mol at the AM1 level [see **Experiment 1**]. Build the bridged cyclohexadienes, **1**, (n=4,5,6,7) and the *meta*-cyclophanes, **2**, (n=4,5,6,7). Subject each to a full conformational search at the MM3 molecular mechanics level, after which perform an AM1 geometry optimization only on the lowest-energy conformation. Does the predicted lowest-energy conformation in each of the bridged cyclohexadienes show the hydrogens disposed for *syn* elimination as suggested above? Are the benzene rings in the *meta*-cyclophanes significantly distorted from planarity? Record the AM1 heats of formation for both bridged cyclohexadienes and *meta*-cyclophanes in the table below.

AM1 heats of formation and hydrogenation energies (kcal/mol)			
n	ΔH_f°		$\Delta H_{dehydrogenation}$
	cyclohexadiene	*meta*-cyclophane	
4			
5			
6			
7			

Work out the heats of reactions (1). You will need to know that the heat of formation of H_2 is -5.2 kcal/mol at the AM1 level. Make a plot of the heat of reaction (1) as a function of tether length; be certain to include on the plot the data for dehydrogenation of benzene itself (n=∞).

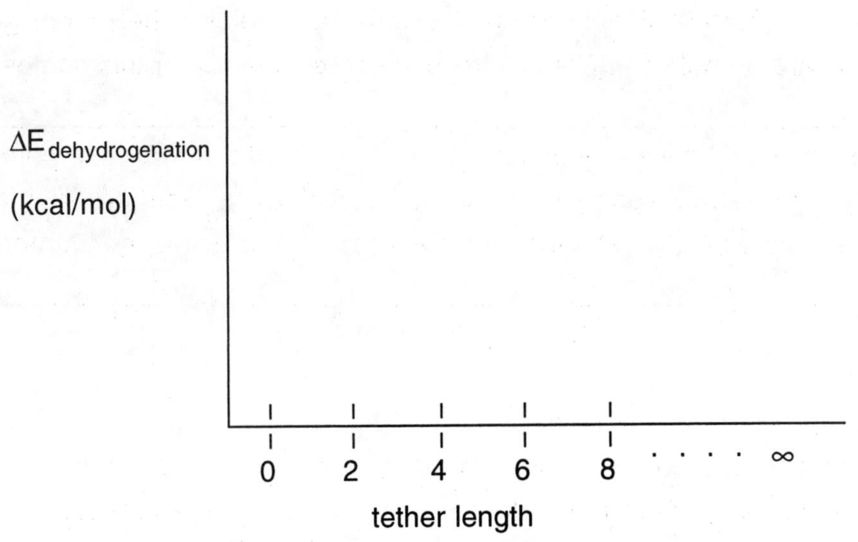

On the basis of your data, what do you conclude about the relative stabilities of *meta*-cyclophanes as a function of tether length. Would you describe any of these systems as unstrained? Is the dehydrogenation endothermic or exothermic for the tethered cyclohexadienes? Is the aromatic driving force or the increase in strain more important?

Chapter 3. Molecular Properties and Spectra

The central goal in the majority of computational investigations is the elucidation of molecular potential energy surfaces. As we have already seen in the first two chapters, this provides detailed connections between molecular structure, including conformation, and chemical stability. As we will see later in this book, the investigation of potential energy surfaces also provides insight into the connection between structure and chemical reactivity. It is not surprising that the quantities most commonly sought from quantum chemical calculations are the molecular geometry and/or the energy. Other quantities are also available, and may be of value in carrying out chemical investigations. Some of these are directly related to the geometry or energy, e.g., acidity is obtained from combining energies, while others are more remote, e.g., the infrared or UV/visible spectrum, and still others represent distinct observables, e.g., the electric dipole moment. Needless to say, the boundaries between energy and geometry and other quantities which may be of interest are often not sharp.

The experiments collected under this chapter cover a range of topics. Infrared spectra for a stable molecule, acetic acid, and for a short-lived species, water dimer, are to be obtained, as are UV/visible spectra for a closely related series of carbonyl compounds. These examples illustrate the procedures involved and provide some calibration as to the performance of available computational methods. A comparison of methods available for the calculation of atomic charges is provided and, closely related to this, discussion of the relationship between charges (which cannot be measured) and dipole moments (which can be measured). Acid/base strengths are addressed at some length. Electrostatic potentials are used to assess structural effects on acid strength in hydrocarbons, and are correlated with solution phase pKa's of carboxylic acids. The basicities of alkylamines both in the gas and water are calculated and differences in acid and base strengths for ground and excited state molecules are addressed. Finally, reduction potentials in substituted quinones and the rates of electrophilic addition to alkynes are correlated with calculated orbital energies.

Experiment 21: Infrared Spectrum of Acetic Acid

We use the semi-empirical PM3 method to compute and assign the vibrational (infrared) spectrum of acetic acid.

Absorption of light in the infrared region of the electromagnetic spectrum excites vibrational motions. Both the absorption frequencies and intensities are very sensitive to detailed molecular geometry and, because of this, vibrational spectroscopy, i.e., infrared and Raman spectroscopy, provides a powerful tool for structure elucidation. Chemists often use vibrational spectroscopy to search for evidence that a particular functional group is present. For example, a strong absorption in the region 1675-1880 cm^{-1} is compelling evidence for carbonyl functionality. Alternatively, the **fingerprint region** of the spectrum (below about 1500 cm^{-1}) may be surveyed to compare an unknown with some authentic sample. If the infrared spectra in this region are identical, then the two materials are almost certainly the same. Finally, vibrational spectra also provide a sensitive barometer of changes both to geometry and to electronic structure due to association, e.g., hydrogen bonding, or to solvation.

In this experiment, we apply the PM3 semi-empirical method to compute and assign the infrared spectrum of acetic acid. This will illustrate the general approach to computing spectra, and will allow us to assess the accuracy of PM3 calculations in this regard.

Procedure

The equilibrium conformation of acetic acid has one of the CH linkages of the methyl group eclipsing the C=O bond. Can you explain why [see **Experiment 12**]? There are two obvious arrangements involving the OH group which need to be considered.

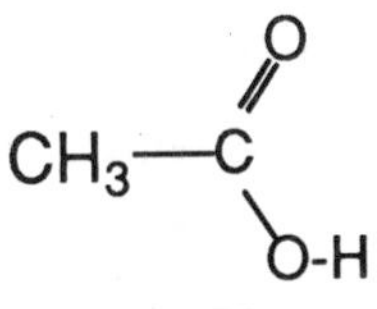

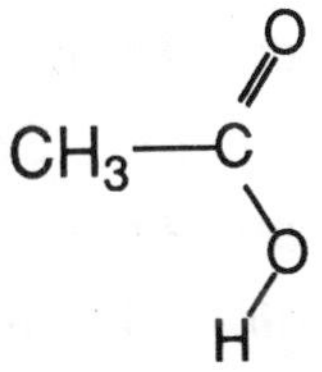

O
CH3—C
O-H

O
CH3—C
O
H

Obtain PM3 structures and heats of formation for both conformers (note: each molecule must have C_s symmetry in order to generate the correct symmetry labels for the vibrations). Which of the two is indicated to be the more stable? Can you rationalize your result? Hint: Calculate and compare electric dipole moments for the two conformers.

Calculate vibrational frequencies and infrared intensities only for the lower-

[7] energy conformer. Once the calculation has completed, animate the normal modes one by one, and try to match the calculated frequencies with those obtained from the experimental infrared spectrum[1] provided in the table below.

Experimental and PM3 infrared frequencies (cm^{-1}) and intensities					
Observed			Calculated		
	description of vibration	frequency (intensity) [a]	description of vibration	frequency	intensity
a'	OH stretch	3583 (m)			
	CH_3 d-stretch	3051 (vw)			
	CH_3 s-stretch	2944 (vw)			
	C=O stretch	1788 (vs)			
	CH_3 d-deform	1430 (sh)			
	CH_3 s-deform	1382 (m)			
	OH bend	1264 (m)			
	C-O stretch	1182 (s)			
	CH_3 rock	989 (m)			
	CC stretch	847 (w)			
	OCO deform	657 (s)			
	CCO deform	581 (m)			
a"	CH_3 d-stretch	2996 (vw)			
	CH_3 d-deform	1430 (sh)			
	CH_3 rock	1048 (w)			
	C=O op-bend	642 (s)			
	C-O torsion	534 (m)			
	CH_3 torsion	93			

a) vs=very strong; s=strong, m=medium; w=weak; vw=very weak; sh=sholder

Pay attention to the symmetry of vibration (a' or a"), and to the description of the vibrational motion provided in the table. Write a brief description of each of the calculated vibrational modes. Do your descriptions fit with those in the table? Point out any major discrepancies.

Experimental infrared intensities for each of the 18 vibrational frequencies of acetic acid are also included in the table. Among the most intense infrared absorptions is that corresponding to stretching of the carbon-oxygen double bond.

[1] T. Shimanouchi, **Tables of Molecular Vibrational Frequencies**, vol. 1, NSRDS-NBS 39, Nat. Bur. Stand., Washington DC, 1972, p. 111.

Other vibrations involving motions of one or both oxygens also exhibit medium to strong absorptions, while modes which do not involve the oxygens generally show weak absorptions. Given your assignments above, how well do the calculated intensities reflect the experimental values? It is usually assumed that the intensity and the change in dipole moment due to a vibration are correlated. Is this assumption consistent with your calculated intensities and vibrations? Hint: compare the animation of the vibration corresponding to the C=O stretch with that for one of the CH stretching motions.

Optional

Recalculate the vibrational spectrum of acetic acid in which the carboxylic acid proton has been replaced by deuterium. Identify frequencies which are shifted by deuterium substitution. The most conspicuous change in the experimental spectrum is the shift in the OH stretching frequency from 3583 cm^{-1} in CH_3CO_2H to 2642 cm^{-1} in CH_3CO_2D. [2] How well do the calculations reproduce this shift? **[11]**

[2] ref 1, p. 112.

Experiment 22: Charges on Atoms in Molecules

We examine and compare two popular ways to calculate charges on atoms in molecules. We emphasize that atomic charge is not a uniquely defined quantity. Not only do different methods give different results, but results from a given method often depend on the level (basis set, etc.) of calculation.

Charges are a part of the everyday language of organic chemistry, so much so that many chemists have come to accept them at face value. Charge distributions imply something about where the electrons reside in molecules, and this in turn tells us something about the "chemistry" which molecules can undergo. For example, the obvious resonance structures for phenoxy anion,

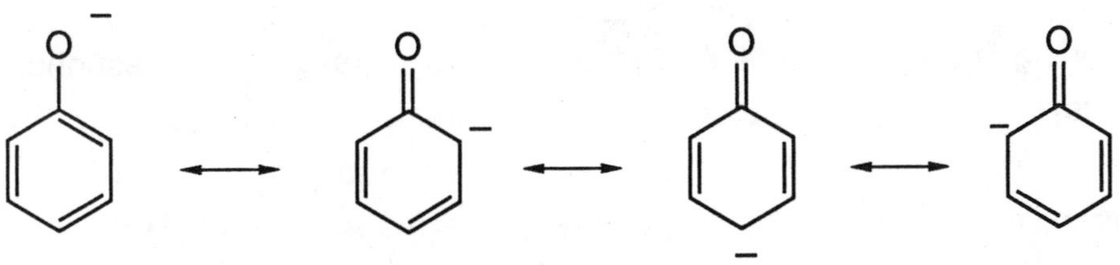

tell us that the molecule's negative charge resides not only on oxygen, but also on the *ortho* and *para* (but not on the *meta*) ring carbons. This, in turn, tells us that addition of an electrophile will occur at these sites.

Despite their obvious utility to chemists, there is actually no way either to measure atomic charges or to calculate them, at least not uniquely. The reason behind this surprising statement is quite simple. Take a careful look at a molecule from the point of view of quantum mechanics. It is made up of nuclei, each of which bears a positive charge equal to its atomic number, and electrons, each of which bears a charge of -1. We usually assume that the nuclei can be treated as point charges, i.e., they do not occupy appreciable space, and furthermore that they are stationary. The latter is a statement of the *Born-Oppenheimer approximation.* Treatment of the electrons is more difficult. They may either be viewed as individual particles each moving at the speed of light, or better as a distribution of negative charge. In the latter view, it needs to be recognized that the distribution extends throughout all space, although it is primarily concentrated in regions around the individual nuclei and in between nuclei which are close together, i.e., are bonded. The region of space occupied by a conventional space-filling or CPK model corresponds roughly to a van der Waals surface and encloses something on the order of 90-95% of the electrons in the entire distribution.

How do we designate charges on individual atoms? We clearly need to account both for the nuclear charge and for the charge of any electrons *associated* with the particular atom. While the nuclear contribution to the total charge on an atom is easy to handle (as already mentioned, it is simply the atomic number), it is not at all obvious how to partition the total electron distribution by atoms. To see that this cannot be done uniquely, consider the heteronuclear diatomic molecule HF, sketched below.

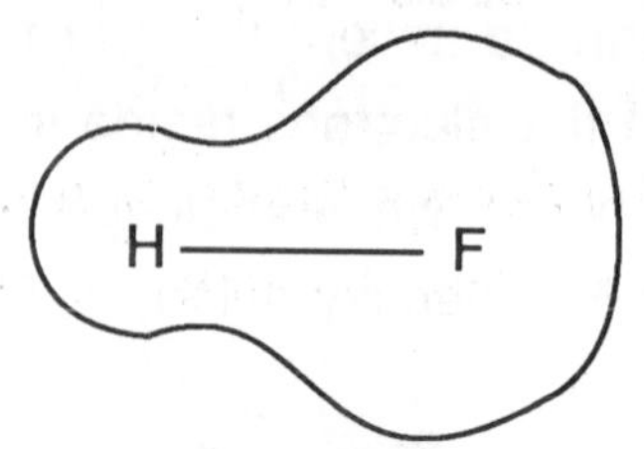

Here, the surrounding line is a particular "isodensity surface", say that corresponding to a van der Waals surface enclosing a large fraction of the total electron density. The surface has been drawn to suggest that more electrons are associated with fluorine than with hydrogen, reflecting the known polarity of the molecule, i.e., $^{\delta+}$H-F$^{\delta-}$, as reflected by the direction of its electric dipole moment [see also **Experiment 28**]. While this is qualitatively reasonable, how exactly do we divide this surface between the two nuclei? Are any of the divisions shown below better than the rest?

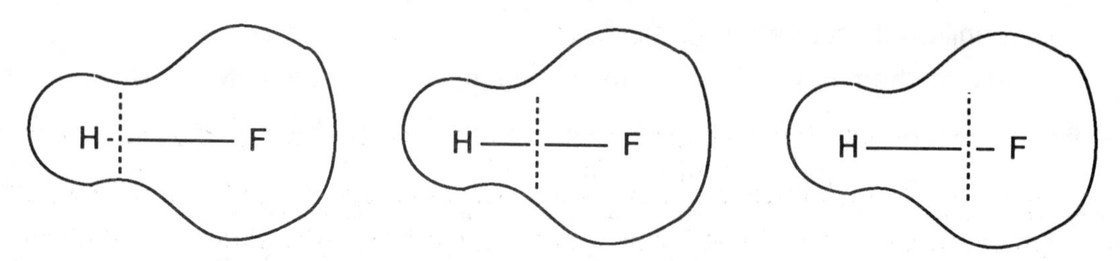

The answer to the first question is that it is not apparent how to divide the surface; the answer to the second question is clearly no! Atomic charge is not a molecular property, and it is not possible to provide a unique definition (or even a definition which will satisfy all). We can calculate (and measure using X-ray crystallography) molecular charge distributions, but we cannot uniquely partition them among the atomic centers.

This said, we need to add that numerous methods have been developed for partitioning charge and are in widespread use. Two of the most popular are the

Mulliken partition method and charge calculation based on fits to electrostatic potentials. We briefly review both of these techniques.

A. Mulliken Method for Charge Partitioning[1]

The electron density function $\rho(\mathbf{r})$ is defined such that $\rho(\mathbf{r})d\mathbf{r}$ is the probability of finding an electron in a small volume element $d\mathbf{r}$. In Hartree-Fock theory,

$$\rho(\mathbf{r}) = \sum_{\mu}^{N}\sum_{\nu}^{N} P_{\mu\nu}\phi_{\mu}(\mathbf{r})\phi_{\nu}(\mathbf{r}) = n \quad ,$$

where $P_{\mu\nu}$ is an element of the density matrix, ϕ_{μ} and ϕ_{ν} are basis functions and n is the total number of electrons. The summations are over the N basis functions. Integrating over all space yields,

$$\int \rho(\mathbf{r})d\mathbf{r} = \sum_{\mu}^{N}\sum_{\nu}^{N} P_{\mu\nu}\int \phi_{\mu}(\mathbf{r})\phi_{\nu}(\mathbf{r})d\tau = \sum_{\mu}^{N}\sum_{\nu}^{N} P_{\mu\nu}S_{\mu\nu} = n \quad ,$$

Where we have defined the overlap integral, $S_{\mu\nu}$. The total electron density may be divided into diagonal (μ=ν, $S_{\mu\nu}$=1) and off-diagonal terms,

$$\sum_{\mu}^{N} P_{\mu\mu} + 2\sum_{\mu>\nu}^{N}\sum^{N} P_{\mu\nu} = n \quad .$$

While it is reasonable to associate the diagonal terms, $P_{\mu\mu}$ to a particular center, the partitioning of the $P_{\mu\nu}$ between the centers is not obvious and is in fact arbitrary. In the Mulliken procedure, each basis function is allocated half the total number of electrons. Within this method, we can define a gross population for basis function ϕ_{μ},

$$q_{\mu} = P_{\mu\mu} + P_{\mu\nu}S_{\mu\nu},$$

where it is easily shown that,

$$\sum_{\mu}^{N} q_{\mu} = n \quad .$$

---

[1] R.S. Mulliken, J. Chem. Phys., **23**, 1833, 1841, 2338, 2343 (1955).

Atomic populations, q_A, and atomic charges, Q_A, follow.

$$q_A = \sum_{\mu}^{\text{on A}} q_\mu$$

$$Q_A = Z_A - q_a$$

The principal advantage of the Mulliken procedure is that it is computationally simple. Aside from being arbitrary, as are all charge analysis schemes, it suffers from the fact that it generally does not converge with increasing complexity of *ab initio* basis set.

B. Charges Based on Fits to Electrostatic Potentials[2]

This method of obtaining atomic charges is not a partitioning scheme as is the Mulliken procedure, but a scheme in which a distribution of energies of interaction of a point positive charge with a molecule is fit to atomic charges. One can then think of the method as providing that set of atomic charges which best reproduces the overall electrostatic potential resulting from the actual molecular electron distribution.

Several steps are involved in its implementation after a quantum mechanical wavefunction has been obtained:

i) Define a grid of points around the molecule. This normally is restricted to the region outside that dictated by the van der Waals surface.

ii) Calculate the electrostatic potential at each of these points.

$$\varepsilon_p = \sum_{A}^{\text{nuclei}} \frac{Z_A}{R_{Ap}} - \sum_{\mu}^{N} \sum_{\nu}^{N} P_{\mu\nu} \int \frac{\phi_\mu^*(1)\phi_\nu(1)}{r_{1p}} dx_1 dy_1 dz_1$$

The first summation is over nuclei A, where Z_A are atomic numbers and R_{Ap} are distances to the test charge. The second summation is over atomic basis functions μ and ν, where $P_{\mu\nu}$ are elements of the density matrix and the integrals measure the Coulombic interaction between the test charge and the molecule's electron distribution.

---

[2] L.E. Chirlian and M. Francl, J. Computational Chem., **8**, 894 (1987); C.M. Breneman and K.B. Wiberg, *ibid.*, **11**, 361 (1990).

iii) Fit the calculated potential to a potential based on atomic charges (treated as variables), subject to the constraint that the sum of atomic charges is equal to the total charge on the molecule.

While fitting charges to electrostatic potentials is computationally expensive (at least relative to the Mulliken procedure), the results generally show convergence with increasing complexity of the *ab initio* basis set. This method of obtaining charges is the obvious choice if the purpose of obtaining the charges is for use in empirical energy functions.

In this experiment, we obtain charges for acetic acid in order to see the variation between the two methods and, in the case of *ab initio* wavefunctions, the variation in charge distributions as a function of basis set.

Procedure

Build acetic acid in the conformation shown below [see also **Experiment 21**] (the numbers are used to assign charges).

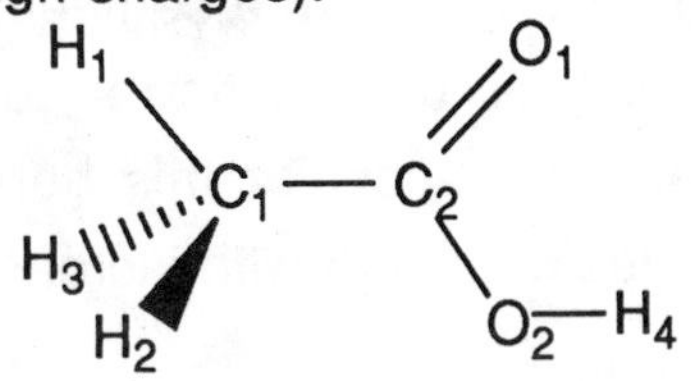

H_1 O_1

C_1 — C_2

H_3

H_2 O_2—H_4

Optimize at the AM1 level. Using the AM1 geometry, perform single-point energy calculations at the MNDO, AM1 and PM3 semi-empirical levels and at the STO-3G, 3-21G and 6-31G* *ab initio* levels.

Charge distributions like electric dipole moments [see also **Experiment 28**] are sensitive to the choice of geometry. We use a common geometry for all calculations to limit our assessment to the method of charge calculation and to the level of theory.

Record the calculated Mulliken and electrostatic fit charges in the table below.

Mulliken and electrostatic-fit charges (electrons)						
	MNDO	AM1	PM3	STO-3G	3-21G	6-31G*
Mulliken						
C_1						
C_2						
O_1						
O_2						
H_1						
H_2=H_3						
H_4						
Fits to Electrostatic Potentials						
C_1						
C_2						
O_1						
O_2						
H_1						
H_2=H_3						
H_4						

Are the calculated charges "chemically reasonable"? For example, is the hydroxyl hydrogen indicated to be more positive than the methyl hydrogens suggesting it as an acidic site [see also **Experiment 23**]? Do the semi-empirical methods all give similar results? The PM3 method has often been criticized for providing "unrealistic" charge distributions. Do you see any evidence for this here? Do either the Mulliken or electrostatic potential fits charges converge with increasing level of *ab initio* theory?

Optional

[1] Perform charge calculations at the MP2/6-31G* level using both Mulliken and electrostatic fit procedures. Make certain you specify use of direct methods. Compare these to the results obtained from the corresponding HF/6-31G* wavefunctions. Focus on the carbonyl carbon and oxygen. What shifts in charges do you observe? Can you rationalize?[1] Hint: recall that correlation involves mixing of excited states into the ground-state wavefunction. How would you describe the lowest-energy excited state of acetic acid? It might help to calculate the HOMO and LUMO for acetic acid (use HF/6-31G*) to see what effect removing an electron from the former and putting it into the latter might have.

---

[1] J.E. Carpenter, M.P. McGrath and W.J. Hehre, **111**, 6154 (1989).

Experiment 23: Electrostatic Potentials as Indicators of Acidity

We use electrostatic potentials obtained from 3-21G *ab initio* calculations to examine changes in gas-phase acidities due to changes in hybridization, to ring strain and to substitution by donor and acceptor groups. We also examine the ability of electrostatic potentials to distinguish between weak and strong acids.

To what extent do charges on acidic hydrogens in neutral molecules anticipate the ease with which these hydrogens may be removed, i.e., their acidity? Do subtle changes in charge distributions resulting from variations in structure and/or from substitution anticipate changes in acidity? To measure charge distribution, we employ the electrostatic potential. As pointed out in **Experiment 22**, this corresponds to the energy of interaction of a positive test charge with the nuclei and electron distribution of the molecule under investigation, i.e.,

$$\varepsilon_p = \sum_{A}^{\text{nuclei}} \frac{Z_A}{R_{Ap}} - \sum_{\mu}^{N} \sum_{\nu}^{N} P_{\mu\nu} \int \frac{\phi_\mu^*(1)\phi_\nu(1)}{r_{1p}} dx_1 dy_1 dz_1$$

The first summation is over nuclei A; Z_A are atomic numbers and R_{Ap} are distances to the test charge. The second summation is over atomic basis functions μ and ν; $P_{\mu\nu}$ are elements of the density matrix and the integrals measure the Coulombic interaction between the test charge and the molecule's electron distribution.

The electrostatic potential may be sampled over the entire *accessible surface* of a molecule (corresponding roughly to a van der Waals contact surface), and then provides a measure of charge distribution from the point of view of an approaching reagent. Regions of positive electrostatic potential indicate excess positive charge, i.e., repulsion for the positively-charged test probe, while regions of negative potential indicate areas of excess negative charge, i.e., attraction of the positively-charged test probe. In this experiment, which is broken into four relatively independent parts, we examine electrostatic potential surfaces for a variety of simple molecules in order to assess qualitatively their relative acidities.

A. Relative Acidities of Ethane, Ethylene and Acetylene

Alkynes are far stronger acids than alkenes, which in turn are stronger acids than alkanes. The usual explanation is that the sp hybrid resulting from deprotonation of an alkyne is lower in energy than the sp^2 hybrid resulting from deprotonation of an alkene (which in turn is lower in energy than the sp^3 hybrid from an alkane), and hence better able to hold the non-bonded electron pair[1] [see also **Experiment 9**]. Let's see if the ordering of acidities in hydrocarbons is anticipated by the electrostatic potentials in the vicinity of the acidic hydrogens or by calculated charges on the "acidic" hydrogens.

Procedure

Build ethane, ethylene and acetylene and optimize at the 3-21G *ab initio* level. Generate total electron density surfaces onto which the electrostatic potential has been encoded. Display the three electrostatic potential surfaces simultaneously and all on

[3] the same scale. Focus your attention on the hydrogens. Which molecule contains the most electron-poor hydrogen? Which molecule contains the least electron-poor hydrogen? Is the charge on hydrogen correlated with the molecule's acidity?

Quantify your visual impressions by "measuring" the value of the electrostatic

[8] potential on the density surface (in the vicinity of the hydrogens). Record these values in the table below.

3-21G electrostatic potentials (kcal/mol) and hydrogen charges (electrons)		
	value of the electrostatic potential	charge on acidic hydrogen
ethane		
ethylene		
acetylene		

Do the potentials support your qualitative conclusions from viewing the image? Calculate and record atomic charges based on fits to electrostatic potentials. Are those charges in line with your expectations based on the graphical surfaces? Point out any discrepancies.

---

[1] March, p. 233.

B. Effect of Ring Strain on Acidity

Hybridization is also commonly invoked to rationalize the higher acidities of strained hydrocarbons relative to unstrained systems.[2] For example, the fact that the CH hybrids in cyclopropane have less *p character* than the sp^3 hybrids in unstrained alkanes is taken as the reason for the higher acidity of the small-ring systems. Here we see whether the electrostatic potential and/or hydrogen charges also parallel the change in acidity from acyclic to strained-ring compounds.

Procedure

Build propane and cyclopropane and optimize at the 3-21G level. Calculate electron density surfaces with electrostatic potentials encoded. Examine the two systems together (and on the same scale). Determine the value of the potential in the vicinity of the methylene hydrogens and record in the table below. **[3,8]**

3-21G electrostatic potentials (kcal/mol) and hydrogen charges (electrons)		
	value of the electrostatic potential	charge on acidic hydrogen
propane		
cyclopropane		

What do you conclude about the relative acidities of the two molecules? Is your conclusion consistent with the experimentally measured pK_a's of these compounds? Evaluate and record hydrogen charges based on fits to electrostatic potentials. Confirm that these provide analogous results to those obtained by inspection of the electrostatic potentials.

C. Substituent Effects on Acidity

Models based on electrostatic potentials or charges fit to electrostatic potentials should be capable of accounting for changes in acidity which result from substitution. In particular, they should be able to elaborate the effects which electron-donor and electron-acceptor substituents have on acidity, and account for the ordering of acidities of related substituted systems. Here we see if the electrostatic potentials and/or

---

[2] Lowry and Richardson, p. 293.

charge calculations are able to reproduce the effects of electron-donor and electron-acceptor substituents on acetylene.

Procedure

Build propyne and 3,3,3-trifluoropropyne, optimize at the 3-21G level and calculate total density surfaces with encoded electrostatic potentials. Trifluoropropyne [1] is large enough that you will probably need to use direct methods. Display the [3] calculated potential surfaces side-by-side and on the same scale. Bring up the encoded surface for acetylene (part **A**) and also put it onto the same scale. Focus your attention on the acetylenic hydrogens. Specifically, determine the value of the [8] potential on the acidic hydrogen and record in the table below.

3-21G electrostatic potentials (kcal/mol) and hydrogen charges (electrons)		
	value of the electrostatic potential	charge on acidic hydrogen
acetylene		
propyne		
trifluoropropyne		

What do you conclude about the effects of methyl and trifluoromethyl substituents in altering the acidity of acetylene? Is your conclusion consistent with experiment? On the basis of your results, would you say that the methyl group is acting as an electron donor or an electron acceptor? What about the trifluoromethyl group? Are your conclusions consistent with conventional chemical wisdom? Calculate atomic charges based on fits to electrostatic potentials. Is the hydrogen's charge correlated with its electrostatic potential? Based on these calculated charges, what do you conclude about the effect of methyl and trifluoromethyl substituents on acetylene acidity?

D. Strong Acids and Weak Acids

Does the relationship between hydrogen charge (as evaluated by examination of electrostatic potential surfaces) and acidity extend beyond the realm of hydrocarbon acids? Let's see if examining electrostatic potentials and/or charges at hydrogen can tell us that ethanol is a weak acid, whereas acetic acid is a moderately strong acid and nitric acid is a very strong acid.

Procedure

Build ethanol, acetic acid and nitric acid and optimize at the 3-21G level. You probably don't need to use direct methods. As before, calculate both electrostatic potentials encoded onto total electron density surfaces and display these three surfaces side-by-side and on the same scale. Orient the molecules such that the acidic hydrogen in each is clearly visible and then determine the magnitude of the electrostatic potential. Record in the table below. [3] [8]

3-21G electrostatic potentials (kcal/mol) and hydrogen charges (electrons)		
	value of the electrostatic potential	charge on acidic hydrogen
ethanol		
acetic acid		
nitric acid		

Do the electrostatic potentials correctly anticipate the relative acidities of these molecules? Do the charges on hydrogen also anticipate the proper ordering of acidities? Can you identify the most acidic hydrogen in each molecule using either the electrostatic potentials or the atomic charges?

Experiment 24: UV Spectra of Conjugated Carbonyl Compounds

We employ semi-empirical AM1 configuration interaction (CI) calculations to obtain UV absorption maxima in a series of conjugated carbonyl compounds.

Chromophores undergoing electronic transitions typically absorb in the UV or visible region. In order for a molecule to absorb, the energy of the photon must exactly equal that of the transition between the ground state and some excited state. Photons with greater or lesser energy will be "ignored". We define an absorption wavelength, λ, in terms of the energy difference between ground and excited states, i.e.,

$$\lambda(\text{nm}) = \frac{hc}{E_x - E_g} ,$$

where E_x is the energy of the excited state, E_g is the energy of the ground state, h is Planck's constant and c is the speed of light.

In this experiment, we calculate λ for a series of related α, β-unsaturated carbonyl compounds,

R_3

R_1 O

R_2 R_4

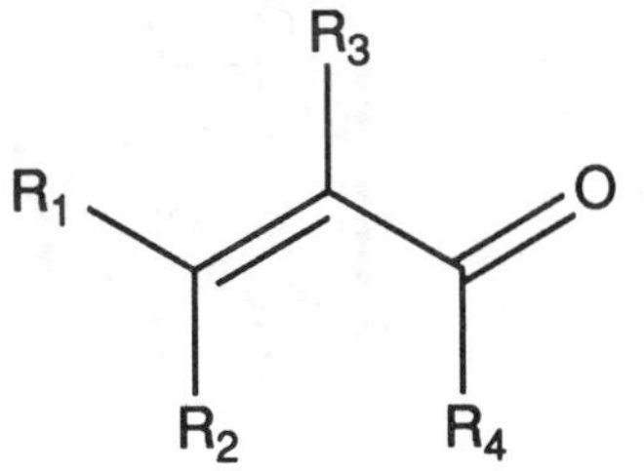

using the semi-empirical AM1 method. These compounds are ideal for study primarily because of a wealth of experimental data available for comparison. Also, the experimental absorption bands for this chromophore are generally very sharp, intense, and not strongly *solvatochromic* (dependent on solvent). This allows for unambiguous comparison with calculated absorptions. The excited-state energies will be obtained through a limited configuration interaction (CI) procedure.

The CI method builds up excited-state descriptions starting from the ground-state description by explicit promotion of electrons from a given set of occupied molecular orbitals to a given set of unoccupied molecular orbitals. Within this "window", wavefunctions resulting from all possible single-electron promotions and all possible double-electron promotions are combined to give a new set of solutions, the lowest energy of which corresponds to a new ground-state description and higher-energy solutions of which correspond to excited-state descriptions. The difference in energies between ground and excited state solutions correspond to absorptions.

Procedure

Build and optimize at the AM1 level each of the compounds in the table below.

AM1 absorption maxima (nm)					
	expt	AM1		expt	AM1
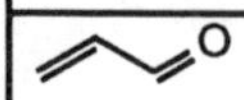 O	209		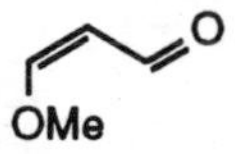 O OMe	239	
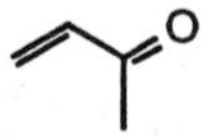 O	215		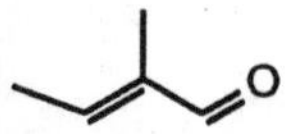 O	241	
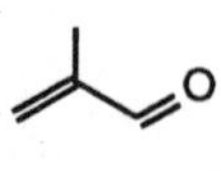 O	219		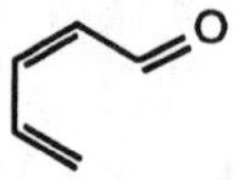 O	251	
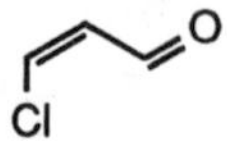 O Cl	221		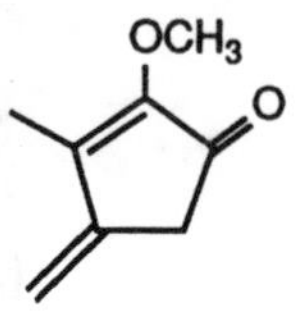 OCH_3 O	259	
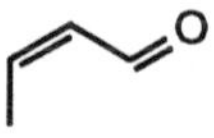 O	221		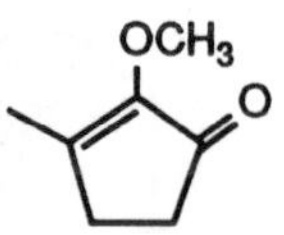 OCH_3 O	266	
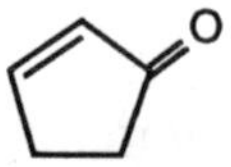 O	219		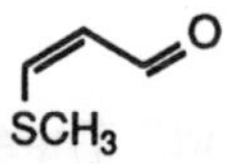 O SCH_3	294	
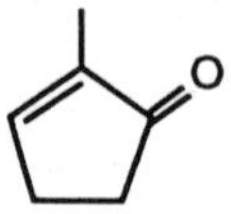 O	229		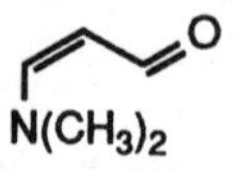 O $N(CH_3)_2$	304	

Perform a single-point AM1-CI calculation using the AM1 ground-state geometry for each. This will provide the energies of all excited states which may be formed from the ground state by absorption of light. The lowest energy of these corresponds to a $\pi \rightarrow \pi^*$ transition in these compounds; there is a lower energy $n \rightarrow \pi^*$ transition, but this is (formally) *forbidden*, and not easily seen in the absorption spectrum. Record the calculated (lowest-energy) transition wavelength in the table. Plot experimental vs. calculated absorption maxima.

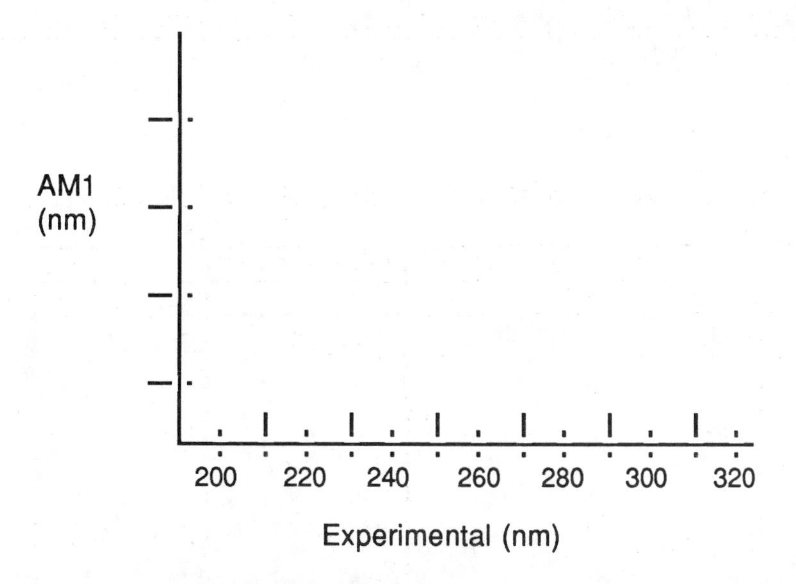

Are the calculations generally successful in reproducing absolute absorption maxima? Do they properly reproduce trends in the data?

Experiment 25: Gas and Aqueous Phase Basicities of Alkylamines

We use both semi-empirical AM1 and *ab initio* STO-3G calculations to obtain the relative basicities of alkylamines both in the gas phase and in water. We investigate the role of solvent in altering intrinsic (gas phase) basicities, and assess the performance of the AM1-SM2 solvent model in reproducing the changes from gas to aqueous-phase relative basicities.

In the gas phase, methylamine is a stronger base than ammonia. As seen by the experimental data in the table below,

amine	gas phase basicity relative to ammonia (kcal/mol)	
NH_3	0	increase in base strength ↓
CH_3NH_2	9	
$(CH_3)_2NH$	16	
$(CH_3)_3N$	19	

additional methyl substitution leads to a further increase in basicity.[1] The ability of methyl to stabilize the positively-charged nitrogen center, while now well established, was long contested. The reason was that experimental aqueous phase pKa's for the methylamines show a different ordering.[2]

amine	aqueous phase pKa	
NH_3	9.24	increase in base strength ↓
CH_3NH_2	10.65	
$(CH_3)_2NH$	10.78	
$(CH_3)_3N$	9.80	increase in base strength ↑

While a significant increase in aqueous pKa is noted from ammonia to methylamine, the pKa of dimethylamine is only slightly greater than that of methylamine, and the pKa of trimethylamine is actually significantly smaller. Note also, that the range of methyl

[1] R.W. Taft in, **Proton Transfer Reactions**, E.F. Caldin and V. Gold., eds., Wiley, New York, 1975, p. 31.

[2] F.M. Jones, III and E.M. Arnett, Prog. in Phys. Org. Chem., **11**, 263 (1974).

substituent effects is an order of magnitude less in water than in the gas phase. These changes clearly reveal the role of the solvent.

In this experiment, we investigate the ability of calculations both to reproduce the ordering of basicities of alkylamines in the gas phase, and then to account for changes in basicities due to solvation. We also use graphical models to understand these changes.

Procedure

Build and minimize at the AM1 level, ammonia, ammonium ion, methylamine, methylammonium ion, dimethylamine, dimethylammonium ion, trimethylamine and trimethylammonium ion. As each finishes, record the heat of formation (ΔH_f^{gas})in the table below.

AM1 heats of formation and solvation energies (kcal/mol) and STO-3G energies (hartrees)

	AM1			STO-3G	
	ΔH_f^{gas}	ΔH_f^{aq}	$E^{solv.}$	E^{gas}	E^{aq}
NH_3					
CH_3NH_2					
$(CH_3)_2NH$					
$(CH_3)_3N$					
NH_4^+					
$CH_3NH_3^+$					
$(CH_3)_2NH_2^+$					
$(CH_3)_3NH^+$					

Resubmit each of the jobs for single-point AM1-SM2 calculations[3] using AM1 equilibrium geometries. Record the AM1 heats of formation in water (ΔH_f^{aq}). Obtain and record the solvation energy (E^{solv}) for each as the difference between "aqueous" and gas-phase heats of formation. Are the calculated solvation energies for ammonium ions smaller or larger than those for the corresponding neutral amines? Rationalize your observation. Do the solvation energies for neutral amines increase,

[3] C.J. Cramer and D.G. Truhlar, Science, **256**, 213 (1992).

decrease or remain about the same with increasing alkyl substitution? What trend do you observe for the corresponding ammonium ions?

The AM1 model generally does not provide a very satisfactory account of gas-phase relative proton affinities, and it is advisable to obtain these values from STO-3G *ab initio* calculations. Even this very low level *ab initio* treatment is generally quite successful in describing relative acid and base strengths. Perform geometry optimizations at the STO-3G level for each of the amines and corresponding ammonium ions (the AM1 results provide good starting structures). You will probably not need to use direct methods as these are relatively small calculations. Record the STO-3G energies (E^{gas}) in the table, and then add to these energies the heats of solvation previously calculated using the AM1-SM2 model. You will need to convert kcal/mol to hartrees (1 hartree=627.5 kcal/mol). Enter these data (E^{aq}) in the table above.

Evaluate energies of reactions (1),

$$BH^{+} + NH_3 \rightleftharpoons B + NH_4^{+}, \quad B = NH_3, CH_3NH_2, (CH_3)_2NH, (CH_3)_3N, \qquad (1)$$

using your calculated data for both gas-phase (STO-3G) and solvated (STO-3G corrected for AM1-SM2 solvation energies) species. Enter your results in the table below.

	STO-3G relative proton affinities (kcal/mol)	
	ΔE^{gas}	ΔE^{aq}
NH_3		
CH_3NH_2		
$(CH_3)_2NH$		
$(CH_3)_3N$		

Do your results reproduce the measured gas-phase relative proton affinities for the methylamines? Do they parallel the experimental pKa's obtained in water?

To better understand the reversal in basicities of alkylamines from the gas phase to water, examine electrostatic potentials encoded onto total electron density surfaces for the four ammonium ions based on STO-3G wavefunctions. Display all [3] four surfaces on screen at the same time and set the range to a common scale. Regions of maximum positive charge (positive electrostatic potential) will be stabilized most effectively by the solvent. Where are the positively-charged regions localized in each of the four ammonium ions? What effect does methyl substitution appear to have on these regions? On the basis of the electrostatic potentials, what would you conclude to be the ordering of solvation energies in these systems? Is this in accord with the calculated solvation energies for these ions?

Experiment 26: Reduction Potentials in Substituted Quinones

We use the AM1 semi-empirical method to calculate the energy of the lowest-unoccupied molecular orbital in a variety of quinones, and attempt to correlate this with experimental one-electron reduction potentials. We compare electrostatic potentials to assess qualitatively the ability of quinones to accept electrons into the π system.

Electron transfer is one of the most fundamental chemical processes. In fact, there is an increasing consensus that many nucleophilic and some electrophilic reactions involve electron transfer at some point in the overall mechanism. It is of particular interest to quantify electron affinity, that is, the ability of a molecule to accept an additional electron. Furthermore, knowledge of how substituents affect electron affinity is crucial to designing molecules with specific properties.

Quinones are an important class of electron-poor compounds which readily accept electrons to yield radical anions, i.e.,[1]

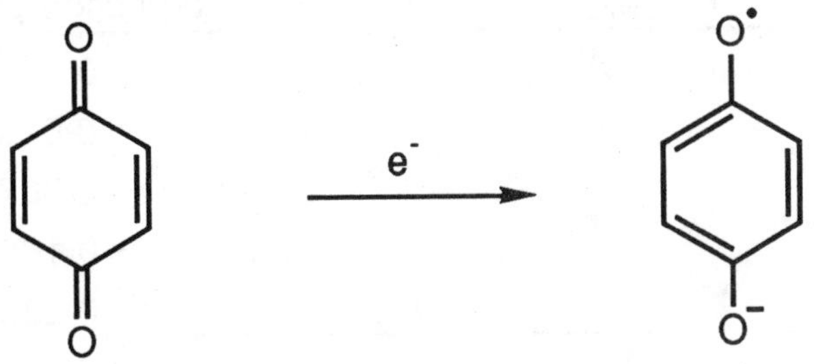

A quinone's ability to accept an electron in solution is defined by its one-electron reduction potential, many of which have been measured experimentally. These values, assuming solvent stabilizes different quinone radical anions to the same degree, are correlated with electron affinity, and we can use them to assess the ability of simple theoretical methods to reproduce and predict trends in reactivity. In this experiment, we compare orbital energies obtained from AM1 semi-empirical calculations to experimental one-electron reduction potentials for a variety of simple quinones.

---

[1] G.J. Gleicher, in **The Chemistry of the Quinoid Compounds**, vol. 1, S. Patai, ed., Wiley, New York, 1974, p. 18.

Procedure

Build and optimize at the AM1 level quinones **1-5**.

1 **2** **3** **4** **5**

Request printing of the molecular orbital energies and record the energy of the lowest unoccupied molecular orbitals (E_{LUMO}) in the table below. Also for each system, calculate a map of the electrostatic potential encoded onto a total electron density surface.

AM1 orbital energies and experimental reduction potentials (eV)		
	E_{LUMO}	reduction potential
1		0.010
2		0.023
3		0.067
4		0.165
5		0.235

Plot the calculated LUMO energies against the experimental reduction potentials.

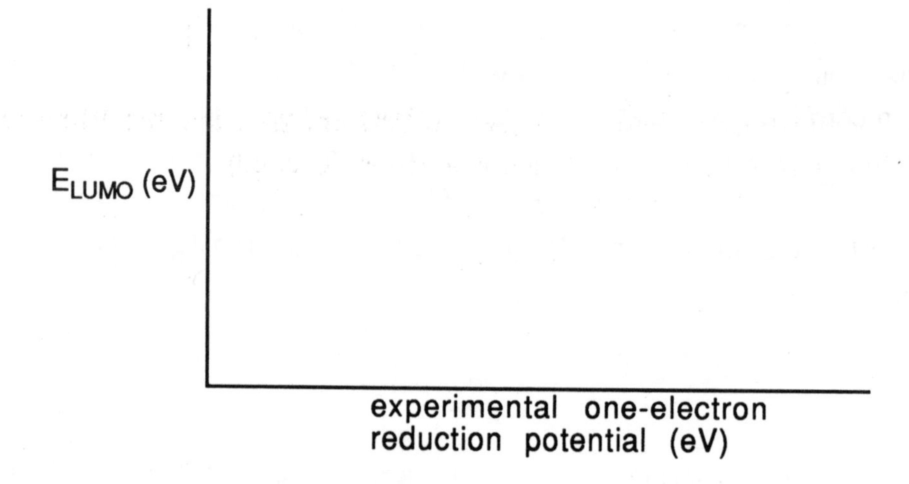

What is the effect of increasing methyl substitution on reduction potential? Can you rationalize your result?

Display the electrostatic potentials (superimposed onto total density surfaces) for quinones **1** to **5**. Put all on a common scale. Examine the potential in the π system for each of the quinones. What is the trend in potentials with increasing methyl substitution? Is there a correlation between potentials and calculated LUMO energies and/or measured reduction potentials? According to your results, does methyl act as an electron-withdrawing or electron-releasing substituent? Is your finding in acord with usual chemical wisdom? [3]

Build quinones **6-11**,

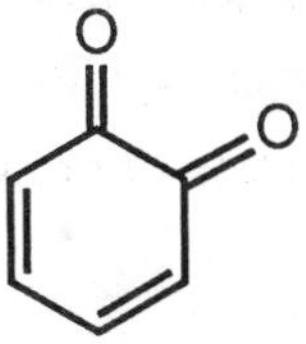

6 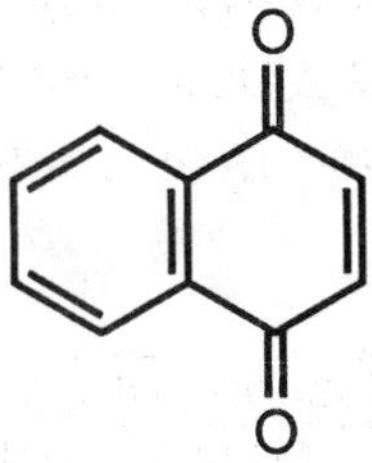 **7** 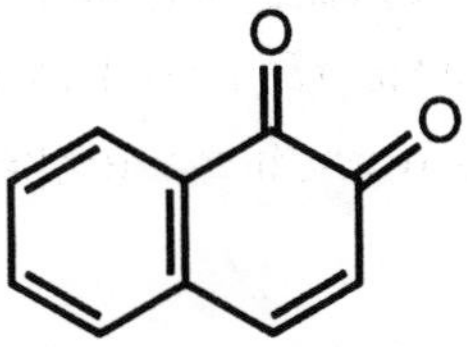 **8**

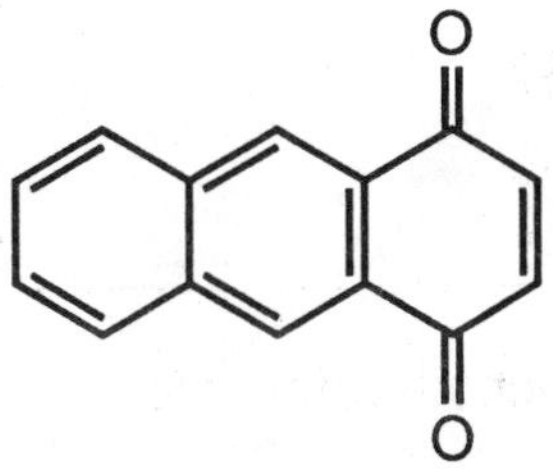

9 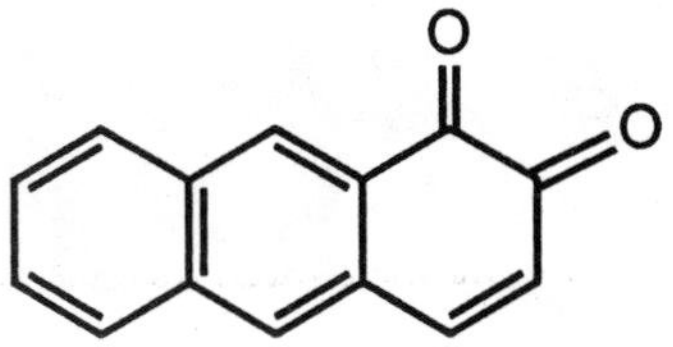 **10** 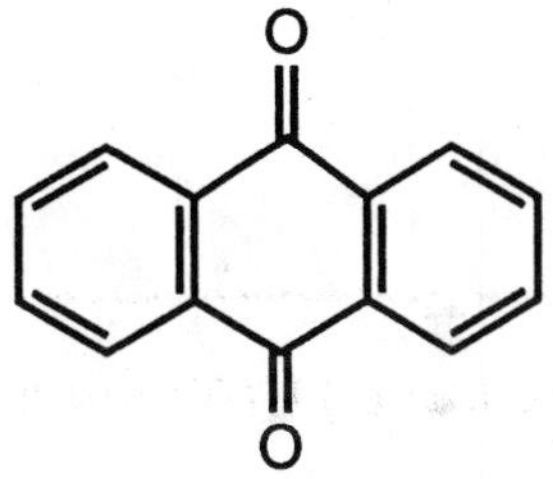 **11**

and optimize at the AM1 level. Calculate LUMO energies and record below (along with that for the parent quinone **1** which you earlier obtained).

AM1 orbital energies and experimental reduction potentials (eV)		
	E_{LUMO}	reduction potential
1		0.715
6		0.783
7		0.484
8		0.576
9		0.401
10		0.401
11		0.154

Again, plot the calculated LUMO energies versus the experimental reduction potentials.

E_{LUMO} (eV)

experimental one-electron reduction potential (eV)

(The experimental reduction potential for **1** is different here than in the previous comparison due to a different reference standard). Is there a correlation between the electron reduction potentials and the energy of the LUMO? Why do you suppose that increasing the number of fused rings lowers the potential for electron transfer to quinones? To answer this you may want to compute, display and compare the LUMOs of quinones **1**, **7**, and **9**.

Experiment 27: Structure and Infrared Spectrum of Water Dimer

We use *ab initio* 3-21G calculations to examine the structure of the water dimer as an example of hydrogen-bonded molecules. We attempt to rationalize changes in structure and vibrational frequencies in water dimer relative to water in terms of specific hydrogen-bond interactions.

The reason that water and simple alcohols have boiling points which are significantly higher than expected based solely on their molecular weights is because they associate in solution. Indeed, liquid water exhibits a highly structured network of hydrogen bonds, i.e.,

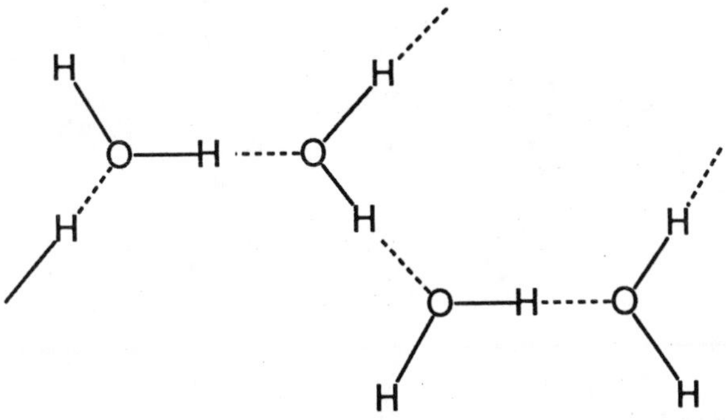

While the individual hydrogen bonds are nowhere as strong as covalent or ionic linkages, they are sufficiently strong to impart a degree of structure to liquid water. This has been observed experimentally using X-ray crystallography, which shows a relatively narrow distribution in the average separation between "nearest neighbor" oxygen atoms.

In this experiment, we explore the structure and vibrational spectrum of one of the simplest, and certainly the most carefully studied, hydrogen-bonded system, the water dimer.[1] Our objective is to uncover the consequences of hydrogen bonding on both structure and vibrational spectrum. Optionally, we illustrate the use of the electrostatic potential to demark the charge distribution in water itself, allowing us to anticipate the geometry of the dimer.

[1] For a review, see: P.A. Kollman, in **Applications of Electronic Structure Theory**, H.F. Schaefer, III, ed., vol. 4, Plenum Press, New York, 1977, p. 109.

Procedure

Build and optimize water (C_{2v} symmetry) at the *ab initio* 3-21G level. Also, request calculation of vibrational frequencies. Record the calculated OH bond distance and the vibrational frequencies in the table below, and indicate the motion to which each of the latter corresponds.

3-21G OH bond lengths (Å) and vibrational frequencies (cm^{-1})			
	OH bond length	frequency	description of vibrational motion
water			
water dimer			

The experimental infrared spectrum of water is given in the table below.

Experimental infrared frequencies (cm^{-1})		
symmetry	frequency	description
a1	3657	symmetric stretch
b1	3757	asymmetric stretch
a1	1595	bend

[7] Are your calculations in qualitative agreement? Animate the three normal modes to see that they correspond to the motions assigned in the experimental spectrum.

Build water dimer in the geometry below (the atom numbers are for later use).

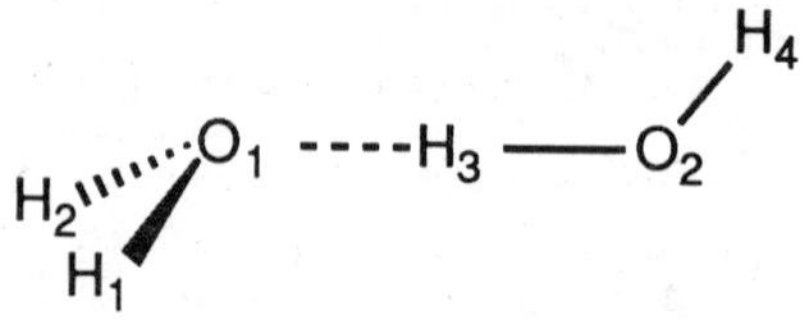

$$H_2 \cdots O_1 \text{ - - - - } H_3 \text{ — } O_2 (H_4), \quad O_1 - H_1$$

Try to get a structure with C_s symmetry. Optimize first at the PM3 level to get a reasonable starting structure, and then at the 3-21G level.

Here again we illustrate the strategy of first obtaining a structure (and Hessian) using a semi-empirical model before proceeding with *ab initio* calculations. This is especially useful with weak complexes such as water dimer where the minimum in the potential energy surface is likely to be very shallow.

Request calculation of vibrational frequencies at the 3-21G level. When completed, record the four OH bond distances and the six highest vibrational frequencies in the table above. (The six lowest frequencies correspond to intermolecular motions. Why?). Provide brief descriptions for each of these vibrations based on animations. Describe differences between the water molecules incorporated into water dimer and "free water". In particular, what do you observe to be the effect of hydrogen bonding on the length of the OH bond involved? [7]

Optional

1. Let's see if we could have anticipated the gross structure of the water dimer from calculations on water itself. Calculate and examine a total density surface for water onto which the electrostatic potential has been superimposed. Delineate the regions of greatest positive charge and of greatest negative charge, and based on this suggest how two water molecules might align to best take advantage of favorable electrostatic interactions [see also **Experiment 10**]. How does this alignment compare with the geometry you have found? [3]

2. A reasonable alternative water-dimer geometry is the bifurcated structure.

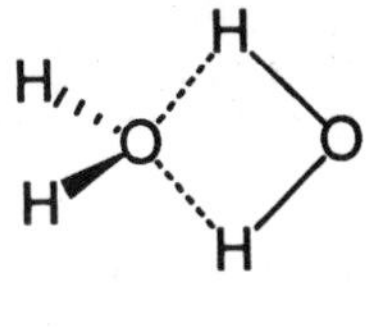

This structure may be favored because it aligns the total dipole associated with each molecule instead of just the dipoles associated with individual OH bonds. On the other hand, this structure seems to bring the oxygens closer together. Thus, we will be able to see what forces are more important for hydrogen-bonding. Obtain a geometry of this structure first at the PM3 level and then using 3-21G. Do the *ab initio* calculations show it to be higher in energy than the linear form? Is it a potential energy minimum?

To answer the latter question, you will need to calculate the normal-mode vibrational frequencies to see if they are all real or if one or more are imaginary.

Experiment 28: Atomic Charges and Electric Dipole Moments

We use *ab initio* 3-21G calculations to explore the influence of molecular geometry on the electric dipole moment and, more generally, to examine relationships between atomic charges, bond dipoles and electric dipole moments.

The *electric dipole moment* is among the most fundamental experimentally measurable quantities related to the charge distribution in a molecule. It is also one of the most heavily used pieces of data for explaining a variety of physical and chemical properties from boiling points to chemical reactivities. The origin of the electric dipole moment is easily understood by considering a molecule to be made up of a set of point charges, positively charged nuclei and negatively charged electrons, or alternatively "atoms" which bear either net positive or negative charge [see also **Experiment 22**]. In either representation, the sum of these individual charges for a neutral molecule must be zero. However, the vector sum leads instead to a simple "two charge" picture, and the notion that a molecule has a "positive end" and a "negative end".

x = positively charged nuclei

• = negatively charged electrons

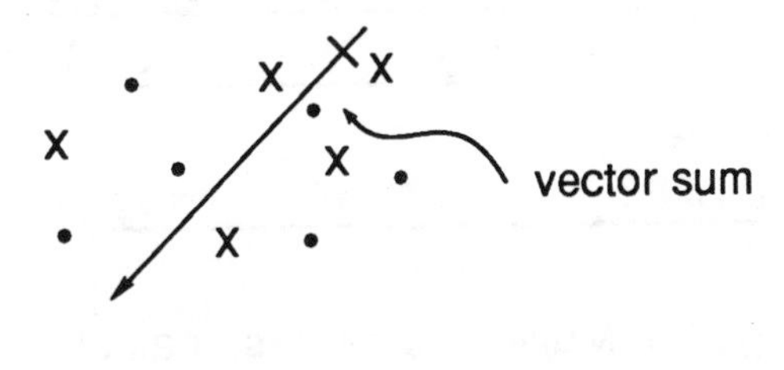

scalar sum=0

The magnitude of the resulting dipole moment vector corresponds to the magnitude of the electric dipole moment, the quantity which is routinely measured and discussed. The direction of the dipole moment vector may also be measured, but this is quite difficult and has only been done in a few cases.

Chemists often view the dipole moment in a slightly different light, as arising from a collection of *bond dipoles*. Covalent bonding results from the sharing of electrons between atoms. If the two bonded atoms are different, or are the same but are in different chemical environments, then the electrons involved in the bond will not be shared equally. As a consequence, the bond becomes *polarized*, with the two constituent atoms attaining slightly different net charges. We can represent the resulting bond dipole by a vector, the direction of which lies along the interatomic axis, and (by convention) points from relative positive to relative negative (the word "relative" here is important since the two bonded atoms need not necessarily be charged or have opposite charges). The electric dipole moment for a molecule is thus the vector sum of the individual bond dipoles. This means that the dipole moment is related not only to bond polarity, but also to the shape of the molecule.

In this experiment, we examine the charge distribution and electric dipole moment in carbon dioxide both in its linear (equilibrium) form and in a hypothetical bent geometry. We seek to clearly distinguish between polar bonds (present in both structures) and an overall dipole moment (present only in the hypothetical bent structure).

Procedure

Build (linear) carbon dioxide and optimize at the 3-21G level. Request both Mulliken charges and the electric dipole moment. Record the CO bond distance, carbon and oxygen charges and the dipole moment in the table below.

CO bond distance (Å), Mulliken charges (electrons) and dipole moments (debyes)				
	r_{CO}	q(C)	q(O)	μ
linear CO_2				
"bent" CO_2				

Using the Mulliken charges, calculate the magnitude of each bond dipole by multiplying the difference in charge between carbon and oxygen by the bond length (number of electrons times distance in Å are acceptable units for the bond dipole). What is the direction of each bond dipole? What is the magnitude of the dipole moment for linear carbon dioxide?

[10] Construct carbon monoxide in which the OCO bond angle is constrained at 120°. Optimize at the 3-21G level (subject to the bond angle constraint). Again calculate Mulliken charges and the electric dipole moment. As you did before, also calculate the dipole moment for each bond based on atomic charges, and then summing the bond dipoles calculate a total dipole moment. How does it compare with that for linear CO_2? Rationalize the difference.

Experiment 29: Rates of Electrophilic Additions to Alkynes

We correlate rates of electrophilic additions to alkynes with the energies of the highest-occupied molecular orbital on the alkyne obtained from AM1 semi-empirical calculations.

Arylalkynes add molecular chlorine to yield dichlorostyrenes.[1]

$$Ar-\!\equiv\!-H \xrightarrow[\text{slow}]{Cl_2} \left[Ar-\overset{+}{C}=C(Cl)H \;\text{ or }\; \text{Ar, H-bridged } Cl^+ \right] \xrightarrow[\text{fast}]{Cl^-} Ar(Cl)C=C(Cl)H \;\text{ or }\; Ar(Cl)C=C(H)Cl$$

The first step in the reaction, involving formation of an intermediate vinyl cation, is rate limiting. Given such a mechanism, we might expect that the more accessible the electrons in the triple bond, the faster will be the initial electrophilic addition and hence the overall reaction. In this experiment, we explore such a possibility, and attempt to correlate the energy of the highest-occupied molecular orbital, E(HOMO), in arylalkynes with reaction rate.

Procedure

Build the arylalkynes.

$X-C_6H_4-\!\equiv\!-H$ X=H, F, CH_3, OCH_3, NO_2

Optimize each at the AM1 level; be certain to specify printing of molecular orbitals and associated orbital energies. For each, record the energy of the highest-occupied molecular orbital in the table below.

---

[1] K. Yates and A.T. Go, J. Org. Chem., **45**, 2377, 2385 (1980).

AM1 orbital energies (eV) and experimental relative rates for *para*-substituted phenylacetylenes		
X	E(HOMO)	relative rate
H		1
F		1.40
CH_3		17.3
OCH_3		1840
NO_2		.0030

Plot E(HOMO) versus $\log_{10}$(relative rate) of Cl_2 addition for these alkynes (log (rate) is used because it is proportional to the energy barrier for the reaction).

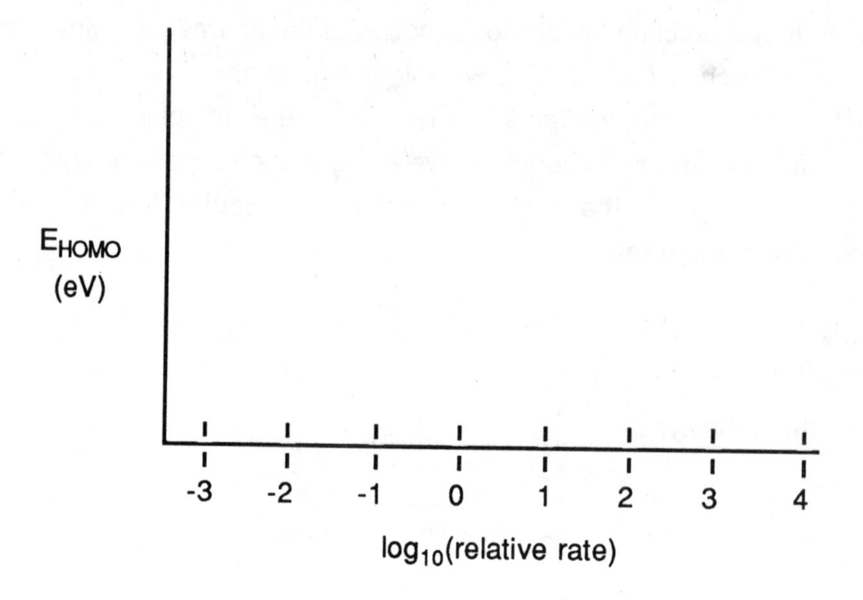

Is the correlation as expected? Build and optimize *meta*-nitrophenylacetylene at the AM1 level. Use E(HOMO) for this compound and your correlation between E(HOMO) and relative rate to predict the relative rate for this compound. How does this compare with the experimental relative rate of 0.00156?

Experiment 30: Aqueous Phase pKa's of Organic Acids

We use electrostatic potentials obtained from semi-empirical AM1 calculations to estimate aqueous-phase pKa's for a variety of carboxylic acids.

The acidity of an organic substrate is often an important factor in determining its chemistry. For example, chemo or regioselective deprotonation of ketones, esters or α,β-unsaturated carbonyls is important in enolate chemistry [see **Experiment 42**]. Another example is provided by the stereoselective deprotonation that often accompanies based-induced elimination reactions [see **Experiment 48**]. Anticipating the selectivity from such reactions requires a working knowledge of the relative kinetic and/or thermodynamic acidities of organic molecules.[1]

In this experiment, we model the relative acidities of carboxylic acids by computing the maximum electrostatic potential at the acidic hydrogen; the greater the electrostatic potential the more acidic the hydrogen.

Procedure

Build each of the molecules below.

Cl_3C–C(=O)–OH **1**; HO–C(=O)–C(=O)–OH **2**; Cl_2CH–C(=O)–OH **3**; $NCCH_2$–C(=O)–OH **4**

$ClCH_2$–C(=O)–OH **5**; HO–C(=O)–CH=CH–C(=O)–OH **6**; HO(O=)C–C_6H_4–C(=O)OH **7**; H–C(=O)–OH **8**

[1] For a discussion of the effect of structure on the strengths of organic acids, see: March, p. 229.

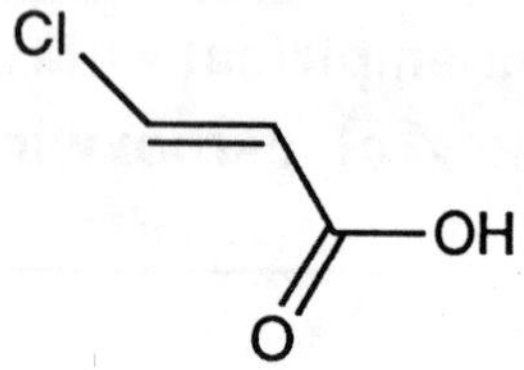

9 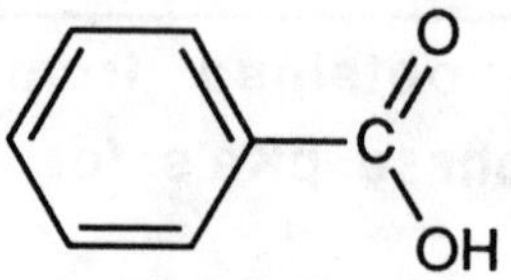　　10 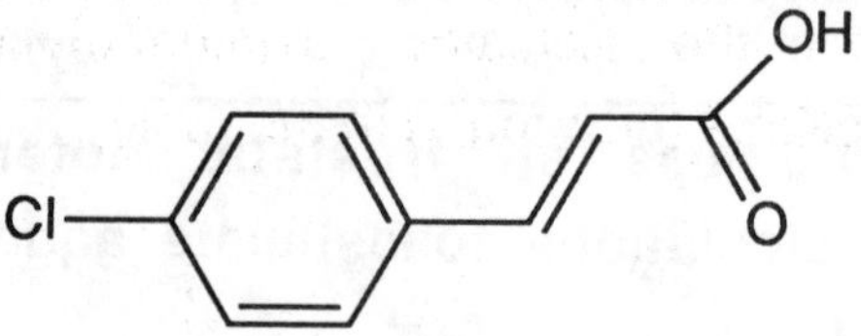　　11

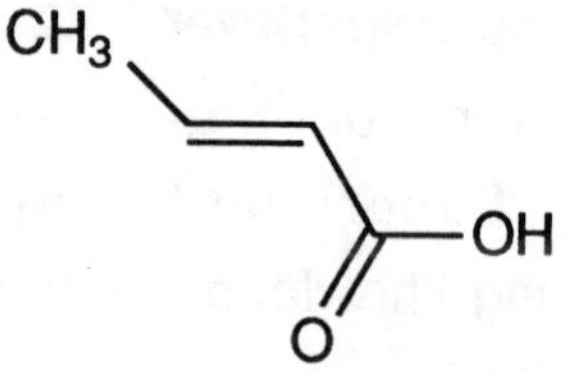

12 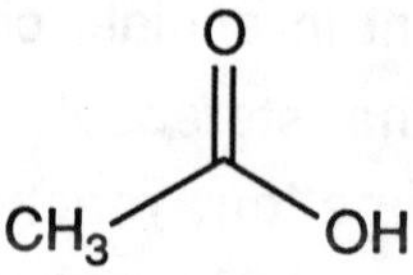　　13 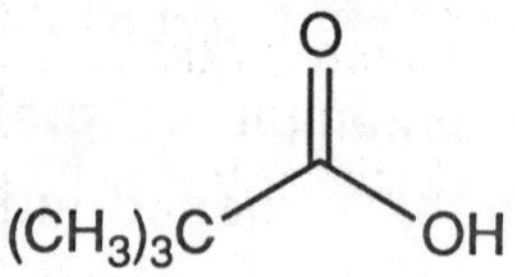　　14

Optimize at the AM1 level. Be certain to request generation of a total electron density surface onto which the electrostatic potential has been encoded. As each calculation completes, record the maximum value of the electrostatic potential (in the vicinity of the carboxylic hydrogen) in the table below. [8]

AM1 electrostatic potentials (kcal/mol) and experimental pKa's		
	maximum value of the electrostatic potential	aqueous phase pKa
1		0.70
2		1.23
3		1.48
4		2.45
5		2.85
6		3.10
7		3.51
8		3.75
9		3.79
10		4.19
11		4.41
12		4.70
13		4.75
14		5.03

Plot the calculated maximum electrostatic potential values against the aqueous phase pKa's[2] (also found in the table).

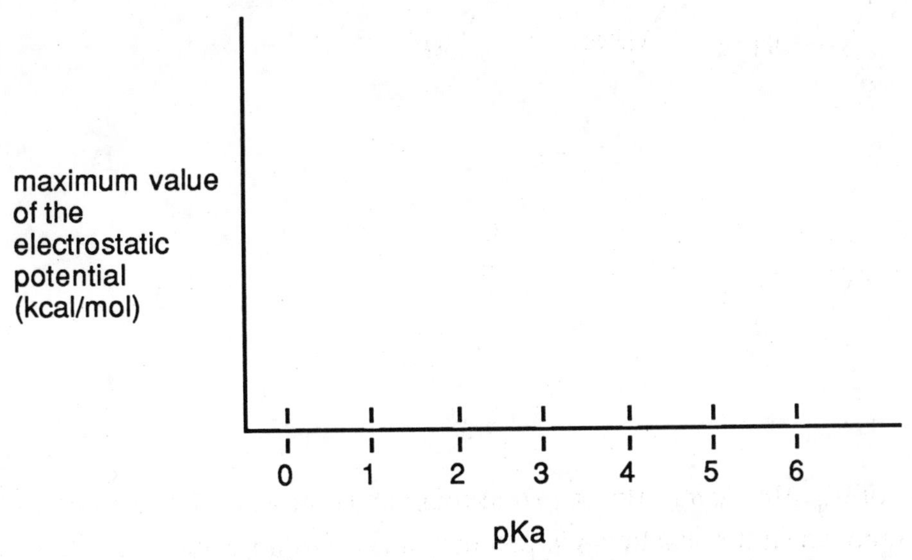

Do you observe a reasonable correlation? How do you account for this result?

Optional

Consider the base-induced *syn* elimination of HX (X=F or Cl) from **15** below.

$NaNH_2$ -HF ← **15** → $NaNH_2$ -HCl

15

Experimentally, HF is eliminated in preference to HCl. Perform an AM1 geometry optimization, and generate a total electron density surface onto which the electrostatic potential has been encoded. Which hydrogen is indicated to be the more acidic? Will its abstraction by $NaNH_2$ lead to the experimentally observed product?

---

[2] E.P. Sarjeant and B. Dempsey, **Ionization Constants of Organic Acids in Aqueous Solution**, IUPAC no. 23, Pergamon Press, 1979.

Experiment 31: Acidities and Basicities of Excited-State Molecules

We use CI corrections to the semi-empirical AM1 method to model changes in acidity as a result of photoexcitation. We try to anticipate changes in acidity by examining the molecular orbitals of ground-state species.

The strength of an organic acid is most commonly expressed in terms of its pKa. This corresponds to the pH above which the acid is fully deprotonated. Hence, the lower the pKa the stronger the acid. While measuring the pKa of an acid in its ground state is routine, measuring the pKa for an excited-state molecule is not nearly as straightforward. To date, only a few excited-state acidities are accurately known. Those that are known show interesting effects. Consider, for example, 2-naphthol and for 2-naphthoic acid, data for which are provided below.

Experimental pKas

	S_0	S_1	acidity change on excitation to S_1
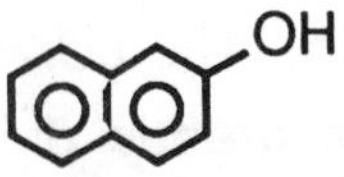 2-naphthol (OH)	9.5	2.8	stronger
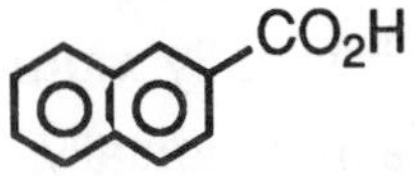 2-naphthoic acid (CO_2H)	4.2	6.6	weaker

Recalling that a change of 1 pKa unit represents an order of magnitude change in acid strength, note the dramatic differences in acidity between an acid in its ground and first-excited states. In the case of 2-naphthol, the acidity in the S_1 state is almost seven orders of magnitude greater than that of the ground state, while the acidity of S_1 2-naphthoic acid is more than 100 times less than in its ground state.

In this experiment, we use semi-empirical AM1/CI calculations to model changes in acidity of 2-naphthol and 2-naphthoic acid upon photoexcitation, and then try to offer explanations for the observed changes. As an approximation, we employ the CI corrections only to model energy differences between ground and excited states, and not to provide equilibrium geometries; ground-state AM1 structures will be used in their place.

Procedure

Build 2-naphthol and 2-naphthoic acid, and optimize at the AM1 level. Record the heats of formation (in the ground state, S_0) in the table below.

AM1 and AM1/CI heats of formation (kcal/mol)		
	S_0	S_1
2-naphthol		
2-naphthoic acid		
2-naphthoxy anion		
2-naphthyl carboxylate		

Generate HOMO and LUMO isosurfaces for each. This will help us to anticipate the energy changes which will occur upon electronic excitation. For 2-naphthol, view the HOMO and LUMO simultaneously. In this case, $S_0 \rightarrow S_1$ excitation essentially corresponds to a HOMO to LUMO electron promotion. What would be the effect of removing an electron from the HOMO and placing it in the LUMO? The HOMO is a π-type molecular orbital with considerable amplitude on the oxygen. The LUMO is also a π molecular orbital; however, the amplitude on oxygen is greatly diminished. Consequently, electron promotion from the HOMO to the LUMO delocalizes some of the oxygen's electron density into the ring system, rendering it slightly more positive. This in turn increases acidity, in accord with what is observed experimentally.

Let's now apply the same arguments to 2-naphthoic acid. Place both orbitals on screen at the same time. Where are the HOMO and LUMO localized? What shifts in electron density would you expect as a result of S_0 to S_1 excitation? What should this do to the acidity? Is this in accord with experiment?

To see if the qualitative arguments stand up to quantitative tests, perform AM1/CI calculations for the species involved in reactions (1) and (2).

[2-naphthol-OH]* + 2-naphthoxide O^- ⟶ [2-naphthoxide O^-]* + 2-naphthol-OH (1)

$$\left[C_{10}H_7CO_2H \right]^* + C_{10}H_7CO_2^- \longrightarrow \left[C_{10}H_7CO_2^- \right]^* + C_{10}H_7CO_2H \quad (2)$$

Here, the asterisk signifies a species in its first (singlet) excited state. If the acid is stronger in the excited state, the energy of the reaction as written will be negative; a positive energy indicates reduction in acidity upon excitation. We will need AM1 heats of formation not only for the acid, HA, but also for its conjugate base, A^-, in both the ground state and in the first excited state, S_1. You have already performed the appropriate calculations on the two acids in their ground states. Build the two conjugate bases, 2-naphthoxy anion and 2-naphthylcarboxylate, optimize at the AM1 level and record the heats of formation in the table. Next, perform single-point AM1/CI calculations on all four species in order ot get heats of formation for the first excited state. Record these values as well in the table. Compute the energies of reactions (1) and (2). Are your calculations in agreement with experiment with regard to trends in ground and excited state acidities? Were they properly anticipated by the inspection of the HOMO and LUMO? **[12]**

Optional

Using an AM1 (ground state) optimized geometry and HOMO and LUMO plots only (no CI calculations) explain why 2-naphthylamine becomes a stronger base upon excitation to S_1.

Chapter 4: Reactive Intermediates

Molecules which are not sufficiently stable to be isolated and characterized using normal methods but nonetheless are involved as intermediates in chemical processes are usually termed reactive intermediates.

Stepwise Reactions

The transformation of one molecule into another during a chemical reaction can be a complex process. Intervening between the reactant and the product are many starts and stops, points where progress seems rapid, and occasions where a newly formed molecule suddenly reverts to its prior structure. If we hope to predict the outcome of a chemical reaction we must take into account the route or *mechanism* that is followed and the structure and chemical properties of any reactive intermediates.

Many of the tools that are used routinely to determine the structures of stable compounds (spectroscopy, crystallography) can only be applied with enormous difficulty to the study of reactive intermediates. The high reactivity and short lifetimes of such intermediates as carbocations, carbanions, free radicals, and carbenes, makes the direct observation of these species impossible or at best very difficult. Consequently, a great deal of effort (and expense) has been directed at developing experimental methods for generating and detecting reactive intermediates. The data provided by these experiments have given chemists a good understanding of many compounds, but progress has been slow. The unusual structures and properties of short-lived intermediates have made interpretation of experimental data difficult, and the chemical literature abounds with incorrect conclusions based on "hard" experimental facts.

Computer modeling of reactive intermediates, on the other hand, is no more difficult than modeling of stable compounds. Computer models are naturally "long-lived" and the computational chemist is free to manipulate the molecular and electronic structure of a reactive substance as part of his or her investigations. Computer models can be used both to explore the properties of new, unusual reactive intermediates and to predict the properties of intermediates for which experimental data is limited or altogether unavailable. This latter use has made modeling an invaluable tool for experimental chemists faced with the problem of interpreting exotic laboratory observations.

One well-documented story illustrates the power of computer modeling[1]. On the basis of extensive computer calculations, methylene, $:CH_2$, had been predicted by Foster and Boys in 1959 to be a bent molecule (H-C-H bond angle =129°) in its triplet ground state. Two years later, Herzberg reported the experimental observation of triplet CH_2 and concluded from these data that the compound was linear. Herzberg's conclusion, based as it was on "hard" experimental observations, was not challenged until 1970, when Bender and Schaefer reported new computational results supporting a bent molecule (H-C-H bond angle = 135°). Subsequent experimental and theoretical investigations confirmed Bender and Schaefer's model. Old ways are hard to change, but many chemists now view computer modeling as a "full partner with experiment" for the study of molecular structures and properties.

The Hammond Postulate

In principle, there is absolutely no connection between the thermodynamics and kinetics of a chemical reaction. An energetically favored process ($\Delta G < 0$) might occur rapidly ($\Delta G^\ddagger$ small) or slowly ($\Delta G^\ddagger$ large). Nevertheless, chemists have found that ΔG and $\Delta G^\ddagger$ are often correlated for closely related processes. This observation is codified in the Hammond postulate which essentially states that the transition state for a highly endothermic single-step reaction resembles the product(s) in structure and energy ($\Delta G^\ddagger$ large), while the transition state for a highly exothermic single-step reaction resembles the reactant(s) in structure and energy ($\Delta G^\ddagger$ small). These statements are reflected in the following reaction coordinate diagrams.

[1] The full story of CH_2 and several other reactive intermediates is recounted in: W.A. Goddard, Science, **227**, 917 (1985); H.F. Schaefer, *ibid.*, **231**, 1100 (1986)

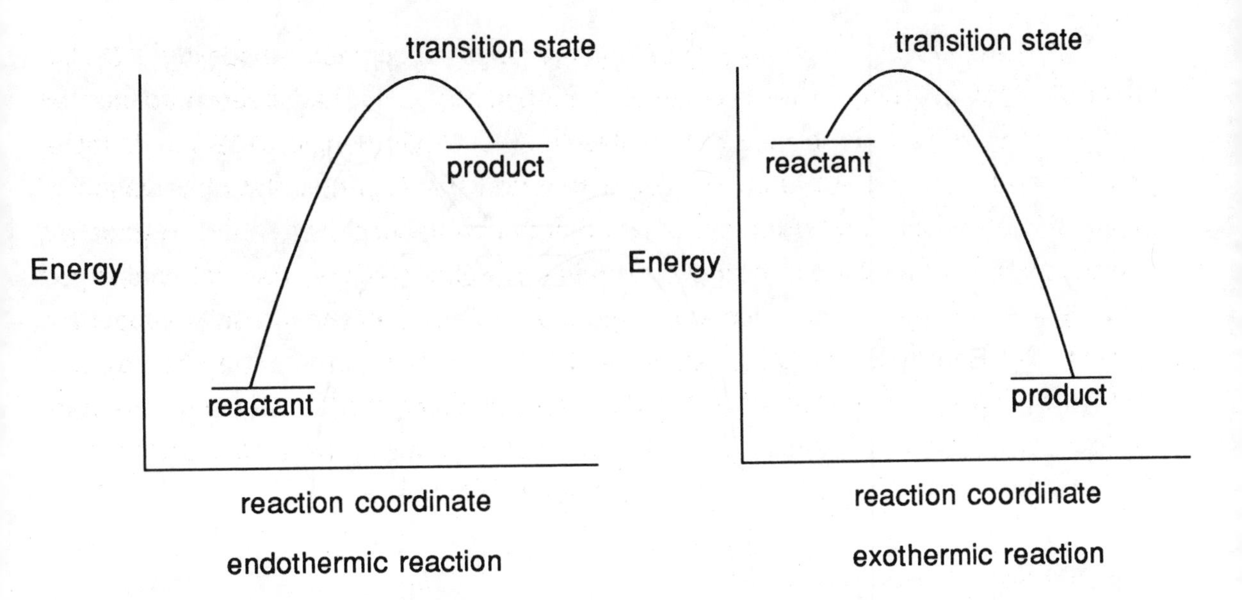

endothermic reaction | exothermic reaction

The usefulness of the Hammond postulate lies in the connection between transition state properties and reactant/product properties. It is much easier to characterize the properties of the latter, even when these compounds are highly reactive intermediates, than it is to characterize the properties of transition states. Indeed, it is really not possible to characterize the properties of transition states by experimental means alone.

Since most chemical reactions are multi-step processes involving high-energy intermediates, the Hammond postulate finds wide application. For example, the bromination of toluene can yield *ortho-*, *meta-*, or *para*-bromotoluene, and the relative amounts of each product will be determined by their respective rates of formation, i.e., by the energy of the transition state in the rate-determining step.

CH_3 $\xrightarrow[FeBr_3]{Br_2}$ CH_3, Br vs. CH_3, Br vs. CH_3, Br

ortho *meta* *para*

Bromination appears to involve two steps: electrophilic attack by "Br^+" to give an unstable cationic intermediate, followed by deprotonation.

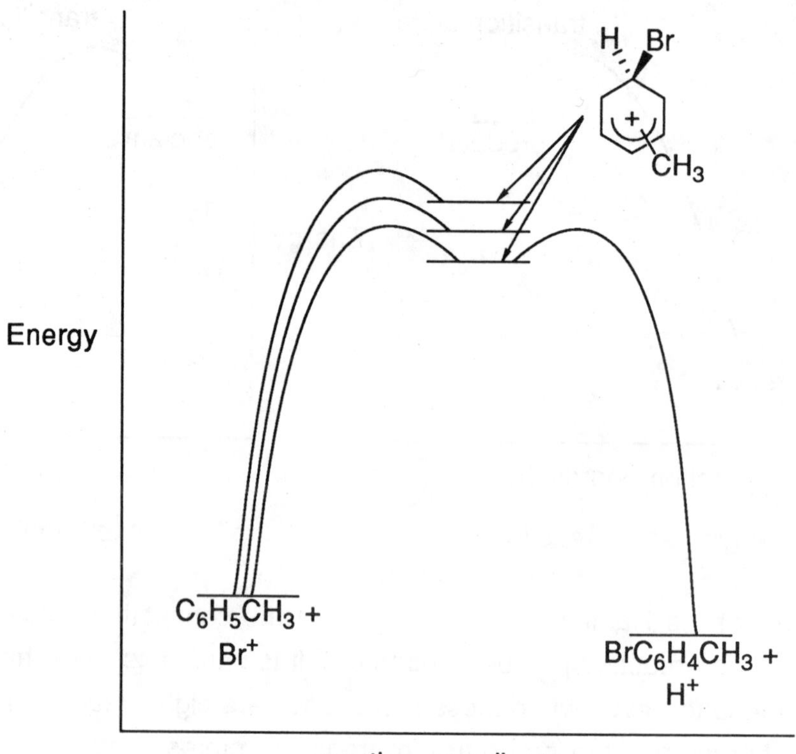

The initial step is rate-determining and highly endothermic. Thus, the Hammond postulate tells us that the energy of the transition state will resemble the energy of the corresponding cationic intermediate (the "product" of the initial step). Computer modeling can be used to evaluate the relative energies of the *ortho*-, *meta*-, and *para*-substituted intermediates and also to identify factors that contribute to these energy trends.

The experiments in this chapter demonstrate the use of computational methods to elucidate the structures and stabilities of several classes of reactive molecules. The properties of these molecules can then be connected to various chemical reactions where they have been proposed as intermediates. The first two experiments address the structures of simple carbocations, with particular emphasis on the relationship between conformation and energy. The role of carbocation intermediates in electrophilic aromatic substitution, and of free radical intermediates in alkene substitution reactions are considered in the next two experiments. The chapter concludes with discussion of the structure and infrared spectrum of *ortho* benzyne and with a general treatment of substituent effects in stabilizing a variety of reactive intermediates.

Experiment 32: Hyperconjugation and the Structures and Stabilities of Alkyl Cations

We use both semi-empirical AM1 and *ab initio* 3-21G calculations to investigate the structures of isopropyl and *tert*-amyl cations. We introduce the concept of hyperconjugation and examine its effect on the structures of simple carbocations. We assess the relative hyperconjugating abilities of CH and CC bonds.

Carbocations play an important role in many simple organic reactions. For example, the regiochemistry of acid-catalyzed additions to alkenes is dictated by the structure of the more stable carbocation resulting from protonation of the double bond [see also **Experiment 38**]. This is usually the carbocation in which the formal positive charge (the carbocation center) resides on the more highly-substituted carbon, leading to products in accord with Markovnikov's rule. In this experiment, we investigate one of the important factors, termed hyperconjugation, which contributes to the structure and stability of simple alkyl carbocations.

Procedure

Build isopropyl cation in the conformation shown below (C_s symmetry).

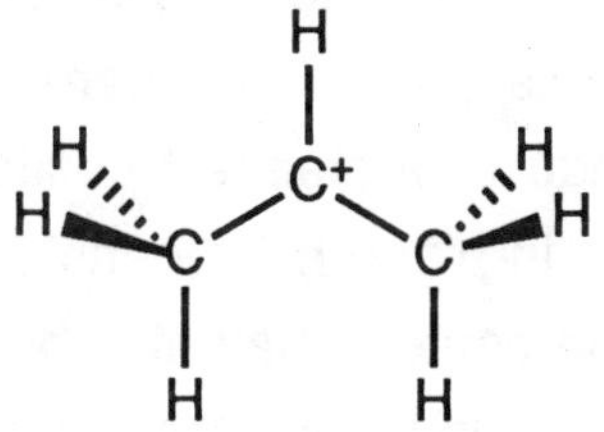

H
H H
H C+ H
C C
H H

Optimize at the 3-21G *ab initio* level. When completed, examine the calculated geometry. You will note that the CC bonds are somewhat shorter than typical (CC) single bonds, but not nearly as short as normal double bonds. This observation suggests "partial double bond character" involving the methyl carbons. How can a formally saturated carbon participate in π bonding? The answer is

hyperconjugation.[1] Hyperconjugation involves participation of the classical resonance forms shown below.

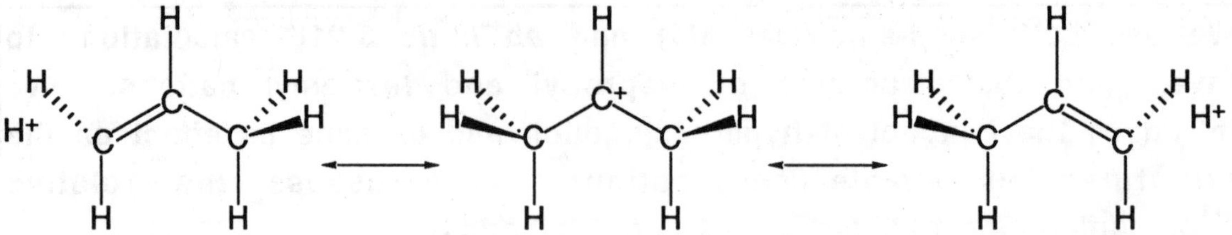

H H H
H, H H, H H, H
H+ C C H H C C+ C H H C C C H+
H H H H H H

What is involved is donation of a pair of electrons formally associated with each of the four out-of-plane CH bonds onto the electron-deficient carbon. Hyperconjugation can also be viewed as a mixing of the vacant molecular orbital at the formal cation center with the adjacent filled CH bond orbitals. This orbital mixing stabilizes the filled orbitals and changes their bonding character in that some of the electron density in the CH bonds is now shifted toward the electron-deficient carbon. The result, regardless of the explanation, should be an elongation of the out-of-plane CH bonds and a contraction in the CC bonds. Is this observed in your structure for isopropyl cation? Can you detect (and rationalize) any angular distortions involving the methyl groups?

As shown by the resonance structures above, hyperconjugation should also lead to delocalization of the positive charge formally associated with the cation center onto the out-of-plane hydrogens, but not onto the in-plane hydrogens. We'll employ a graphical display to try to uncover evidence for this movement of charge. Calculate and display a total electron density surface onto which the electrostatic potential has [3] been encoded. According to this measure, where is most of the positive charge concentrated? Is there evidence of increased positive charge on the out-of-plane methyl hydrogens (relative to the in-plane hydrogens)?

Stabilization of carbocation centers may also be afforded by "hyperconjugation" with CC bonds. There is experimental evidence, however, that CH hyperconjugation is more effective. Specifically, the equilibrium geometry of *tert*-amyl cation has been established experimentally as an "in-plane" structure (allowing for maximum CH hyperconjugation but for no CC hyperconjugation) rather than an out-of-plane structure (allowing for maximum CC hyperconjugation at the cost of reduced CH hyperconjugation).[2]

---

[1] Carey and Sundberg A, p. 54; Lowry and Richardson, p. 431; March, p. 143.

[2] For a review, see: D.E. Sunko and W.J. Hehre, Prog. Phys. Org. Chem., **14**, 205 (1983).

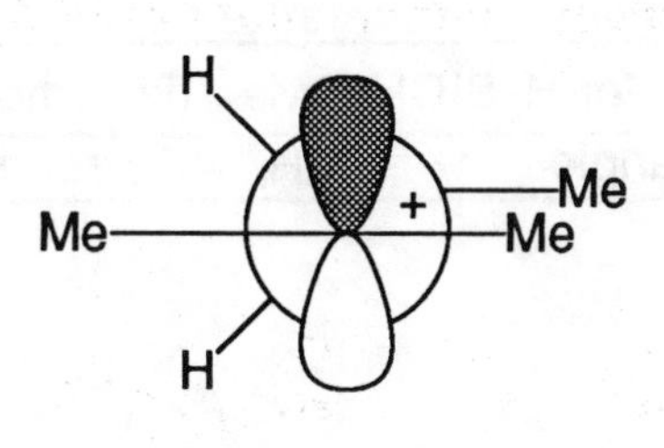

methyl in-plane

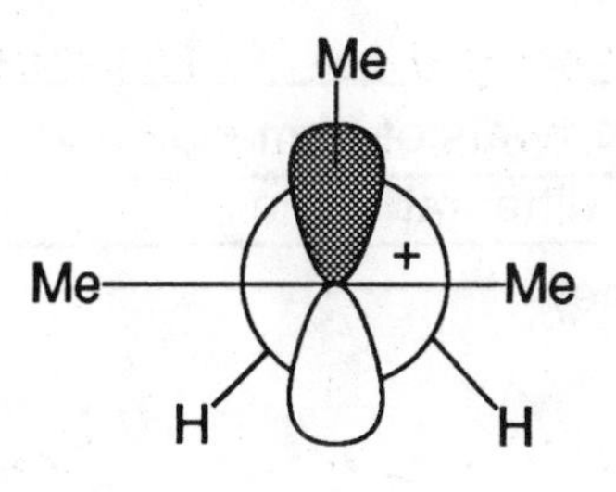

methyl out-of-plane

Build conformers of *tert*-amyl cation in which the methyl group is in the plane of the cation center (in-plane), and constrained to be approximately 30°, 60° and 90° (out-of-plane) away from the plane. Optimize (constrained optimization) at the AM1 level and record the heats of formation in the table below. **[6]**

AM1 heats of formation and relative energies for *tert* amyl cation (kcal/mol)			
ideal dihedral angle	actual dihedral angle	ΔH_f°	rel. energy
0 (in-plane)			
30			
60			
90 (out-of-plane)			

Identify the most stable conformer and compute the energies of other conformers relative to this form. Record these data in the table. Are your results in agreement with the experimental conformation of *tert*-amyl cation, supporting the notion that CH hyperconjugation is of greater benefit than CC hyperconjugation?

Optional

Repeat your conformational calculations for the silicon substituted cation **1**.

$$H_3Si-CH_2-\overset{+}{C}Me_2 \ ,$$

1

by setting the SiCCC dihedral angle at approximately 0°, 30°, 60° and 90°. Record the data in the table below.

AM1 heats of formation and relative energies for $H_3SiCH_2CMe_2^+$ (kcal/mol)			
ideal dihedral angle	actual dihedral angle	ΔH_f°	rel. energy
0 (in-plane)			
30			
60			
90 (out-of-plane)			

Describe the differences with your previous results for *tert*-amyl cation. What do the calculations suggest about the relative hyperconjugating abilities of CH and CSi bonds? Can you rationalize your results?

Experiment 33: Structures and Stabilities of Allyl, Benzyl and Cyclopropylcarbinyl Cations

We use AM1 semi-empirical calculations to investigate the structures of and charge distributions in allyl, benzyl and cyclopropylcarbinyl cations. We employ molecular orbital and electrostatic potential displays to monitor the extent of charge delocalization as a function of geometry.

Allyl and benzyl cations,

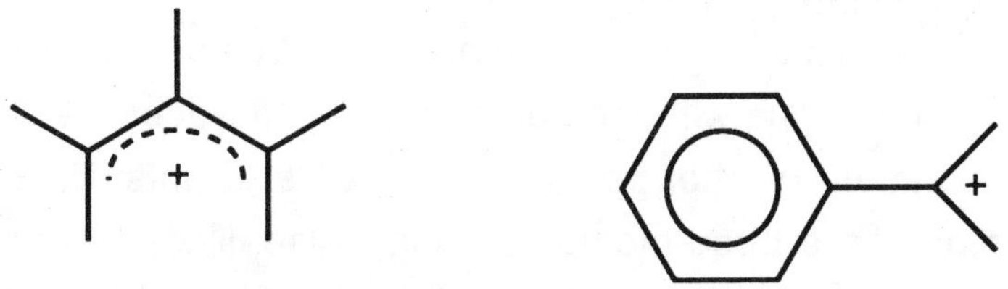

are unusual in that they possess very high stability. They are often seen as *thermodynamic sinks* in mass spectral fragmentation patterns. Also, many derivatives of each have been characterized by NMR spectroscopy (among other techniques) in very strong acids[1]. The usual reason given for the unusual stability of these species is the availability of high-energy π orbitals for donation into the vacant p orbital at the carbocation center, i.e., in the language of resonance theory:

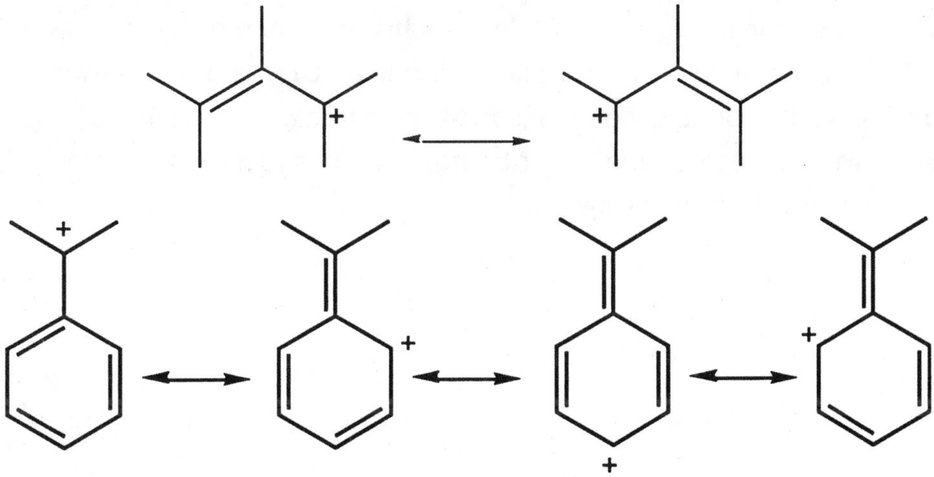

[1] G.A. Olah, **Carbocations and Electrophilic Reactions**, Verlag-Chemie-Wiley, 1973.

Such a picture implies both that the geometries of allyl and benzyl cations will be significantly delocalized (with CC bond lengths intermediate between single and double linkages), and furthermore that they will adopt planar geometries.

Bisected cyclopropylcarbinyl cation,

H
$\overset{+}{C}$—CH CH_2 CH_2
H

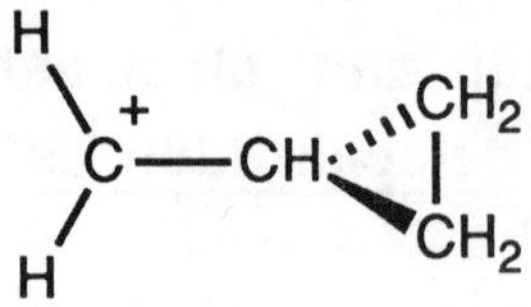

is another species like allyl and benzyl cations which is known to possess unusually high stability. It's structure is less familiar, however, and many chemists will find drawing additional resonance forms problematic. Interaction of the high-energy bond orbital of the cyclopropane ring with the carbocation center does, nevertheless, lead to significant delocalization of the positive charge, and this is accompanied by goemetrical distortion of the three-membered ring. Also, like allyl and benzyl cations, the extent and consequences of interaction are highly sensitive to conformation.

In this experiment, we apply semi-empirical AM1 calculations together with a variety of graphical models to examine both the geometries of and charge distributions in allyl, benzyl and cyclopropylcarbinyl cations both in conformations which facilitate and those which exclude charge delocalization.[2]

Procedure

Build and optimize at the AM1 level planar and perpendicular forms of allyl cation. The latter, in which one of the terminal CH_2 groups is twisted to be perpendicular to the double bond, must be constructed to exhibit C_s symmetry, otherwise it will collapse to the lower-energy planar structure during optimization. Record your data in the table below.

---

[2] For reviews of previous theoretical work, see: W.J. Hehre, in **Methods in Electronic Structure Theory**, H.F. Schaefer, III, ed., Plenum, New York, 1977, p. 277; L. Radom, D. Poppinger and R.C. Haddon, in **Carbonium Ions**, vol. 5, G.A. Olah and P.v.R. Schleyer, eds., Wiley, New York, 1976, p. 2303.

AM1 heats of formation and relative energies (kcal/mol)		
	ΔH_f°	rel. energy
allyl cation (planar)		
(perpendicular)		
benzyl cation (planar)		
(perpendicular)		
cyclopropylcarbinyl cation (bisected)		
(eclipsed)		

Which structure (planar or perpendicular) do the calculations suggest is the lower in energy? Is the magnitude of the calculated energy difference similar to that for rotation about a single bond [see **Experiment 11**] or closer to that for rotation about a double bond [see **Experiment 5**]? Examine the geometries of each. How do the CC bond lengths in the two allyl cations compare with "normal" single and double bonds in a molecule like propene? Do you see evidence for electron delocalization in the planar structure? In the perpendicular structure?

Calculate and display the lowest-unoccupied molecular orbitals for planar and perpendicular allyl cation.

> One way to think about the lowest-unoccupied molecular orbital is that it represents the distribution of positive charge, that is, it identifies the electrophilic site in the ion.

Is the LUMO for planar allyl cation consistent with the simple resonance picture given above, i.e., is the charge delocalized over both terminal carbons equally? What does it tell you about the ability of a π-donor substituent, such as dimethylamino, to stabilize allyl cation? Would such a substituent have the same effect if it were attached to the central carbon as it would if it were attached to a terminal carbon? Would such a substituent have a greater stabilizing effect on allyl cation or 1-propyl cation? Point out any significant differences which you see between the LUMO of planar and perpendicular cations.

Calculate and display total electron density surfaces onto which the electrostatic [3] potential has been encoded for both planar and perpendicular conformers of allyl cation. [This tells us about the charge distribution in the ion; see **Experiment 22**]. Put both cation displays onto the same scale. Are both ions equally effective at delocalizing positive charge? Does this provide you a similar picture with regard to the distribution of positive charge as the LUMO? As the simple resonance picture?

Repeat the entire procedure above for planar and perpendicular conformers of benzyl cation. Again, be certain that the structure you build for the perpendicular cation has C_S symmetry or it will collapse to the lower-energy planar form. Record the heats of formation in the table, identify the more stable conformer and work out the energy of the alternative form relative to this conformer. Do you find planar benzyl cation to be more stable than the perpendicular form? Is the planar-perpendicular energy difference greater or smaller than that calculated for allyl cation? Is your result consistent with the greater number of resonance structures open to planar benzyl cation than to planar allyl cation?

Calculate and display the LUMO for planar benzyl cation. Identify positions on the phenyl ring where π-electron-donor groups are likely to be effective in stabilizing benzyl cation. Do these correspond to what you expect based on the simple resonance picture? Calculate and display the LUMO surface of the perpendicular cation. Describe the difference between the lowest-unoccupied molecular orbital in this system and that for planar benzyl cation. On the basis of these displays, which cation would you expect to be the more stable? Why? For the perpendicular cation, predict where substitution by a π-electron donor would have the greatest stabilizing effect. How would this affect the relative stabilities of the planar and perpendicular ions? Is this in accord with what you expect from the resonance picture?

Calculate and display electron density surfaces onto which electrostatic potentials have been encoded for both planar and perpendicular forms of benzyl [3] cation. Put both conformers onto the same scale. Describe the difference between the two graphics. For which (if either) do you see evidence of delocalization of the positive charge away from the formal carbocation center? On the basis of the electrostatic potentials, which conformer (planar or perpendicular) would you expect to be the favored (recall that charge delocalization implies energetic stabilization)? How does this compare with the calculated energies for the two systems?

Build the bisected form of cyclopropylcarbinyl cation and optimize at the AM1 level. Also build and optimize the corresponding eclipsed conformer.

$H_2\overset{+}{C}—CH(CH_2)_2$ (eclipsed conformer)

It is necessary to build the eclipsed conformer with C_s symmetry, otherwise the optimization will likely lead to the more stable bisected form. Record the heats of formation in the table, identify the more stable conformer and work out the energy of the alternative form relative to this conformer. What do the calculations tell you about the relative energy of bisected and eclipsed conformers of cyclopropylcarbinyl? How does it compare with the calculated relative energies of planar and perpendicular forms of allyl cation, and of planar and perpendicular conformers for benzyl cation? On the basis of your results, comment on the ability of the cyclopropane ring to stabilize a carbocation center relative to the abilities of ethylene (allyl cation) and of benzene (benzyl cation).

Compare the calculated equilibrium CC bond lengths in the three-membered ring incorporated into both bisected and eclipsed conformers of cyclopropylcarbinyl with the value of 1.50Å in cyclopropane at the AM1 level. Which of the two conformers shows the more severe geometrical distortions? Try to rationalize the direction of the bond length changes. It might help you to perform an AM1 geometry optimization on cyclopropane and, following this, display the two highest-occupied molecular orbitals.

The highest-occupied molecular orbitals of cyclopropane, commonly known as the **Walsh orbitals**,[3] form a degenerate (equal energy) pair.

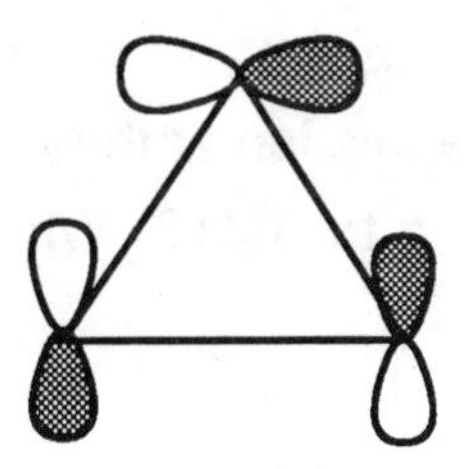

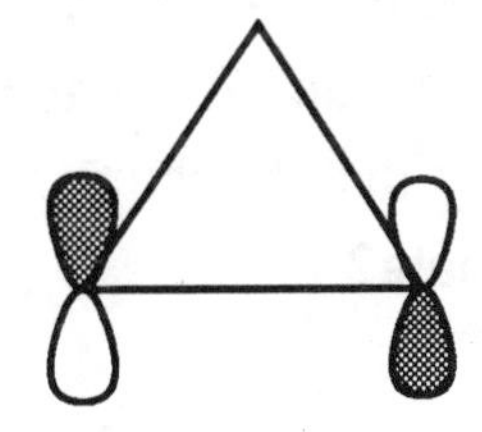

You can easily see that one member of this pair is of the appropriate symmetry to interact strongly with the vacant orbital in bisected cyclopropylcarbinyl, while the other member is of proper symmetry to interact with the vacant orbital in eclipsed cyclopropylcarbinyl but only weakly.

[3] Lowry and Richardson, p. 31; A.D. Walsh, Trans. Faraday Soc., **45**, 179 (1949).

Recognize that antibonding orbital components imply bond lengthening, while bonding orbital components imply bond shortening.

[3] Calculate and display electron density surfaces for bisected and eclipsed conformers of cyclopropylcarbinyl onto which the electrostatic potential has been encoded. Bring both maps onto the same scale. For which (if either) do you see evidence for delocalization of the positive charge away from the formal carbocation center?

[3] Bring up together electrostatic potential maps of planar allyl cation, planar benzyl cation and bisected cyclopropylcarbinyl cation. Put all onto a common scale. Rank the systems according to the extent of positive charge on the formal carbocation center. Does your ranking agree with what is commonly believed to be the ordering of carbocation stabilities?

Optional

The NMR spectrum of dimethylcyclopropylcarbinyl cation in very strong acid media has been measured at a variety of temperatures.[4] Lineshape analysis of the methyl resonances indicates that there is a barrier of 13.7 kcal/mol for their exchange, and this barrier has been assigned to rotation of the Me_2C^+ group relative to the cyclopropane ring. Build and optimize both the bisected and eclipsed ions at the AM1 level. Which is more stable? What is the barrier to rotation according to AM1? How does this compare to the barrier to rotation in cyclopropylcarbinyl cation? Rationalize your result.

Another possible mechanism for exchange is reversible formation of 2,2-dimethylcyclobutyl cation. Build and optimize this ion at the AM1 level. What is the barrier to exchange by this mechanism according to AM1? Which mechanism better fits the experimental data?

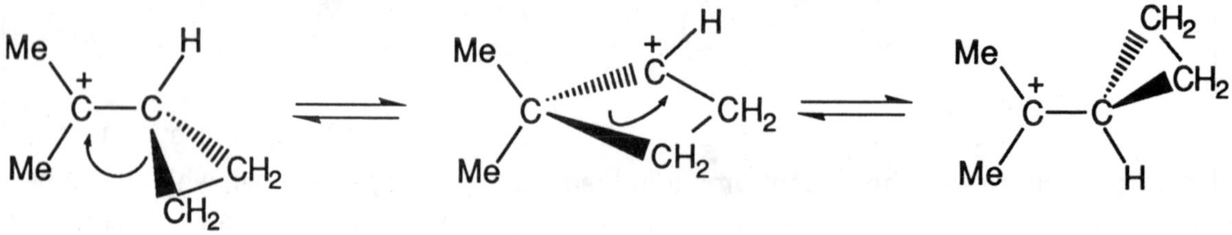

[4] D.S. Kabakoff and E. Namanworth, J. Am. Chem. Soc., **92**, 3234 (1970).

Experiment 34: Directing Effects in Electrophilic Aromatic Substitution

We use AM1 semi-empirical calculations to model the stabilities of σ complexes resulting from electrophilic nitration of substituted benzenes, and on this basis assign preferred substitution products.

One of the most important classes of reactions of aromatic compounds is the substitution of a ring hydrogen by an electrophile.[1] Electrophilic substitution in benzene occurs in two stages: initial attack leads to a σ complex (benzenium ion), which can then go on to eliminate a proton leading to the substituted aromatic.

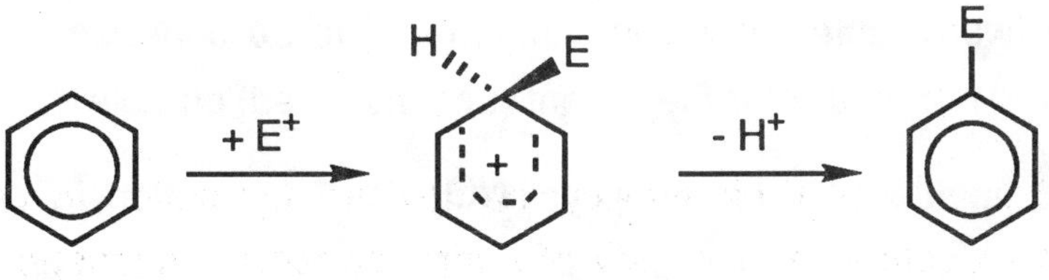

$+E^+$ $-H^+$

σ complex

Of course, all six carbon atoms in benzene are equivalent and therefore present identical environments to an approaching electrophile. Electrophilic addition to a monosubstituted benzene can, however, lead to three different products, corresponding to initial attack on carbons *ortho*, *meta* and *para* to the substituent, i.e.,

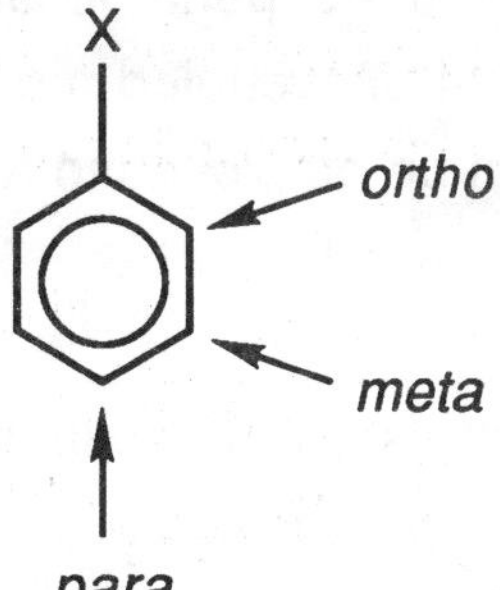

X

ortho

meta

para

There are actually four possible products, but we will not be concerned here with *ipso* attack, i.e., onto the same carbon as the substituent.

---

1 Carey and Sundberg A, p. 554; Lowry and Richardson, p. 623; March, p. 447.

The preferred site of attack is presumably that which leads to the most stable σ complex. This in turn dictates the eventual product.

In this experiment, we use AM1 semi-empirical calculations to determine the preferred site of attack of nitronium cation (NO_2^+) on toluene, aniline, nitrobenzene and trifluorotoluene.

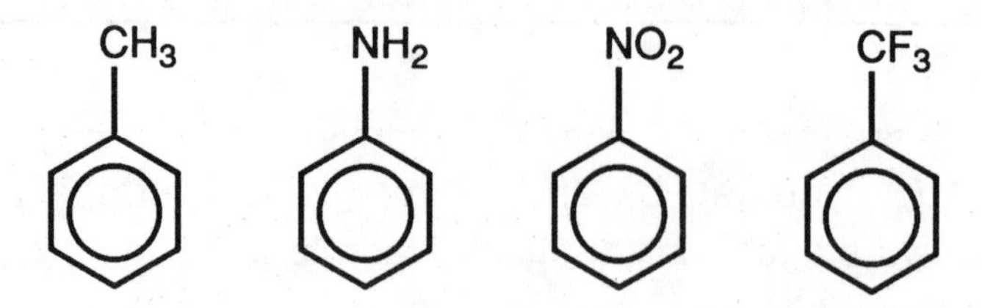

Procedure

A total of twelve different σ complexes need to be constructed and optimized. First, obtain an AM1 structure for the parent (unsubstituted) complex.

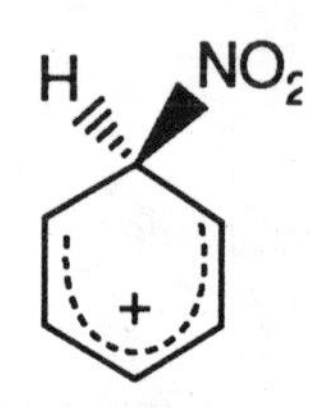

Pick a reasonable conformation of the NO_2 group relative to the ring and stick with this conformation throughout. Is its structure you calculate consistent with the delocalized picture above? Obtain two graphical displays to characterize the distribution of charge, first, the electrostatic potential superimposed onto the total electron density, [3] and second, the value of the lowest-unoccupied molecular orbital superimposed onto the total density. Both of these can be employed to represent the charge distribution in the ion.

While the connection between electrostatic potential and distribution of positive charge is obvious, use of the LUMO for this purpose may be less so. The easiest way to think about the situation is to assume that the LUMO indicates the electrophilic sites in the ion.

At which ring positions do these show buildup of positive charge? Is this consistent with a classical resonance picture for the σ complex?

Use the structure of the parent σ complex as a template for each of the substituted complexes.

Here we illustrate a common strategy for performing structure optimizations on a series of closely-related compounds, mainly optimizing one structure first and, following this, using this structure as a template for the remaining optimizations.

As each job finishes, record its heat of formation in the table below.

AM1 heats of formation (kcal/mol)			
σ-complex resulting from nitration of:	*ortho*	*meta*	*para*
toluene			
aniline			
nitrobenzene			
trifluorotoluene			

Which substituents direct attack to the *meta* position, and which direct attack to the *ortho* or *para* positions? For which substituents are the directing effects the greatest? For those substituents which direct *ortho/para*, which position (*ortho* or *para*) is the preferred? Are *ortho/para* energy differences larger, smaller, or of the same order of magnitude as differences between *ortho/para* and *meta* substitution? Are your conclusions generally in accord with what is commonly known experimentally, i.e., electron-donor groups lead to *ortho-para* direction and electron-acceptor groups lead to *meta* direction?

Experiment 35: Free Radical Substitution Reactions of Alkenes

We use semi-empirical AM1 calculations to rationalize the observed regioselectivity in free-radical substitutions in terms of stabilities of intermediate free radicals. We examine the distribution of spin in free radicals as an indicator of selectivity.

Alkenes containing allylic hydrogens undergo a substitution reaction with N-bromosuccinimide (NBS) in which an allylic hydrogen is replaced with bromine and the double bond is maintained intact (eq. 1)[1].

$$RCH_2CH{=}CH_2 \xrightarrow{NBS} RCH(Br)CH{=}CH_2 + RCH{=}CHCH_2Br \qquad (1)$$

The reaction is known to involve molecular bromine, Br_2, and occurs via a radical chain reaction. The three propagation steps are shown below (eqs. 2-4). The first step involves abstraction of an allylic hydrogen by bromine, $Br^{\bullet}$ (eq. 2). The allylic radical that is produced abstracts a bromine atom from molecular bromine (eq. 3). Since the allylic radical is a resonance hybrid, two different allylic bromides can be formed. Finally, NBS and HBr react to give succinimide and molecular bromine (eq. 4).

$$Br^{\bullet} + CH_3CH_2CH{=}CH_2 \xrightarrow{slow} HBr + CH_3\dot{C}HCH{=}CH_2 \qquad (2)$$

$$Br_2 + CH_3\dot{C}HCH{=}CH_2 \xrightarrow{fast} Br^{\bullet} + CH_3CH(Br)CH{=}CH_2 \qquad (3)$$

$$(\text{or } CH_3CH{=}CHCH_2Br)$$

$$\text{NBS} + HBr \longrightarrow \text{N-H (succinimide)} + Br_2 \qquad (4)$$

NBS

[1] Carey and Sundberg A, p. 688; March, p. 615, 624.

There are five possible sites for hydrogen abstraction from 1-butene, yielding five possible different free radical intermediates, **1-5**.

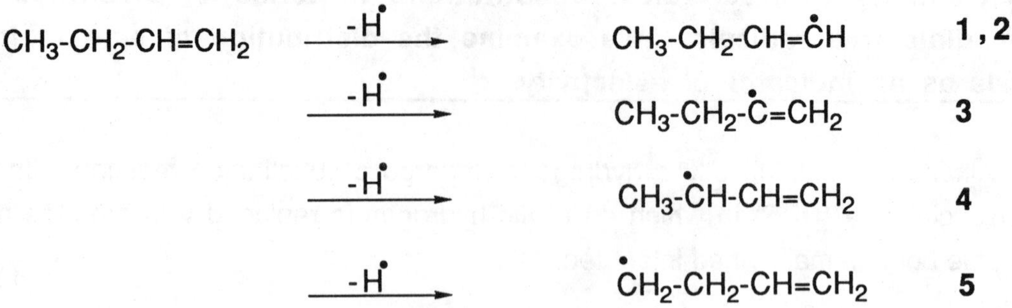

$$CH_3\text{-}CH_2\text{-}CH{=}CH_2 \xrightarrow{-H^\bullet} CH_3\text{-}CH_2\text{-}CH{=}\dot{C}H \qquad \mathbf{1,2}$$

$$\xrightarrow{-H^\bullet} CH_3\text{-}CH_2\text{-}\dot{C}{=}CH_2 \qquad \mathbf{3}$$

$$\xrightarrow{-H^\bullet} CH_3\text{-}\dot{C}H\text{-}CH{=}CH_2 \qquad \mathbf{4}$$

$$\xrightarrow{-H^\bullet} \dot{C}H_2\text{-}CH_2\text{-}CH{=}CH_2 \qquad \mathbf{5}$$

Note that radicals **1** and **2** are stereoisomers, unless of course the radical assumes a linear geometry. As indicated in (3) above, two different products are known to result, seemingly both arrived at via the intermediacy of the free radical **4**.

In this experiment, we examine the radical intermediates involved in NBS bromination of alkenes in order to explain the observed regioselectivity. Specifically, we consider the bromination of 1-butene and employ both radical stabilities to identify the radical first formed, and spin densities to examine the fate of this radical.

Procedure

To build radicals **1-5**, start with *gauche* 1-butene and, one after the other, remove the hydrogens indicated.

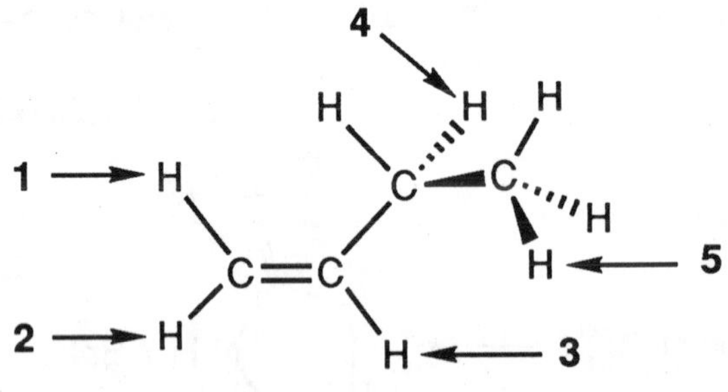

1 → H, 2 → H, 3 → H, 4 → H, 5 → H

Optimize each radical at the AM1 level and record its heat of formation in the table below.

AM1 heats of formation (kcal/mol)
1
2
3
4
5
6
7
8
9

Do you obtain five distinct radicals? In particular, are radicals **1** and **2** distinguishable? Which of the possible structures is the energetically most favored? Is your result consistent with experimental observation? Identify any other structures of comparable energy.

You should have identified the allylic hydrogen as the one actually abstracted, i.e., leading to the most stable radical. Why does this result in a mixture of isomers instead of just the isomer resulting from abstraction of the allylic hydrogen? A spin density map for **4** should provide some clues. The most reactive site in the radical should be the site of highest spin density. By plotting a spin density map, we can identify where the unpaired electron is actually localized and compare this with our simple valence structure. Calculate and display a total electron density surface onto which the spin density has been superimposed. Locate the regions of high spin density. Is the spin density concentrated on more than one carbon? Would Br• attack at these carbons lead to the observed isomeric mixture? **[3]**

Optional

Using semi-empirical AM1 calculations and spin density maps, predict the reaction products of *trans*-3,6-dimethylcyclohexene with N-bromosuccinide. There are four different sites from which hydrogen atoms can be removed

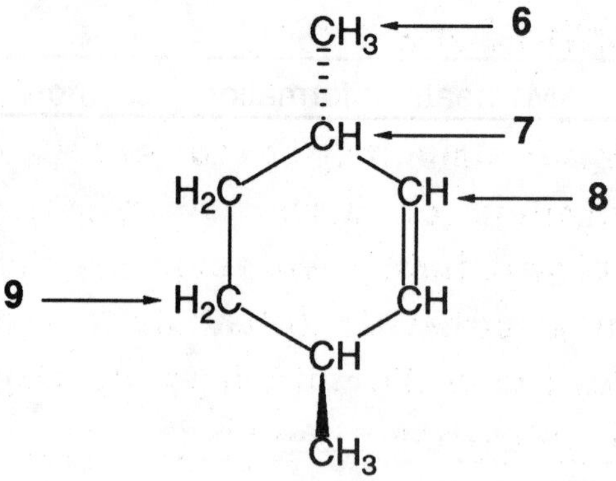

(Five different sites actually appear in a 3d rendering of dimethylcyclohexene,

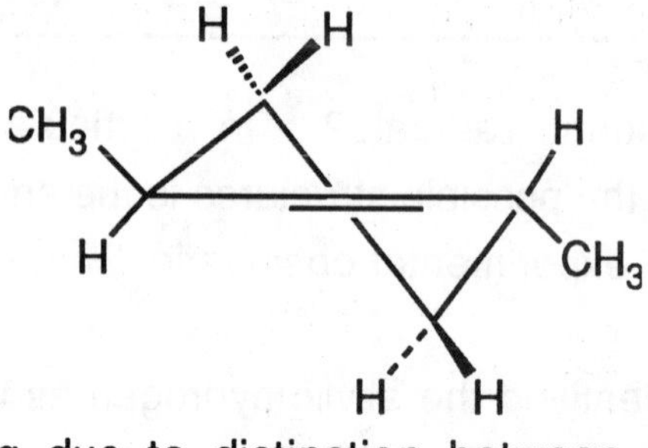

the additional site arising due to distinction between axial and equatorial ring hydrogens. However, these lead to identical free radicals.) Perform calculations on all free radicals and record your data in the table above. Which is the most stable radical? How does this relate to your observations for radicals formed from 1-butene? Calculate a spin density map for the stable radical. Does this indicate more than one possible addition site?

Experiment 36: *ortho* Benzyne

We use 3-21G *ab initio* calculations to examine the geometry and valence molecular orbitals of *ortho* benzyne in order to provide a representation of its structure. We examine the valence molecular orbitals and molecular electrostatic potentials to classify the reactivity of *ortho* benzyne. We calculate the vibrational spectrum for *ortho* benzyne in order to support or refute the experimental assignment.

The commercially important synthesis of phenol from chlorobenzene is believed to involve a two-step elimination/addition mechanism, in which *ortho* benzyne is an intermediate.[1]

Cl

OH⁻

-HCl

H_2O

OH

There is considerable evidence for this mechanism and for the participation of a symmetrical *ortho* benzyne. Most important is the observation that reaction of chlorobenzene labelled by ^{14}C in the *ipso* position and KNH_2 leads to equal amounts of two labelled anilines.

Cl

*

KNH_2

NH_3

*

NH_2 NH_2

* *

+

1 : 1

This would seem to demand a symmetrical intermediate. Further evidence for *ortho* benzyne follows from the isolation of its "trapping products" resulting from Diels-Alder cycloaddition of cyclopentadiene.

---

[1] Cary and Sundberg A, p. 583; Lowry and Richardson, p. 643; March, p. 580; the classic account of benzynes is: R.W. Hoffmann, **Dehydrobenzene and Cycloalkynes**, Academic Press, New York, 1967.

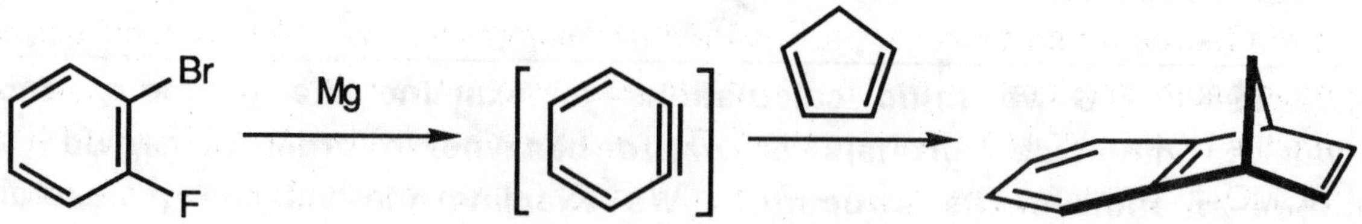

Finally, the infrared spectrum of *ortho* benzyne has been recorded in a low-temperature matrix, and a peak at 2085 cm^{-1} has been assigned to the C≡C stretching frequency. This is consistent with the molecule incorporating a triple bond (typical "C≡C" absorptions occur about 2200 cm^{-1}).

This experiment is divided into three parts. In the first, we use both the calculated geometry and valence molecular orbitals of *ortho* benzyne to provide a realistic representation of its electronic structure. In the second, we examine both the valence molecular orbitals and molecular electrostatic potential for clues as to how the molecule will react. In the third part, we compare the calculated vibrational spectrum for *ortho* benzyne with that reported for the species in a low-temperature matrix.

Procedure

[13] [1] Build *ortho* benzyne. Optimize at the 3-21G level. Be certain to specify use of direct methods. When completed, write down the calculated CC bond lengths in the figure below, and compare them to bond distances in benzene and in hexa-1,5-diene-3-yne obtained at the same level of calculation.

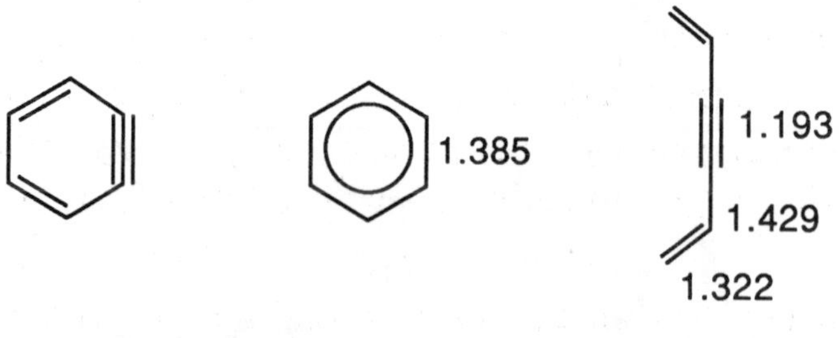

On the basis of its calculated bond lengths, how best would you represent *ortho* benzyne? Does it incorporate a carbon-carbon triple bond? Has the remainder of the benzene skeleton been significantly distorted? Is the π system significantly localized or is it delocalized?

Comparison of the valence molecular orbitals, in particular, the π orbitals, of *ortho* benzyne and benzene provides further information with which to construct an appropriate structural description. For *ortho* benzyne at the 3-21G level, the π orbitals are the HOMO, HOMO-1 and HOMO-3; for benzene, they are the HOMO, HOMO-1 and HOMO-4. Generate and display the π orbitals for both systems; also obtain the orbital energies. Notice that the HOMO and HOMO-1 in benzene are degenerate (have the same energy). Why? Do you see any degeneracies (or near degeneracies) in the π system of *ortho* benzyne? Do the orbital comparisons between the two systems provide a picture which is consistent with that obtained from structural comparisons alone? [15]

Let's now see if what the calculations tell us about the electronic structure of *ortho* benzyne is consistent with its role as a dienophile in reaction with cyclopentadiene. In particular, is *ortho* benzyne as good a dienophile as molecules such as acrylonitrile and acrolein. The key indicator is the LUMO energy [see also **Chapter 5** and **Experiment 43**]; obtain this for *ortho* benzyne and compare to the 3-21G values for acrylonitrile and acrolein given in the table below.

3-21G LUMO energies (hartrees)	
acrylonitrile	0.104
acrolein	0.096
ortho benzyne	

Is the role of *ortho* benzyne as a dienophile consistent with your LUMO energy data? Do the calculations suggest that *ortho* benzyne will be a better dienophile, a poorer dienophile, or about as good a dienophile as acrylonitrile and acrolein?

Construct the graphical surface corresponding to the LUMO in *ortho* benzyne. Is it a σ orbital or a π orbital? Based on what you find, speculate on the geometry of the transition state for the Diels-Alder addition of *ortho* benzyne with cyclopentadiene.

As noted above, the vibrational spectrum of a molecule presumed to be *ortho* benzyne in a low-temperature matrix has been recorded, and a band at 2085 cm^{-1} has been assigned as the "C≡C stretch". This is about 200 cm^{-1} lower than the C≡C stretch in a typical acyclic alkyne, e.g., 2240 cm^{-1} in "2-butyne", suggesting that *ortho* benzyne does incorporate a triple bond, but that this bond is not fully formed, perhaps because of severe bond angle distortion. Calculate the vibrational spectrum of *ortho* benzyne. The resulting normal-mode analysis may also be used to confirm that the molecule is indeed a minimum. Is it?

Potential energy minima are characterized by all frequencies resulting from a normal mode analysis being real. Imaginary frequencies (usually represented as negative frequencies) correspond to motions which lead to lower energies. Potential surfaces which are described by a single imaginary frequency correspond to transition states. It is often a very good idea to perform a normal mode analysis to verify disposition on a complex potential energy surface, especially in cases where symmetry has been imposed.

[7] Identify the frequency corresponding to the "C≡C stretch" (use animation). How close is it to the measured value? As a calibration, the calculated (3-21G) frequency corresponding to the "C≡C stretch" in 2-butyne is 2565 cm^{-1} compared to 2240 cm^{-1} experimentally.

Hartree-Fock level calculations with basis sets such as 3-21G typically lead to vibrational frequencies which are 12% larger than experimental values,[2] and it is common to scale calculated values by 0.88. About half of this difference is due to anharmonic contributions and the other half to electron correlation effects.

On the basis of this comparison, do you conclude that the experimental assignment of *ortho* benzyne is correct?

---

[2] W.J. Hehre, L. Radom, P.v.R. Schleyer and J.A. Pople, **Ab Initio Molecular Orbital Theory**, Wiley, New York, p. 226.

Experiment 37: Stabilizing Reactive Intermediates[1]

We use 3-21G *ab initio* calculations to examine the effects of substituents on carbocations, carbanions and carbon-centered free radicals. We classify substituents in terms of their σ and π electron-donating/accepting abilities.

It is commonly accepted among organic chemists that π-donor substituents will stabilize carbocations, while π-acceptor groups will stabilize carbanions, i.e.,

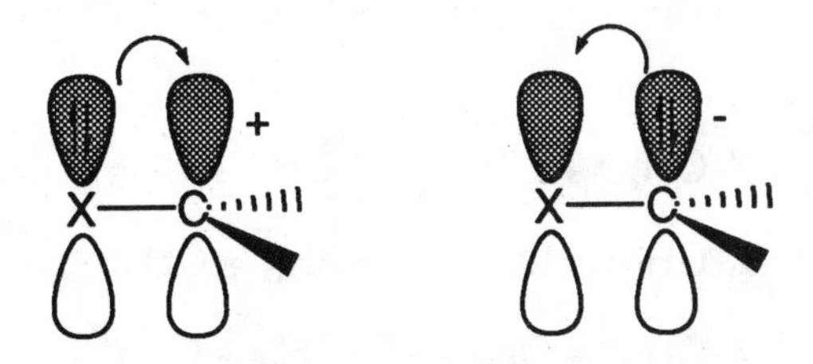

The effect of π-acceptor groups on cation centers and π-donor substituents on anion centers is less apparent. Will they be destabilizing or will they have little overall effect? The role of σ effects is even less well understood. Will strong σ-donor groups, e.g., Li, stabilize electron-deficient carbocation centers, even though they also function as strong π acceptors seeking to withdraw electrons from an empty orbital?

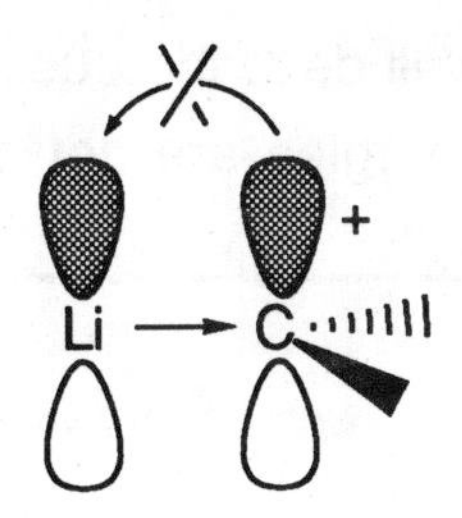

Will the σ-donor properties of a substituent such as Li destabilize an already electron-rich carbanion center despite the strong benefit of π acceptance?

[1] W.J. Hehre, L. Radom, P.v.R. Schleyer and J.A. Pople, **Ab Initio Molecular Orbital Theory**, Wiley, New York, 1986, p. 346.

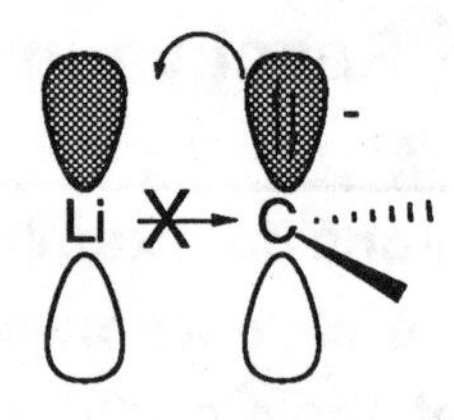

Finally, would you expect substituent effects on free radicals to parallel those of cations or of anions or to lie somewhere in between?

These and related questions are the subjects of the present laboratory. Here, we'll use 3-21G *ab initio* calculations to evaluate the energetics of *isodesmic* reactions (1)-(3).

$$X\text{-}CH_2^+ + CH_4 \rightarrow X\text{-}CH_3 + CH_3^+ \quad (1)$$

$$X\text{-}CH_2^- + CH_4 \rightarrow X\text{-}CH_3 + CH_3^- \quad (2)$$

$$X\text{-}CH_2^\bullet + CH_4 \rightarrow X\text{-}CH_3 + CH_3^\bullet \quad (3)$$

These relate the effect of a substituent X directly attached to a carbocation, carbanion and carbon radical center, respectively, to that for the same substituent attached to a methyl group

> *Isodesmic* reactions maintain the same number of each kind of formal chemical bond, and their energies are generally well described using simple levels of *ab initio* theory (see also **Appendix B**). Their energies are not, however, well (reliably) described using semi-empirical methods.

Procedure

Build all the molecules required to evaluate the energetics of equations (1)-(3), for X=Li (σ donor, π acceptor), CH_3 (σ and π donor), NH_2 (σ acceptor, π donor) and CN (σ and π acceptor), and optimize using the 3-21G *ab initio* model. All of these molecules are small and direct methods will not be needed. Record the total energies in the table below.

3-21G energies (hartrees)				
X	XCH_3	XCH_2^+	XCH_2^-	$XCH_2^\bullet$
H	-39.97688	-39.00913	-39.23940	-39.34261
Li	-46.75248			
CH_3	-78.79395			
NH_2	-94.68166			
CN	-131.19180			

Note that data for methane, methyl cation, methyl anion and methyl radical as well as for substituted methanes have already been provided in the table. Work out the energetics of (1)-(3) and enter in the table below.

3-21G stabilization energies (kcal/mol)			
X	XCH_2^+	XCH_2^-	$XCH_2^\bullet$
H			
Li			
CH_3			
NH_2			
CN			

What is the effect of methyl in stabilizing carbocation, carbanion and carbon radical centers? Is this in accord with expectations? In particular, do you see the expected stabilization of the cation center by the amino group (a strong π donor) and of the anion center by cyano (a strong π acceptor)? What is the effect of the amino substituent on the carbanion and of cyano on the carbocation? Do you see significant stabilizing or destabilizing effects associated with the lithium substituent (a very strong σ donor and a π acceptor)? What are the effects of π-donor and π-acceptor groups on radical centers?

Optional

Are substituent effects able to distinguish between singlet and triplet states of carbenes? We might expect that singlet carbenes, with an empty π orbital, would be stabilized by π donors,

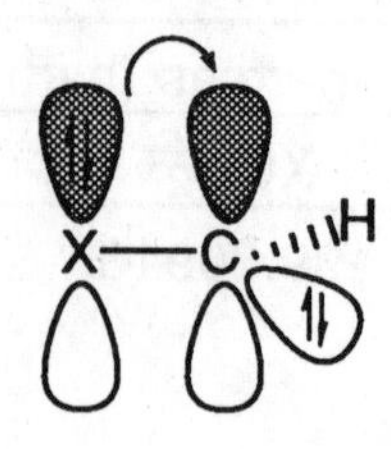

while triplet carbenes would be expected to behave like radicals. Obtain 3-21G energies for all molecules required to evaluate the energetics of (4) and (5) for X=Li, CH_3, NH_2 and CN.

$$X\text{-}\ddot{C}H + CH_4 \rightarrow X\text{-}CH_3 + \ddot{C}H_2 \qquad (4)$$

$$X\text{-}\dot{C}H\bullet + CH_4 \rightarrow X\text{-}CH_3 + \bullet\dot{C}H_2 \qquad (5)$$

Record in the table below,

3-21G energies (hartrees) and stabilization energies (kcal/mol)				
	energies		stabilization energies	
X	$X\ddot{C}H$	$X\dot{C}H\bullet$	$X\ddot{C}H$	$X\dot{C}H\bullet$
H	-38.65185	-38.70907	0	0
Li				
CH_3				
NH_2				
CN				

Work out the stabilization energies and record these as well. Do you see the expected parallels between singlet carbenes and carbocations and between triplet carbenes and radicals? Are the calculated substituent effects for singlet and triplet carbenes different enough to allow distinction between the two?

2. Diffuse functions are normally considered important for the description of the relative energies of carbanions. Recalculate the energies involved in reactions (2) using the 3-21+G basis set (and the 3-21G equilibrium geometries you previously obtained). Do you see significant differences in the stabilization energies from those obtained using 3-21G energies? Are any of your earlier qualitative conclusions altered?

Chapter 5. Reactivity and Selectivity

Let us now return to the reaction coordinate diagram introduced in **Chapter 1** and focus on its use in anticipating the detailed distribution of products in chemical reactions.

Kinetic vs. Thermodynamic Control

Chemical reactions can display complex, and even paradoxical, behavior. A certain experiment might yield one mixture of products under one set of conditions and a completely different mixture of products under a different set of conditions. In addition, many factors (temperature, reagent concentrations, solvent and reaction time) can affect the outcome of an experiment. Thus, understanding the relationship between these experimental factors and the outcome of chemical processes is a major goal of chemistry.

The way in which experimental conditions might favor one chemical reaction over another can best be explained by invoking the notions of *kinetic control* and *thermodynamic control*. A kinetically controlled system is one where the outcome is determined by the relative rates of competing reactions. A thermodynamically controlled system is one where the outcome is determined by the relative stability of competing reaction products. The difference between these reaction types can be more easily understood using a reaction coordinate diagram.

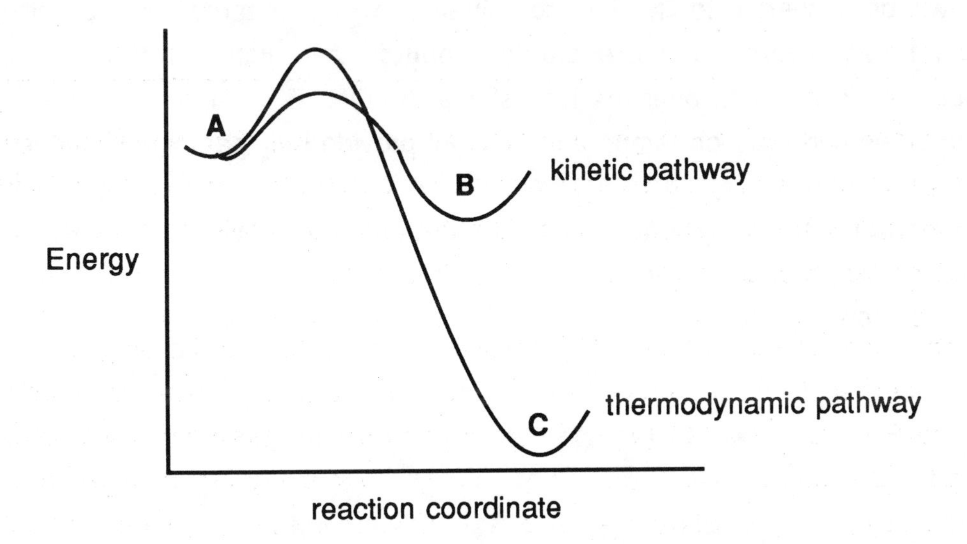

The reaction coordinate diagram above describes the energy changes required for two different competing reactions: **A** $\rightarrow$ **B** and **A** $\rightarrow$ **C**. Both reactions are exothermic because the energies of **B** and **C** are both lower than the energy of **A**. However, the energy of **C** is much lower than the energy of **B**. There is also an energy barrier for both reactions, and the size of the barrier(s) will determine how much heat must be added before a reasonable reaction rate can be achieved. The barrier for formation of **C** is higher than the barrier for formation of **B**, and **B** will form more rapidly than **C** during the first stages of reaction regardless of how much heat is applied.

We can now see one way in which the reaction conditions, in this case, temperature and reaction time, can affect the outcome of the experiment. At relatively low temperatures, more **A** molecules can cross the barrier leading to **B** than can cross the barrier leading to **C**. Since it takes less time to equilibrate **A** and **B** than it does **A** and **C**, a short reaction time will yield [**B**]>>[**C**] at the end of the experiment. In other words, the combination of low temperature and short reaction time favors the faster process, **A** $\rightarrow$ **B**, over the slower process, **A** $\rightarrow$ **C**, and the system is kinetically controlled. **B** is often referred to as the *kinetic product* for just this reason.

If the experiment is carried out at a higher temperature, the formation of **B** will still be favored. However, if the reaction time is extended beyond the time required for equilibration of **A** and **B**, then **C** will gradually accumulate. This occurs because there is enough energy for some **A** molecules to cross the barrier leading to **C**, and because there is enough energy for some **B** molecules to return to **A** (remember that all chemical equilibria are dynamic). Given a long enough reaction time, nearly all of **A** and **B** will be converted to **C**. The combination of higher temperatures and longer reaction times favors the more stable product, **C**, which is referred to as the *thermodynamic product*, over the less stable product, **B**. (Of course, intermediate reaction times and reaction temperatures might provide only partial equilibration of **A**, **B**, and **C**.)

Another commonly encountered situation is one where the kinetic and thermodynamic products are the same. A reaction coordinate diagram for this type of process is shown below.

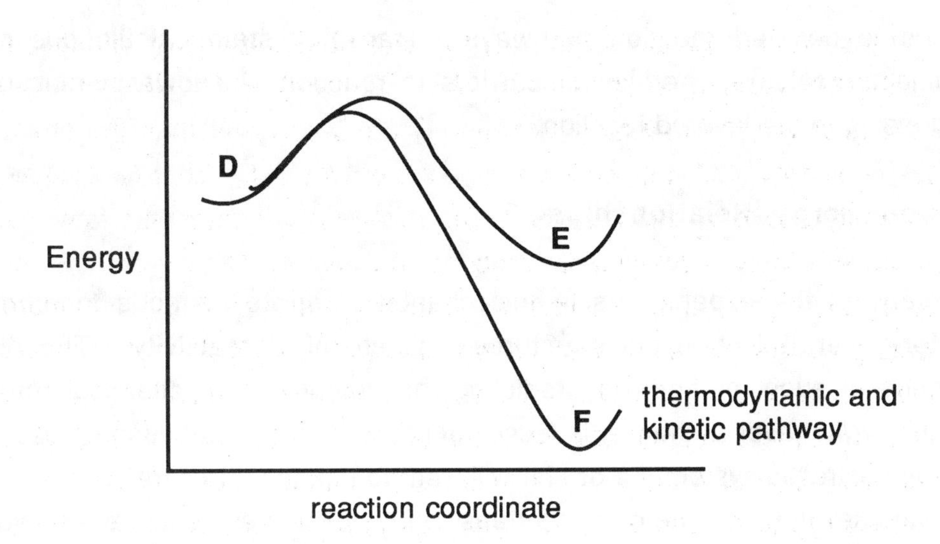

Although **F** is both the kinetic and thermodynamic product, different mixtures of **E** and **F** will be obtained depending on the experimental conditions. High temperatures and long reaction times will cause complete equilibration of **E** and **F**, and their ratio will be determined by their relative energies. Low temperatures and short reaction times will give a different product ratio, one that is determined by the relative barrier heights. As a result, the product ratio can be used to determine whether the reaction occurred under kinetic or thermodynamic control.

Computer modeling can be used to study both kinetically and thermodynamically controlled reactions. In the latter case, the chemist usually wants answers to the following two questions: "which product is preferred thermodynamically and by how much energy?", and "what is the relationship between each product's structure and its energy?" Modeling can be used to calculate the energy of each product and can also be used to derive structure-energy relationships (see **Chapter 1. Structure and Energetics** and **Chapter 2. Conformation**).

Kinetically controlled reactions present a more difficult problem for the chemist. The questions that need to be answered depend a great deal on the type of reaction and may include: "what is the mechanism of the reaction?", "what are the energy barriers for any competing reactions?", "what is the structure of the key transition state?", "what is the energy and structure of the key reaction intermediate?", and so on. Most of the experiments in this chapter illustrate modeling techniques which can be used to answer these questions. These techniques are divided into two categories. Structure-reactivity relationships seek to relate chemical reactivity and product selectivity to the structures of the reactants and/or of key intermediates without reference to detailed reaction pathways. Transition state calculations seek to determine the relative energies of barriers to reaction, the lowest energy barrier corresponding to the favored reaction.

Structure-Energy Relationships

Many of the experiments in this chapter illustrate methods for correlating computer-generated chemical structures with chemical reactivity. The potential importance of such methods in predicting the outcome of a chemical reaction is enormous. Whenever a chemist is faced with two or more competing processes in a kinetically controlled system, he or she will want to use the structures of the reactants (or of some key intermediate or of the transition state) to predict the favored outcome. This is possible only if an appropriate structure-reactivity relationship is available to guide the chemist's predictions. The following discussion describes some of the techniques that can be employed to derive structure-reactivity relationships.

Electrostatic Interactions[1]

Many chemical reactions occur between electron-poor and electron-rich reagents. In most cases, these reagents either carry an electrical charge or are characterized by an unsymmetrical distribution of charge. Electrostatic interactions between such reaction partners can occur over long distances and may favor one orientation or reaction site over another, particularly in solvents with small dielectric constants (recall that the strength of an electrostatic interaction is inversely proportional to the magnitude of the solvent's dielectric constant).

The distribution of charge can be assessed in various ways including the calculation of an electrostatic potential map or an isopotential surface, the calculation of atomic charges from the electrostatic potential, and the calculation of atomic charges from a population analysis.

---

[1] Examples of the use of electrostatic interactions in assigning reactivity and selectivity include: S.D. Kahn, C.F. Pau, L.E. Overman and W.J. Hehre, J. Am. Chem. Soc., **108**, 7381 (1986); S.D. Kahn, C.F. Pau, A.R. Chamberlin and W.J. Hehre, *ibid.*, **109**, 650 (1987); S.D. Kahn and W.J. Hehre, *ibid.*, **109**, 663 (1987); S.D. Kahn, K.D. Dobbs and W.J. Hehre, *ibid.*, **110**, 4602 (1988).

Steric Effects

There are many ways in which a molecule's steric demands may affect its chemical reactivity. One of the most important is *steric hindrance*, i.e., a situation where a large bulky group interferes with or prevents the approach of two reactants. Steric hindrance is a short-range effect since it requires close contact and repulsive overlap of the electron clouds surrounding the two reactants.

Steric hindrance can often be detected by examining a space-filling (CPK) model of the reactant (or a key intermediate or transition state). The 0.002 electrons/au^3 isodensity surface can be used in place of a space-filling model, and may be superior since it more accurately reflects the shape of the electron cloud.

Frontier Molecular Orbital Theory[2]

According to Frontier Molecular Orbital (FMO) theory, many chemical reactions involve an attractive interaction between an electron donor and an electron acceptor. In some cases, this interaction is electrostatic. In others, the interaction occurs mainly via overlap of molecular orbitals on the two reactants. Specifically, overlap of the electron donor's HOMO (or some high-energy filled molecular orbital underneath the HOMO) with the electron acceptor's LUMO (or some low-energy unfilled molecular orbital above the LUMO) may lead to a stabilizing interaction (the HOMO and LUMO are referred to as "frontier molecular orbitals").

The strength of this stabilizing $HOMO_{donor}/LUMO_{acceptor}$ interaction is given by:

$$E_{stabilization} \propto \frac{\left[\int \phi_{donor}^{HOMO} \phi_{acceptor}^{LUMO} d\tau\right]^2}{\varepsilon_{donor}^{HOMO} - \varepsilon_{acceptor}^{LUMO}}$$

Large $E_{stabilization}$ leads to a low energy barrier (high reaction rate). It is easy to identify two factors that can enhance $E_{stabilization}$. The first factor is a small energy gap between $HOMO_{donor}$ and $LUMO_{acceptor}$. Where two or more electron donors compete for the same acceptor, the donor with the higher ε_{HOMO} should prove the more reactive.

---

[2] A readable account of frontier molecular orbital theory is: I. Fleming, **Frontier Orbitals and Organic Chemical Reactions**, Wiley, New York, 1976.

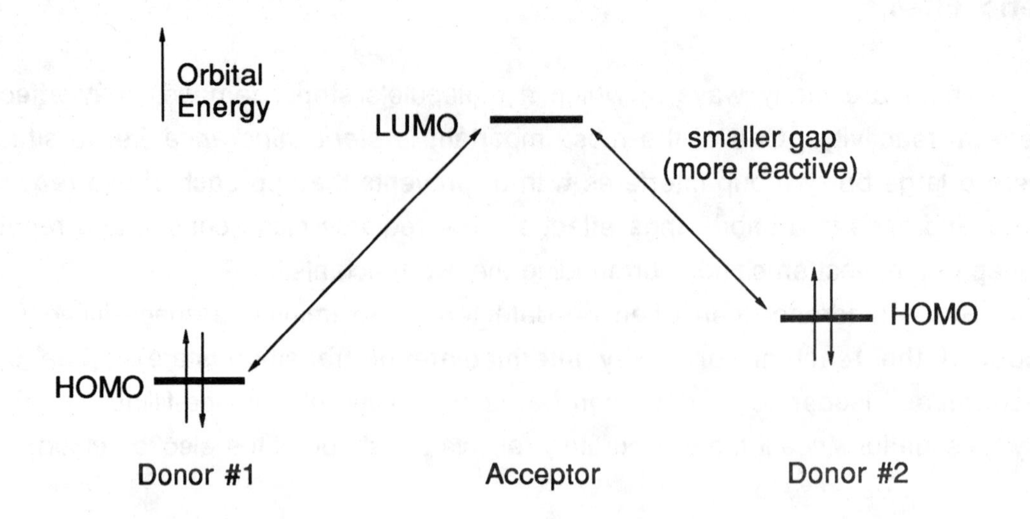

Conversely, where two or more electron acceptors compete for the same donor, the acceptor with the lower ε^{LUMO} should prove the more reactive.

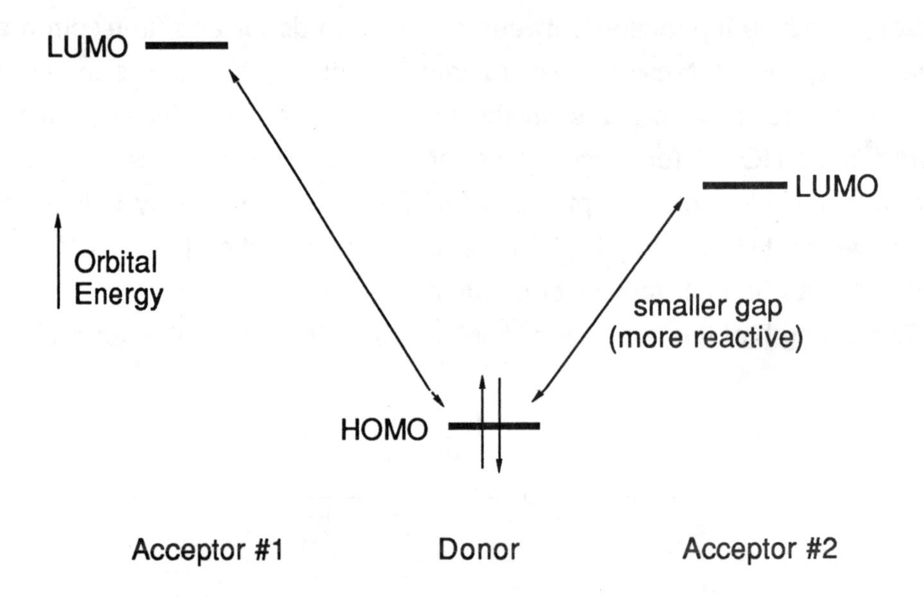

Frontier orbital energies can be obtained from electronic structure calculations and can be compared directly. One must be careful, however, to ascertain that the orbital in question is actually associated with the molecule's reactive site.

A second factor that enhances $E_{stabilization}$ and hence increases chemical reactivity is good overlap between the frontier orbitals (the integral in the numerator is the frontier orbital overlap). This factor plays a role whenever a pair of reactants can select from two or more reaction geometries. Since the gap in orbital energies (the denominator) is unaffected by reaction geometry, the preferred geometry will be the one that yields the best orbital overlap.

Orbital overlap is usually estimated qualitatively and is rarely calculated (although this is not difficult). For example, one might be interested in selectivity towards the two faces of a π system. Since π orbitals are normally symmetrical with respect to their nodal plane, overlap between reactant **Z** and each face of the π system should be the same. However, differing degrees of steric hindrance around each face could affect **Z**'s approach and the amount of orbital overlap that might actually be possible. Steric hindrance can be evaluated by overlaying the orbital with the 0.002 electrons/au^3 isodensity surface (or mapping the orbital onto the isodensity surface). In general, the more the orbital "extends" beyond the isodensity surface, the better the overlap with an incoming reagent.

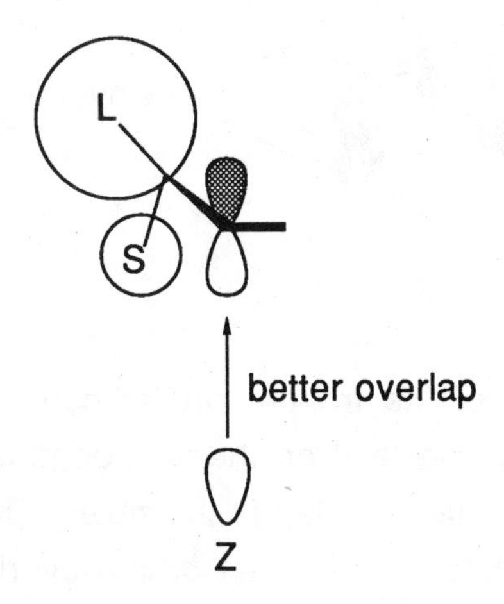

Facial selectivity can also arise from asymmetry in the π orbital itself. Certain atoms might interact with the π system to polarize the π orbitals toward a particular face. In this case, better overlap is achieved at the face where the orbital is larger. Again, examination of the isoorbital surface or mapping the orbital onto the 0.002 electrons/au^3 isodensity surface should indicate which face is larger.

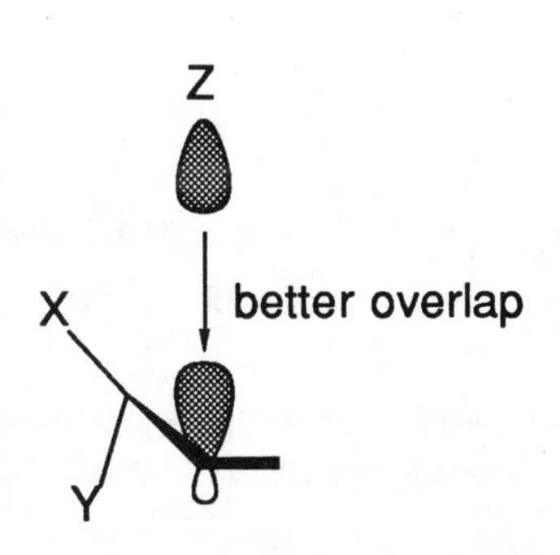

One often encounters π systems that contain several reactive atoms and the question of site selectivity becomes important. If one assumes that steric effects do not play an important role and furthermore that the orbital is not polarized significantly toward one face or the other, overlap should be best at the atom making the largest contribution to the π orbital. Relative atomic contributions can be determined by examining the atomic orbital coefficients, or more conveniently by examining the shape of the isoorbital surface (again, mapping of the orbital onto the 0.002 electrons/au^3 isodensity surface is often useful).

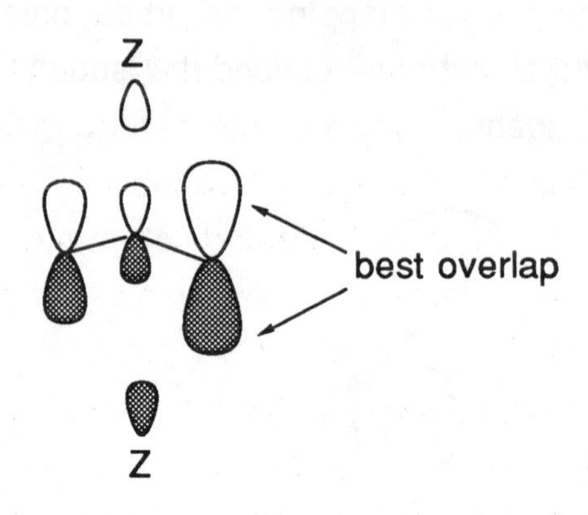

The nodal properties of the frontier orbital can also affect orbital overlap.[3] Backside attack by a nucleophile (Nu) on the C-X bond is favored even in relatively hindered systems because better overlap is possible. Frontside attack would occur along a node in the C-X orbital and the net orbital overlap between $HOMO_{Nu}$ and $LUMO_{CX}$ would be small.

Nu ⟶ C X (better overlap)

Transition States

One of the most exciting, and potentially most useful, methods for investigating structure-reactivity relationships is to construct models of competing transition states

---

[3] This is of course the basis of the Woodward-Hoffmann orbital symmetry rules: R.B. Woodward and R. Hoffmann, **The Conservation of Orbital Symmetry**, Verlag Chemie-Academic Press, New York, 1970.

and calculate their energy barriers directly. Unfortunately, the construction of reliable computer-generated models of transition states and other reactivity species is still in its infancy and will probably undergo significant change and development during the next decade. Part of the problem comes from the fact that transition state structures cannot be detected or characterized experimentally, at least not directly. Transition states are unstable structures on the reaction coordinate and a stable, experimentally accessible population of transition state compounds does not exist. This means that we lack the experience in knowing what transition states "look like". In time this experience will be gained and transition-state structures will be as familiar to us as equilibrium geometries are today.

It might be argued that experimental quantities such as activation energies, activation entropies, and activation volumes provide information about transition state structures. However, there is no unique correspondence between these experimental quantities and transition state structure. Many different structures could, in principle, produce the same barriers, entropies, etc. Thus, interpretation of these parameters requires a theoretical analysis that includes the construction of model transition state structures. In the final analysis, theory and modeling are on their own!

Fortunately, quantum chemical calculations do not (cannot) distinguish between systems which are stable and which can be scrutinized experimentally, and those which are labile (reaction intermediates), or which do not even correspond to energy minima (transition states) and may not even be detectable, let alone characterized. The theory underlying quantum chemistry is general. One must hope that the lack of (intentional) bias in formulating the theory, and the practical computational methods used to implement it, will ensure that calculated changes in structure and energy will be reliable. Given the intrinsic shortcomings of experimental chemistry when it comes to characterizing short-lived species, and in particular transition states, the modeling of these species and the elucidation of reaction pathways represents one of the most important applications of computational chemistry.

Experiment 38: Rates of Electrophilic Additions to Alkenes

We use electrostatic potentials obtained from semi-empirical AM1 calculations to examine the intermediates in electrophilic additions to alkenes. We investigate the relationship between the stability of intermediates and rates of addition of electrophiles to olefins, in particular, the effects of alkyl substitution and of ring strain on the rates of addition of electrophiles to olefins.

The rate of hydrolysis of an alkene is known to depend on the number and size of substituents attached to the double bond.[1] For example, the rate of hydrolysis increases in the alkenes **1-5**,

$$\underset{\mathbf{1}}{H_2C{=}CH_2} < \underset{\mathbf{2}}{CH_3CH{=}CH_2} < \underset{\mathbf{3}}{CH_3CH_2CH{=}CH_2} < \underset{\mathbf{4}}{(CH_3)_2C{=}CH_2} < \underset{\mathbf{5}}{(CH_3)_2C{=}C(CH_3)_2}$$

that is, with increasing alkyl substitution on the double bond. The rate-determining step in the acid-catalyzed hydrolysis of an alkene leading to an alcohol is usually assumed to involve the formation of an intermediate carbocation, i.e.,

$$\text{R-CH=CH}_2 \xrightarrow[\text{slow}]{H_3O^+} \text{R-}\overset{+}{\text{C}}\text{H-CH}_3 \xrightarrow[\text{fast}]{H_2O} \text{R-}\underset{}{\overset{\text{OH}}{\overset{|}{\text{C}}}}\text{H-CH}_3$$

This suggests that overall rate should be related to the "basicity" of their alkene precursors.

In this experiment, we first investigate the basicity, of a series of acyclic alkenes using electrostatic potential maps obtained from semi-empirical AM1 calculations. We attempt to correlate these with known relative rates for alkene hydrolysis. We then examine the extent to which ring strain affects the proton affinities of alkenes, and (by implication) the rates of acid-catalyzed addition reactions.

---

[1] Carey and Sundberg A, p. 349; Lowry and Richardson, p. 572.

Procedure

Build and optimize at the semi-empirical AM1 level the alkenes **1-5**. For each, calculate an electron density isosurface onto which the electrostatic potential has been [3] encoded. Display all the surfaces together. You might find it convenient to first use transparent surfaces, as this will allow you to see the underlying molecular skeleton. Protons attack regions of high negative electrostatic potential, and this occurs in the vicinity of the π system. Locate and measure the magnitude of this "hot-spot" (the minimum value of the electrostatic potential) on each molecule **1-5**. Record the [8] magnitude of the potential in the table below. Is the location of the hot spot consistent across the series?

AM1 electrostatic potentials (kcal/mol)
ethylene
propene
1-butene
iso-butene
tetramethylethylene
cyclopropene
cyclobutene
cyclopentene
cyclohexene
cis-cycloheptene
trans-cycloheptene

Next, place all displays on the same scale, i.e., the widest limits necessary to fully represent the entire range of electrostatic potentials across molecules in the series. Arrange the molecules on the screen so that the magnitude of the "hot-spot" increases from left to right. It will now be easier to observe differences by displaying the surfaces as solid instead of transparent. Does your arrangement follow the observed series for relative hydrolysis rates?

Build and minimize at the AM1 level, cyclopropene, cyclobutene, cyclopentene, cyclohexene and both *cis* and *trans* isomers of cycloheptene. As you did for the acyclic alkenes, calculate and display electron density isosurfaces onto which the electrostatic potential has been encoded. Record the minimum (most negative) value of the electrostatic potential for each in the table above. Bring the displays to the common scale used previously and line up the cycloalkenes on screen (include one or two acyclic alkenes in your "lineup") in order of increasing electrostatic potential. Comment on the effects (if any) of ring strain on the electrostatic potential surfaces [see also **Experiment 3**]. Infer what this says about the reactivity of cycloalkenes. **[3]** **[8]**

Optional

1. Using semi-empirical AM1 calculations and electrostatic potential maps, predict what effect replacing all the methyl groups by trifluoromethyl groups would have on the hydrolysis rate of **5**. What does this say about the character of the trifluoromethyl group? Is it a π-electron acceptor or a π-electron donor? Is your finding consistent with the usual characterization of CF_3 as a substituent?

2. Electrostatic potentials suggest that tetramethylethylene and *trans*-cycloheptene should undergo electrophilic addition with equal facility. This is not the case. Explain.

3. Inspection of *cis*- and *trans*-cycloheptene reveals several conformational minima for each. Perform a conformational search on the two isomers using the MM3 molecular mechanics force field, followed by geometry optimization and graphics calculation on the lowest-energy conformer (only) at the AM1 level. Do any of your conclusions change?

Experiment 39: Structure and Reactivity of Cyclic Bromonium Ions

We use semi-empirical AM1 and *ab initio* STO-3G calculations to examine the geometrical structures and charge distributions in simple cyclic bromonium ions. We relate asymmetry in structure, charge distribution and electrostatic potential in substituted bromonium ions to preferred direction for nucleophilic attack.

Addition of Br_2 to an alkene in acidic media is presumed to occur in a stepwise fashion. The first bromine adds as an electrophile (formally Br^+) giving a cation known as a *bromonium ion*. The bromonium ion can be captured by Br^-, as well as by other nucleophiles, to given an isolable product, e.g.,

"Br+"   Br⁻   only

The stepwise mechanism involving a symmetric cyclic bromonium ion is supported by direct observation of these ions by NMR spectroscopy.[1]

The situation becomes more complex when the alkene is unsymmetrically substituted. For example, bromination of styrene in acetic acid yields the expected dibromide along with an acetoxybromo derivative.[2]

$$\text{PhCH=CH}_2 \xrightarrow[\text{AcOH}]{\text{Br}_2} \underset{80\%}{\text{PhCH(Br)CH}_2\text{Br}} + \underset{20\%}{\text{PhCH(OAc)CH}_2\text{Br}}$$

The regiochemistry of addition for the latter product suggests that the cyclic bromonium ion (if indeed there is one) has an unsymmetrical structure that favors nucleophilic attack at the benzylic carbon. One can easily imagine the bromonium ion favoring a

---

[1] G.A. Olah, P.W. Westerman, E.G. Melby and Y.K. Mo, J. Am. Chem. Soc., **96**, 3565 (1974); for an extensive review, see: G.A. Olah, **Halonium Ions**, Wiley, 1975.

[2] J.H. Rolston and K.J. Yates, J. Am. Chem. Soc., **91**, 1469 (1969).

distorted structure in which ring strain is released by elongation of a C-Br bond and any positive charge on the benzylic carbon is partially stabilized by the electron-releasing phenyl group.

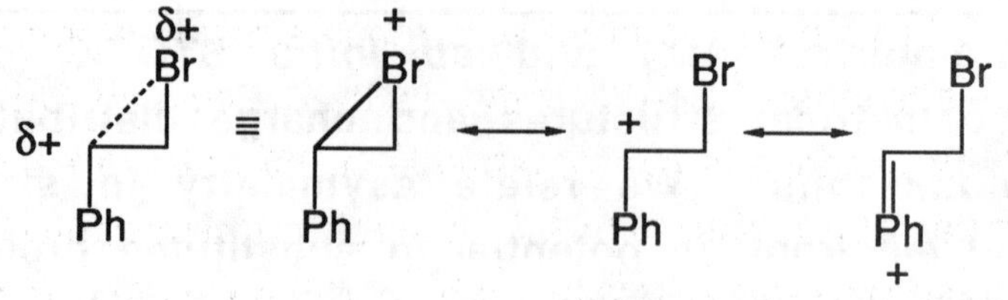

In this experiment we examine the geometrical structure and charge distribution predicted for the simplest cyclic bromonium ion, ethylenebromonium ion. An important question to be answered is whether the ion is more like a weak ion-dipole complex or a covalent three-membered ring.

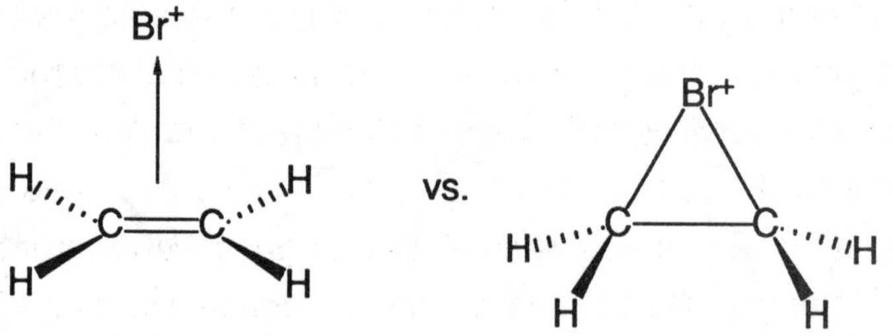

We shall then examine an unsymmetrical ion, the isobutenebromonium ion. Specifically, we want to see what effect methyl substitution has upon the geometry and charge distribution in this ion, and whether the regiochemistry of nucleophile addition is consistent with the ion's calculated charge distribution and electrostatic potential.

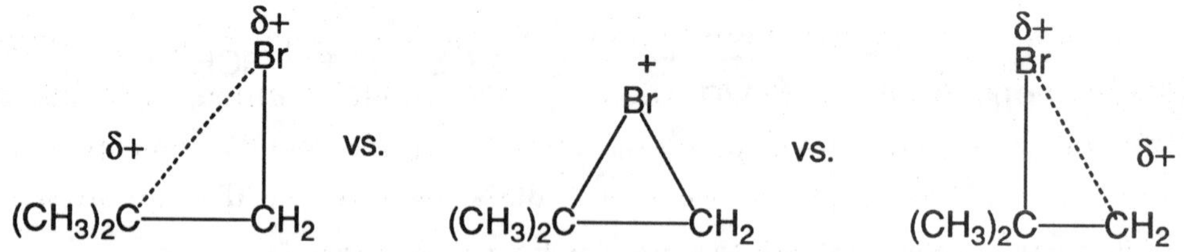

Procedure

Build ethylenebromonium ion and optimize at the AM1 level. Then use the AM1 structure as a starting point for an *ab initio* STO-3G geometry optimization. How does the calculated C-C bond distance in each of these structures compare with the C=C bond distance in ethylene (1.34Å)? How do the calculated C-Br bond distances compare to the C-Br distance in methyl bromide (1.93Å) and to the sum of the carbon and bromine van der Waals radii (3.55Å)? A stable tetrasubstituted cyclic bromonium ion has been studied by X-ray crystallography and the C-C and (average) C-Br bond distances are 1.50Å and 2.16Å respectively.[3]

Calculate an electron density isosurface onto which the electrostatic potential has been mapped. Use both AM1 and STO-3G models. According to this measure, what is the most electron-poor site in each model? Calculate the charge distribution for each model using the Natural Bond Orbital method[4] and record the charges on each atom. Is the charge distribution consistent with the electrostatic potential map? Is the charge distribution consistent with a full positive formal charge on bromine?

Build isobutenebromonium ion and optimize at the AM1 level. Then use the AM1 structure as a starting point for an *ab initio* STO-3G geometry optimization. Use the calculated bond distances and bond angles to describe the bonding pattern in the AM1 and STO-3G models. Do both calculations produce cyclic ions?

For both AM1 and STO-3G models, calculate an electron density isosurface onto which the electrostatic potential has been mapped. What is the most electron-poor site in each model? Display the electrostatic potential maps for ethylenebromonium ion and isobutenebromonium ion using the same scale, i.e., first compare the AM1 maps, then compare the STO-3G maps. In which ion does bromine carry more positive charge? [3]

Calculate the charge distribution for the AM1 and STO-3G models of isobutenebromonium ion using the Natural Bond Orbital method. Are the results consistent with the electrostatic potential maps? Are the results consistent with the ion's geometry? Does the charge distribution account for the observation that nucleophiles preferentially attack the more substituted carbon?

---

[3] H. Slebocka, R.G. Ball and R.S. Brown, J. Am. Chem. Soc., **107**, 4505 (1985).
[4] A.E. Reed, R.B. Weinstock and F. Weinhold, J. Chem. Phys., **83**, 735 (1985).

Optional

1. Frontier molecular orbital theory predicts that the shape of the LUMO of a bromonium ion will determine the site of nucleophilic attack [see **Chapter 5**]. Calculate the LUMO's (or the LUMO map of the isodensity surface) for each bromonium ion and determine the preferred site of attack.

2. Leanna, Martinelli, Varie and Kress[5] observed high selectivity in reaction of **1**,

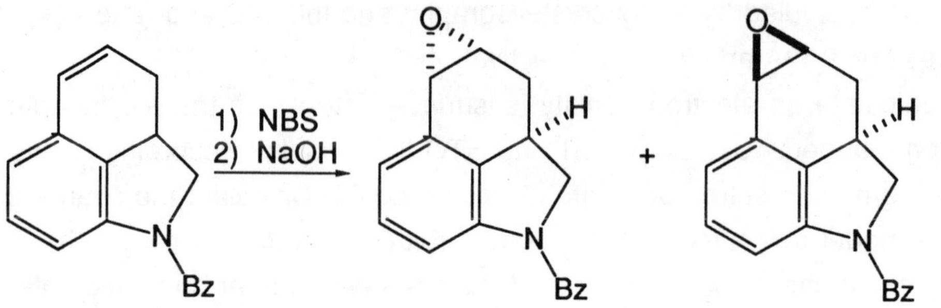

1) NBS
2) NaOH

1 1 : 99

the first step of which is presumed to involve formation of isomeric bromonium ions.

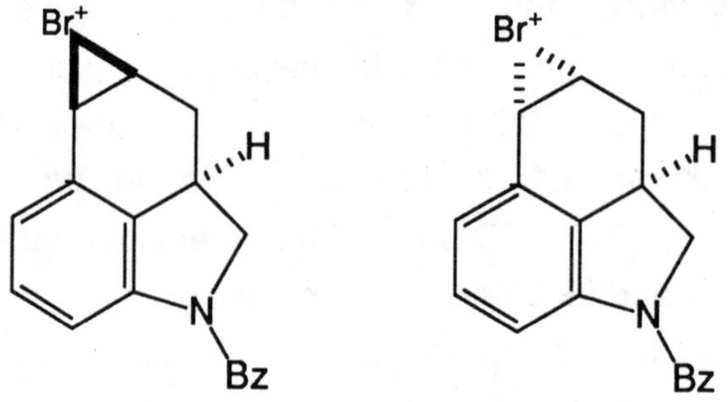

Perform AM1 calculations on model compounds, where CHO replaces the Bz substituent. Do you reproduce the experimental observation? Provide a rationale.

---

[5] M.R. Leanna, M.J. Martinelli, D.L. Varie and T.J. Kress, Tetrahedron Lett., **30**, 3935 (1989).

Experiment 40: Stereochemistry in the Synthesis of Bicyclic Alcohols

We use both semi-empirical AM1 and *ab initio* 3-21G calculations to model stereochemistry in reactions leading to bicyclic alcohols, specifically facial selectivity in nucleophilic attack. We interpret the noted stereochemical preferences in terms of steric and/or stereoelectronic effects.

There are two obvious synthetic routes to the isomeric alcohols **1** and **2**.

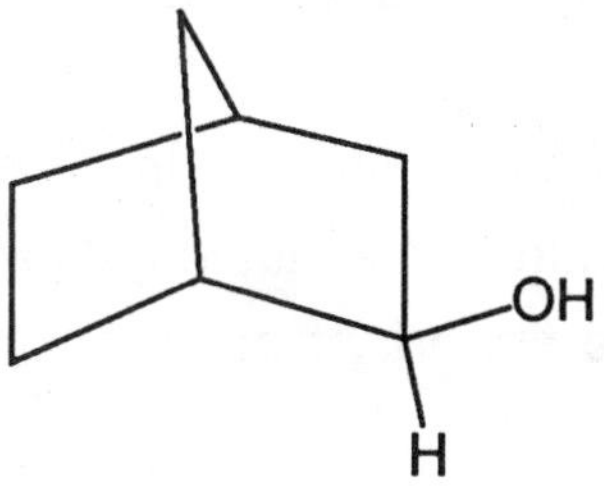

OH
H
1

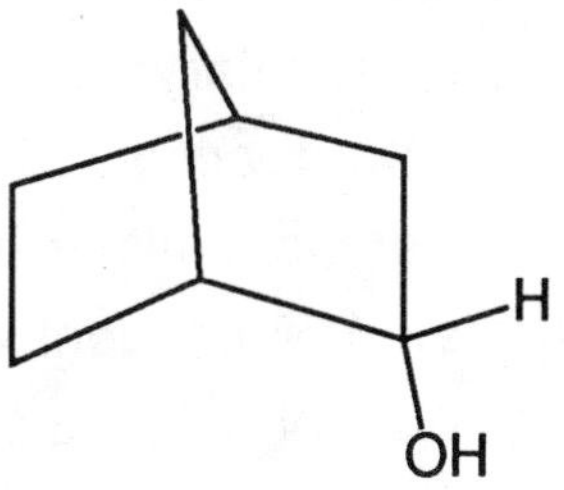

H
OH
2

The first involves hydration of norbornene **3** in the presence of acid,

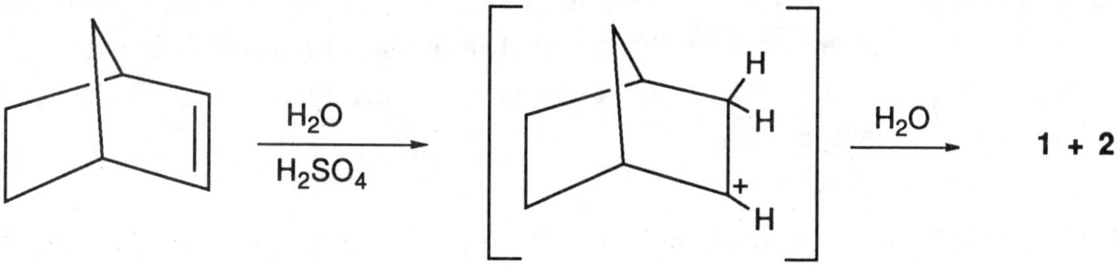

3 $\xrightarrow[H_2SO_4]{H_2O}$ [**4**] $\xrightarrow{H_2O}$ **1** + **2**

and is presumed to occur via a carbocation intermediate **4**, which is then trapped by water. The same carbocation is required for formation of both **1** and **2** so the *product-determining* step is the subsequent reaction between **4** and water. Steric effects might influence the reaction by differentially hindering one face of the carbocation. Stereoelectronic effects may also play a role since FMO theory predicts that the more rapid reaction will be the one characterized by the better overlap between the LUMO of **4** and the HOMO of water.

A second route involves borohydride reduction of norcamphor **5**.[1]

$NaBH_4$ → **6** ($O^- M^+$, H) $\xrightarrow{H_2O}$ **1** (14%) + **2** (86%)

5 **6**

Here, product stereochemistry is determined by the initial attack of borohydride on the carbonyl. The steric environment around the carbonyl group and/or the overlap between the LUMO of **5** and the HOMO of the borohydride should dictate which alcohol will form preferentially.

While these two reactions are chemically very different, in both the step which dictates product stereochemistry involves addition of a nucleophile to an electron-deficient substrate. Independent of route, the important question for the synthetic chemist is "which alcohol will be the major product?"

In this experiment, we model the stereochemistry of products formed in both of these synthetic routes. The model we employ breaks down the interaction between reagent and substrate into two short-range terms: a **steric** term, which is energetically unfavorable, and an **orbital** term, which is energetically favorable. The more favorable approach of a nucleophile to a substrate is that in which interactions between the pair of electrons on the nucleophile and filled molecular orbitals on the substrate are minimized while those involving empty molecular orbitals on the substrate are maximized, i.e.,

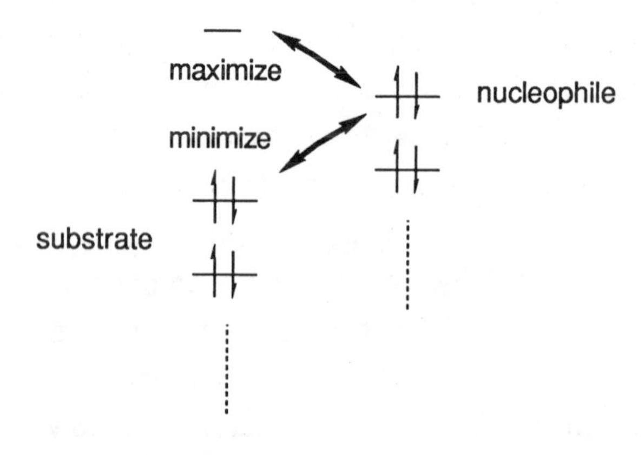

[1] H.C. Brown and J. Muzzio, *J. Am. Chem. Soc.* **92**, 6894 (1970).

Addition of water (a weak nucleophile) to norbornyl cation will occur preferentially to that face in which the LUMO (where the nucleophile's electrons are to go) is the more exposed relative to the total electron density (where the substrate's electrons already are). Addition of a nucleophile to norcamphor, **5**, will occur preferentially to that face in which the LUMO is the more exposed relative to the total electron density resulting from the manifold of filled molecular orbitals.

Procedure

Build norbornyl cation, **4**, optimize at the AM1 level and then perform a single-point 3-21G *ab initio* calculation; use direct methods. Determine the cation's steric and stereoelectronic properties by calculating an isodensity surface, a LUMO isovalue surface and an isodensity surface onto which the (absolute) value of the LUMO has been encoded. **[1]** **[16]**

The reactive sites in **4** are revealed by displaying the LUMO isovalue surface. The LUMO is delocalized throughout the molecule, but the best opportunities for stabilizing it with the HOMO of water are in the immediate vicinity of the carbocation carbon. This is where the orbital is largest. The role of steric hindrance can be assessed by simultaneously displaying the LUMO and isodensity surface (as a mesh or transparent solid so you can see the LUMO underneath). Most of the LUMO lies "inside" the electron cloud and cannot overlap effectively with a nucleophile. In which direction does the LUMO extend further beyond the electron cloud? Are there other groups which might hinder the approach of a water molecule and HOMO-LUMO overlap?

An alternative is to display the LUMO map on the isodensity surface. Identify the regions where the LUMO is largest and where good overlap (absent steric hindrance) with HOMO of water is possible. Which face of the cation provides the better overlap opportunity? Which alcohol should be the major product? Is your conclusion regarding addition preference consistent with experimental observation?

Build norcamphor, **5**, optimize at the AM1 level and then submit for a single-point 3-21G *ab initio* calculation. [1] Again, be certain to specify direct methods. As with norbornyl cation, construct graphical surfaces for the total electron density, the LUMO and the total density onto which the value of the LUMO has been encoded. [16] Examine the three surfaces using the same procedures described above. What reactive site(s) is identified by the LUMO surface? Given hydride reduction of the carbonyl group as the principal reaction, which face of the carbonyl group is more accessible and provides the better opportunity for the LUMO in **5** to overlap with the HOMO in BH_4^-? Is this prediction consistent with the experimental observations of Brown and Muzzio?

Optional

1. It is believed that Na^+ complexes to the oxygen of **5** prior to hydride reduction. The **5**-Na^+ complex should have a lower energy LUMO than **5** itself. How should this change in LUMO energy affect the reaction rate according to FMO theory?

2. $Li^+ [HB(CH(CH_3)CH_2CH_3)_3]^-$ reduces **5** to a mixture of **1** and **2**, probably by a mechanism similar to one followed by a mechanism similar to one followed by $NaBH_4$.[2] Given the greater steric bulk of this reagent, what should happen to the overall reaction rate and to the ratio of **1**:**2**?

3. It has been observed experimentally that reduction of camphor, **7**,

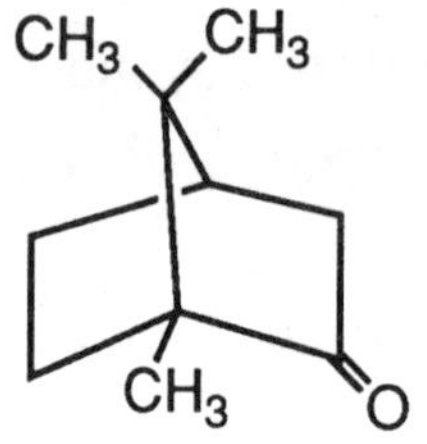

7

with sodium borohydride gives the opposite stereoselectivity as the corresponding reduction of norcamphor, **5**. Following the same procedure as you employed to assign the stereochemistry of nucleophilic addition in norcamphor, use semi-empirical AM1 and *ab initio* 3-21G calculations (direct methods) and graphical displays to determine [1] the preferred face for nucleophilic addition in camphor. Do you see the experimentally observed reversal in stereochemistry of nucleophilic addition? What do you think is the cause?

---

[2] H.C. Brown and S. Krishnamurthy, J. Am. Chem. Soc. **94**, 7159 (1972).

Experiment 41: Acid-Catalyzed Ring Opening of Epoxides

We examine AM1 semi-empirical equilibrium structures of protonated epoxides to account for the regiochemistry of acid-catalyzed ring opening.

Epoxides undergo acid-catalyzed ring opening to yield alcohols, e.g.,[1]

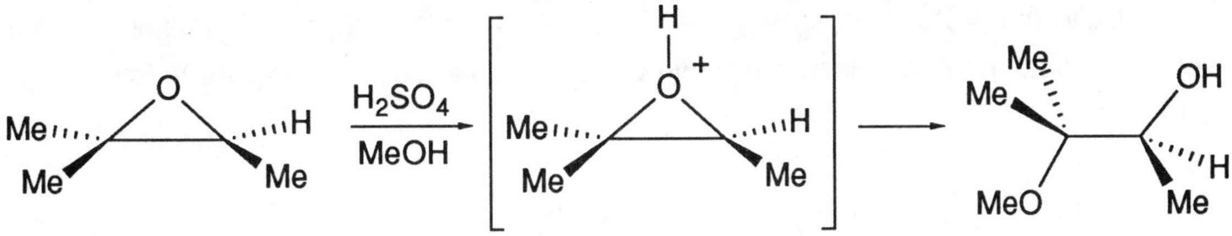

The observed regiochemistry is usually ascribed to the greater participation of resonance structures in which the positive charge is localized on the more-substituted carbon than those where it is localized on the less-substituted carbon, i.e.,

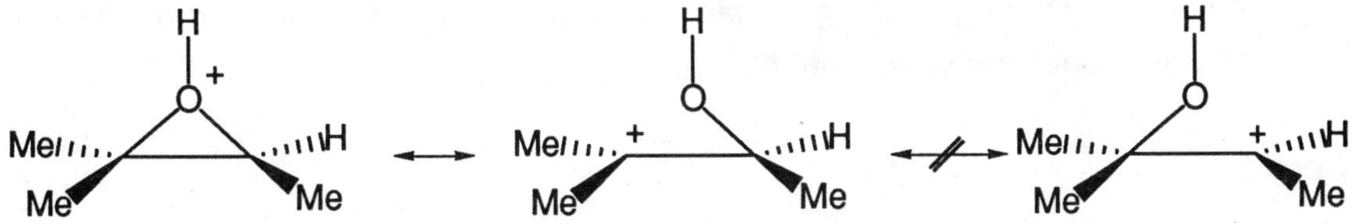

Prediction of the preferred mode of ring opening in more complicated systems, e.g., the decalin epoxide, **1**,[2]

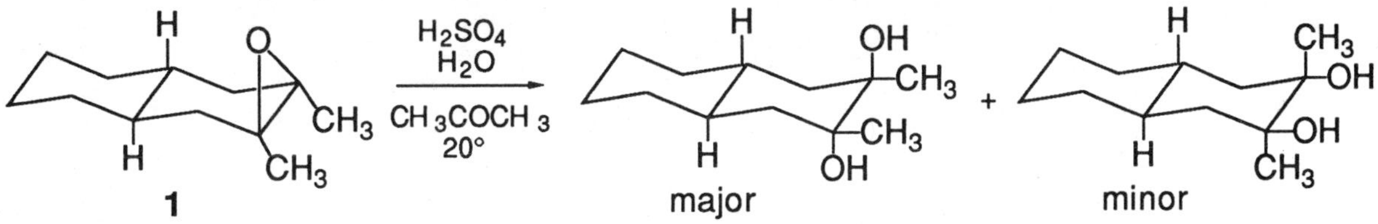

is not as easily realized. Here, it is not obvious which of the possible resonance structures will dominate. We need a more quantitative model to account for the

[1] S. Winstein and L.L. Ingraham, J. Am. Chem. Soc., **74**, 1160 (1952).
[2] B. Rickborn and D. Murphy, J. Org. Chem., **34**, 3209 (1969).

observed product distribution. In this experiment, we examine the AM1 geometry of the protonated form of **1** for evidence of preferential CO bond cleavage. This system is ideal for consideration by such a simple model, as both ring carbons present nearly identical steric environments to the approaching nucleophile and the selectivity of the reaction will likely dominate the selection.

Procedure

Build the protonated form of the decalin epoxide **1**, and optimize using the AM1 semi-empirical method. Record the two CO bond distances in the figure below.

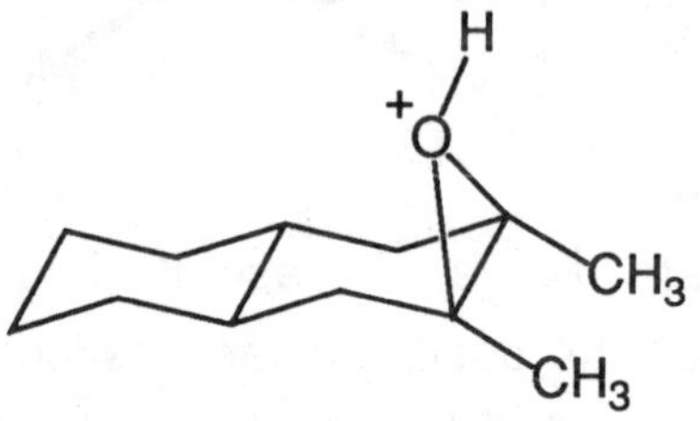

H
+O
CH_3
CH_3

Do you detect asymmetry in the geometry of the protonated 3-membered ring? If so, which product would you expect on this basis?

Optional

The location of the LUMO in the protonated form of **1** should reveal the disposition of positive charge. Calculate and display an isodensity surface onto which the LUMO has been encoded. Does it suggest buildup of positive charge on the epoxide carbons? Can you detect polarization toward one carbon or the other? [3]

Experiment 42: Nucleophilic Addition to α,β-Unsaturated Carbonyl Compounds

We use both semi-empirical AM1 and *ab initio* 3-21G calculations to demonstrate that nucleophilic attack on an α,β-unsaturated carbonyl compound may either occur at the carbonyl carbon or at the β olefin position.

α,β-Unsaturated ketones, e.g., cyclohexenone, are not only able to undergo nucleophilic addition at the carbonyl carbon, but also add onto the olefin position β to the carbonyl, i.e.,

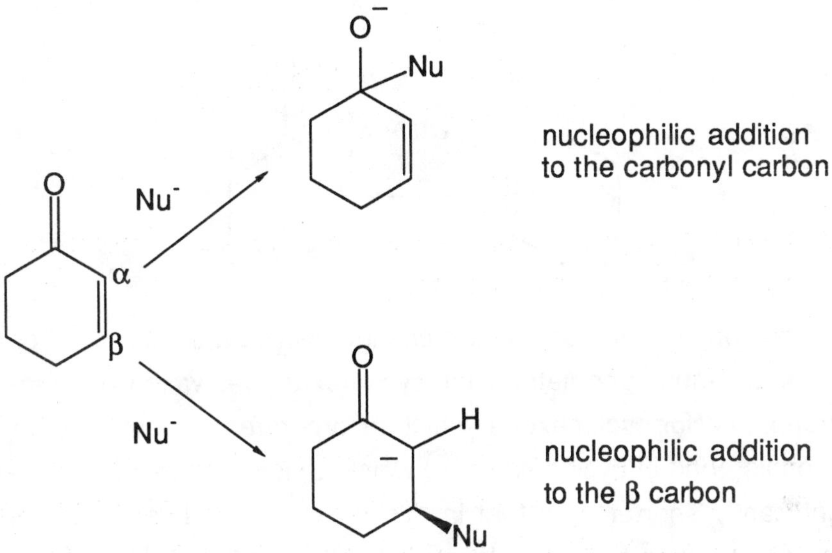

O^- Nu α β Nu^- Nu^- O H Nu

nucleophilic addition
to the carbonyl carbon

nucleophilic addition
to the β carbon

A number of synthetically important reactions, such as the Michael reaction[1], involve addition of a nucleophile, a "Michael donor", to an α,β-unsaturated carbonyl compound, a "Michael acceptor", e.g.,

$$CH_3\overset{\overset{O}{\|}}{C}CH_2CO_2CH_2CH_3 + H_2C{=}CH\overset{\overset{O}{\|}}{C}CH_3 \longrightarrow CH_3\overset{\overset{O}{\|}}{C}\text{-}\underset{\underset{CO_2CH_2CH_3}{|}}{C}HCH_2CH_2\overset{\overset{O}{\|}}{C}CH_3$$

Michael donor Michael acceptor

---

[1] Carey and Sundberg B, p. 39; March, p. 713.

In this experiment, we seek evidence for reactivity of α,β-unsaturated carbonyl compounds both at the carbonyl and β olefin positions, both in terms of equilibrium geometry and as reflected by localization of the lowest-unoccupied molecular orbital. Optionally, we examine the extent of geometrical distortions implied by resonance structures.

Procedure

Build cyclohexenone and minimize at the AM1 level. Examine the resulting structure for evidence of electron delocalization as implied by the resonance structures.

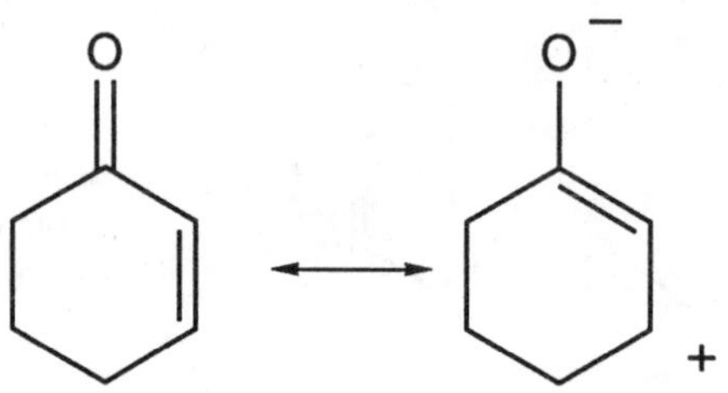

In particular, do you see the bond length changes which are implied? For comparison, obtain AM1 equilibrium geometries for cyclohexanone, which contains a "normal" carbonyl group, and for cyclohexene, which incorporates a "normal" CC double bond. Is the CO double bond in cyclohexanone, which is not capable of resonance forms as above, significantly shorter than that in cyclohexenone? Is the CC double bond in cyclohexene shorter than that in cyclohexenone?

Perform a single-point 3-21G *ab initio* calculation on cyclohexenone using the [1] AM1 geometry obtained previously. Be certain to use direct methods. Calculate and display two graphical surfaces: the LUMO and the total electron density onto which the value of the LUMO has been encoded. From the first, you will see that the LUMO is delocalized over several centers, and it is not easy to assign at which center nucleophilic attack is expected. The composite display (value of the LUMO [3] superimposed onto the total electron density surface), provides a much clearer picture. This indicates the availability of the LUMO to accept electrons (from the attacking nucleophile) at the surface of contact between reagent and substrate. Does this show two likely sites for nucleophilic attack? If so, which appears to be the more prominent?

Optional

The AM1 calculations above for cyclohexenone should have revealed only very small geometrical distortions resulting from participation of alternative zwitterionic resonance structures. Let's examine another system to see if this result is more general. Obtain structures at the AM1 level for both *meta*-and *para*-nitroaniline. Sketch the critical bond lengths in the figures below.

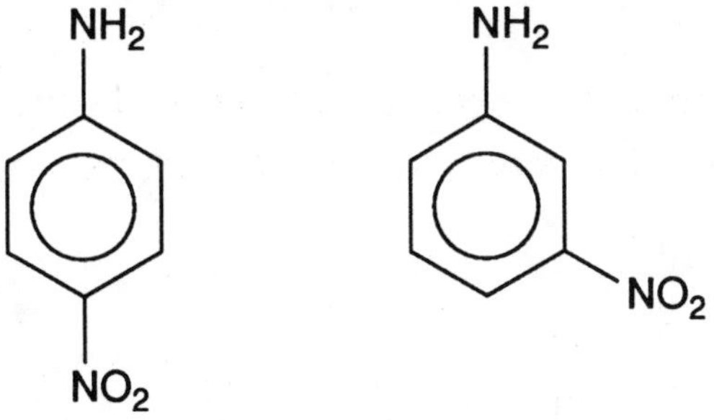

NH_2 NH_2

NO_2

NO_2

Do you see evidence for the distortions implied by the resonance structures available to the *para* compound,

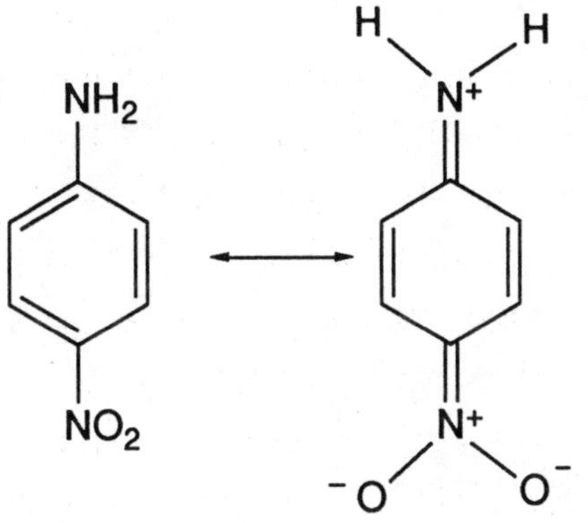

H H

NH_2 N^+

NO_2 N^+

^-O O^-

but not available in the *meta* system? What do the calculations seem to imply about the magnitudes of geometrical distortions resulting from resonance?

Repeat the calculations at the 3-21G level (use direct methods) to see if the [1] conclusions reached above hold as one moves to a better computational model.

Experiment 43: Activated Dienophiles in Diels Alder Reactions

We employ both semi-empirical AM1 and *ab initio* 3-21G calculations to investigate the utility of Frontier Molecular Orbital (FMO) theory in ordering the rates of Diels-Alder reactions involving a common diene but different dienophiles, and in accounting for regioselectivity in additions involving asymmetrical dienophiles. We also investigate correlations between calculated electrostatic potentials and rates and regioselectivities of Diels-Alder reactions

The most common (and synthetically most useful) Diels-Alder reactions involve electron-rich dienes and electron-deficient dienophiles, e.g.,

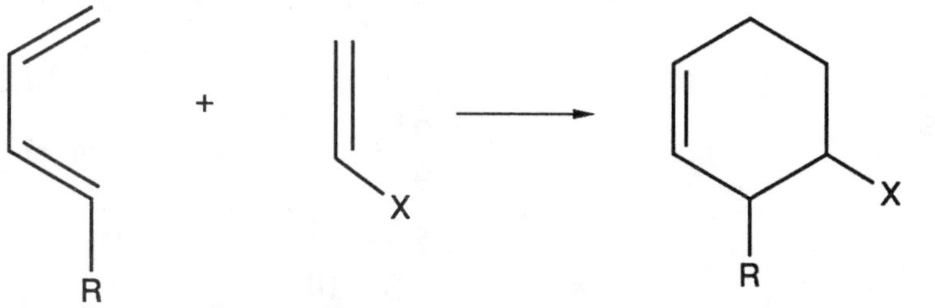

R=alkyl, alkoxy

X=CN, CHO, COOH

The rate of these reactions generally increases with increasing π-electron-donor ability of substituents on the diene, and with increasing π-electron-acceptor ability of substituents on the dienophile. This may be rationalized using frontier molecular orbital (FMO) theory, where the important interaction is assumed to be that between the highest-occupied molecular orbital (HOMO) on the diene and the lowest-unoccupied molecular orbital (LUMO) on the dienophile, i.e.,

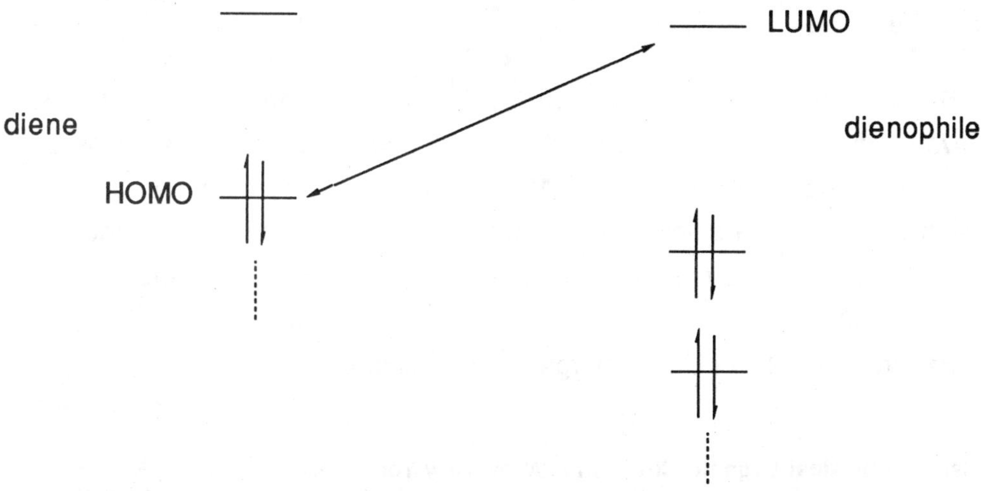

diene

HOMO

LUMO

dienophile

This interaction is stabilizing, the extent of stabilization increasing with decreasing energy separation between the interacting orbitals and with their increased overlap. We should, therefore, be able to increase the overall rate of reaction simply by raising the energy of the diene HOMO or by lowering the energy of the dienophile LUMO.

In this experiment, we first explore to what extent the rate data parallel LUMO energies in the respective dienophiles. Experimentally determined relative rates for Diels-Alder cycloadditions of ethylene and cyano-substituted ethylenes with cyclopentadiene are tabulated below.[1]

Relative rates	
reaction: cyclopentadiene +	relative rate
ethylene	6×10^{-6}
acrylonitrile	1
trans-1,2-dicyanoethylene	81
cis-1,2-dicyanoethylene	91
1,1-dicyanoethylene	4.55×10^{4}
tricyanoethylene	4.8×10^{5}
tetracyanoethylene	4.3×10^{7}

These data provide an excellent opportunity to test the simple model, in that they show a change in rate spanning thirteen orders of magnitude with increasing electron deficiency of the dienophile. Next, we examine two different graphical models both for evidence of structure-rate correlations and to indicate preferred regiodirection in Diels-Alder cycloaddition.

Procedure

Build ethylene, acrylonitrile, *trans*-1,2-dicyanoethylene, *cis*-1,2-dicyanoethylene, 1,1-dicyanoethylene, tricyanoethylene and tetracyanoethylene, and optimize using the AM1 method. After each AM1 optimization completes, resubmit for a single-point 3-21G calculation. You will need to use direct methods only for the larger systems. Print the molecular orbitals and associated orbital energies.

[1]

Record the 3-21G LUMO energies in the table below.

---

[1] N.S. Isaacs, **Physical Organic Chemistry**, Wiley, New York, 1987, p. 661.

3-21G orbital energies (hartrees)	
ethylene	
acrylonitrile	
trans-1,2-dicyanoethylene	
cis-1,2-dicyanoethylene	
1,1-dicyanoethylene	
tricyanoethylene	
tetracyanoethylene	

Plot the calculated LUMO energies against the experimental relative rates.

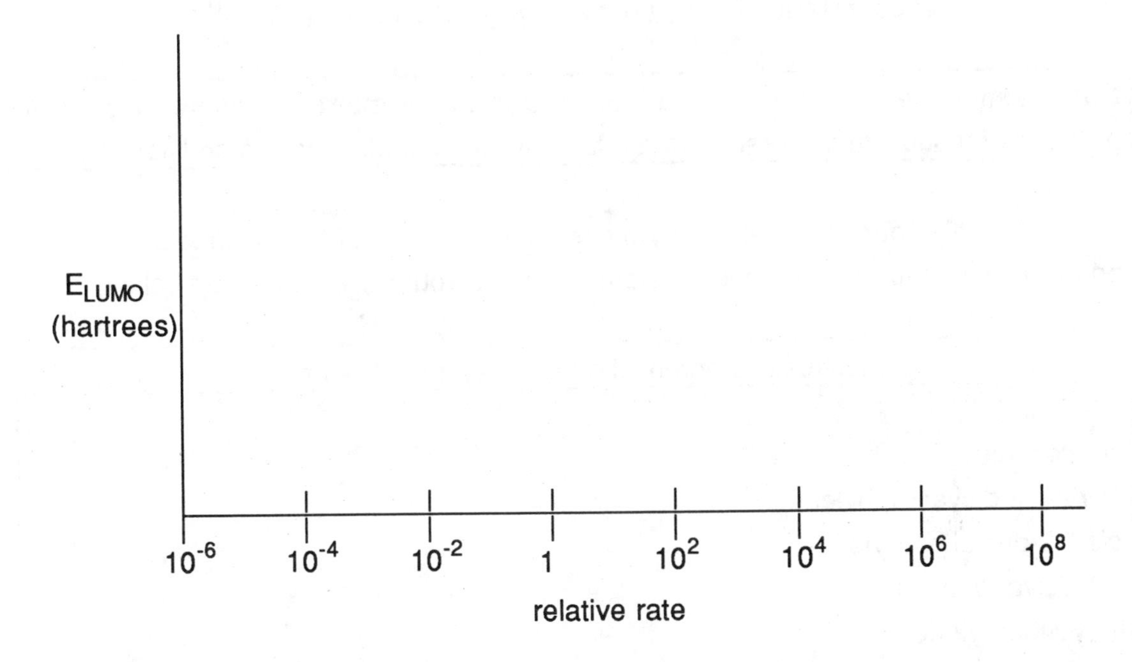

Do you observe a reasonable correlation? Try to rationalize any significant deviations. Hint: recall that stabilization is a function not only of HOMO/LUMO energy separation but also of the overlap between the interacting orbitals, i.e.,

$$E_{stabilization} \propto \frac{\left[\int \phi_{diene}^{HOMO} \phi_{dienophile}^{LUMO} \, d\tau\right]^2}{\epsilon_{diene}^{HOMO} - \epsilon_{dienophile}^{LUMO}}$$

where the numerator involves the overlap of the diene HOMO and dienophile LUMO, and the denominator involves their energy difference. Remember that the diene is held constant in the rate variations.

Another measure of dienophile reactivity is provided by the molecular electrostatic potential.[2] This measures the attraction of a molecule for a point positive charge as a function of position. In this case, dienophile reactivity corresponds to repulsion of the point charge in the region of the π system. Calculate electrostatic potentials encoded onto electron density surfaces for all dienophiles. Arrange them on screen such that you are looking directly at the π system and in the order of their experimental Diels-Alder reactivity, and put all on the same scale. On the basis of electrostatic potentials, comment on the ordering of reactivities. Is it consistent with that observed experimentally? Point out any major discrepancies.

[3]

Our treatment here is analogous to that used in **Experiment 38**, where electrostatic potentials for substituted alkenes was related to rates of electrophilic addition.

Quantify your observations by measuring the value of the electrostatic potential on the π system for each of these systems. Record your data in the table below,

[8]

Electrostatic potential on the π system (kcal/mol)	
ethylene	
acrylonitrile	
trans-1,2-dicyanoethylene	
cis-1,2-dicyanoethylene	
1,1-dicyanoethylene	
tricyanoethylene	
tetracyanoethylene	

and plot vs. experimental relative rate.

[2] S.D. Kahn, C.F. Pau, L.E. Overman and W.J. Hehre, J. Am. Chem. Soc., **108**, 7381 (1986).

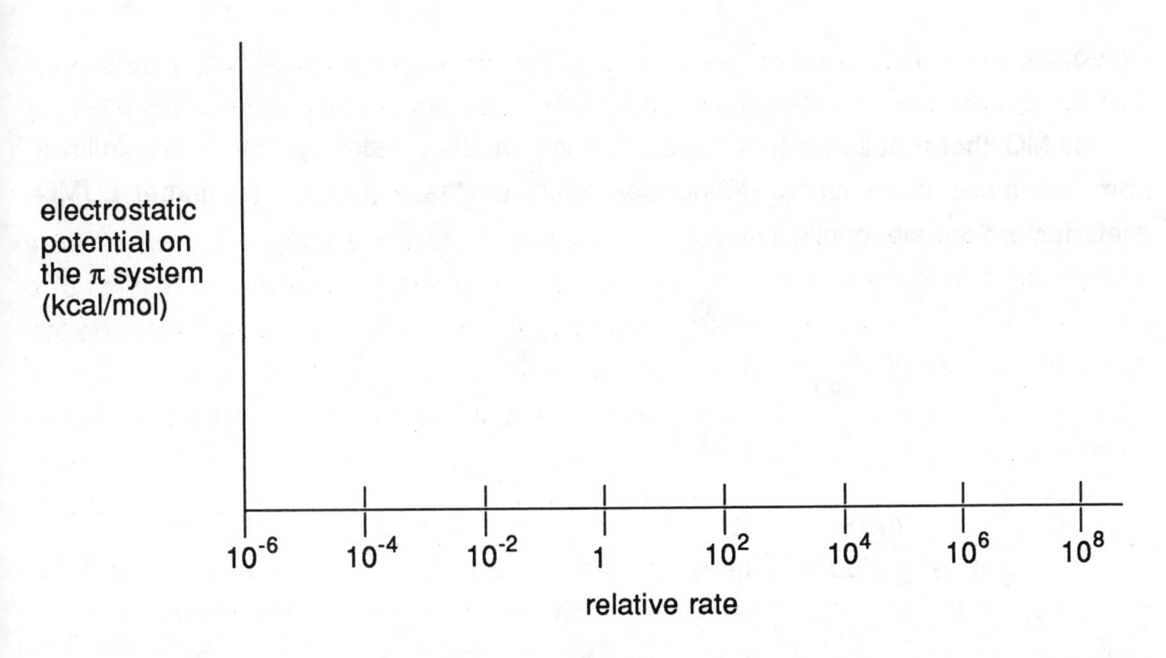

Do you observe a reasonable correlation? Point out any significant deviations and try to rationalize.

Examine the three asymmetrical dienophiles (acrylonitrile, 1,1-dicyanoethylene and tricyanoethylene) in more detail. For each, calculate graphical surfaces corresponding to the LUMO and to the total electron density onto which the value of the LUMO has been encoded. Turn off the previously displayed electrostatic potential surfaces and simultaneously display the LUMO plots for these three systems. Which way is the LUMO polarized in each of these systems? Is this consistent with what you would expect based on drawing resonance structures? Another representation which might provide a clearer picture is the value of the LUMO displayed on the total electron surface. This allows you to quantify your observations by actually measuring the magnitude of the LUMO over the two carbons in the double bond. **[3]**

Reexamine the electrostatic potential maps for the three asymmetrically substituted dienophiles. Does the polarization you observe in the LUMOs also appear here? Quantify your observations with measurements of the value of the electrostatic potentials on the different double bond positions. **[8]**

Optional

FMO theory tells us that regioselectivity in Diels-Alder cycloadditions follows from alignment of the larger HOMO coefficient on the diene and the larger LUMO coefficient on the dienophile,[3] i.e.,

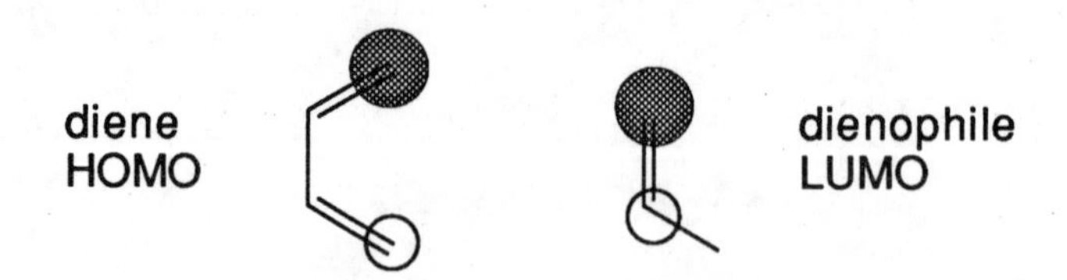

What does such a model say about the preferred adduct of 1-methylcyclopentadiene with acrylonitrile? You will need to perform 3-21G calculations (use the AM1 geometry) on the diene in order to establish on which position the HOMO is most heavily localized. Is your finding in agreement with the experimental preference?

---

[3] I. Fleming, **Frontier Orbitals and Organic Chemical Reactions**, Wiley, New York, 1976.

Experiment 44: Addition of Singlet Difluorocarbene to Ethylene

We use AM1 semi-empirical calculations to examine the electronic structure of singlet difluorocarbene for clues as to how it will add to olefins. We then examine the transition state for CF_2 addition to ethylene to see if it follows these expectations.

Singlet carbenes add to olefins to yield cyclopropanes.

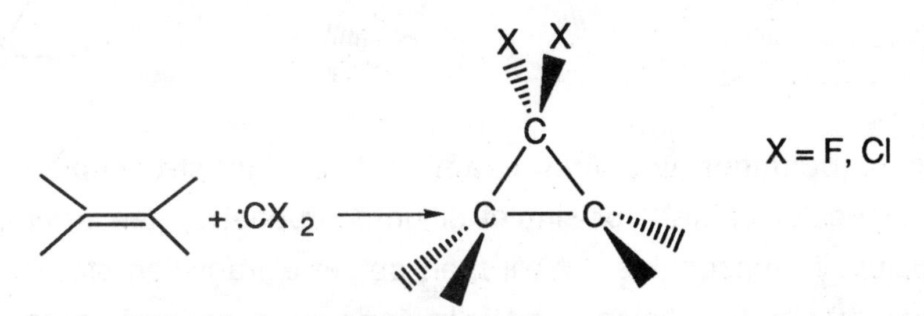

Because a singlet carbene possesses both a high-energy filled molecular orbital in the plane of the molecule and a low-energy out-of-plane unfilled molecular orbital, i.e.,

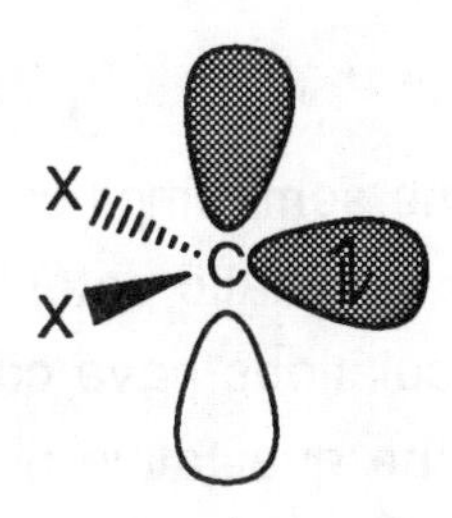

this reaction presents an interesting dilemma. Clearly it would be most advantageous for the vacant orbital on the carbene to interact with the olefin π system during its approach, i.e.,

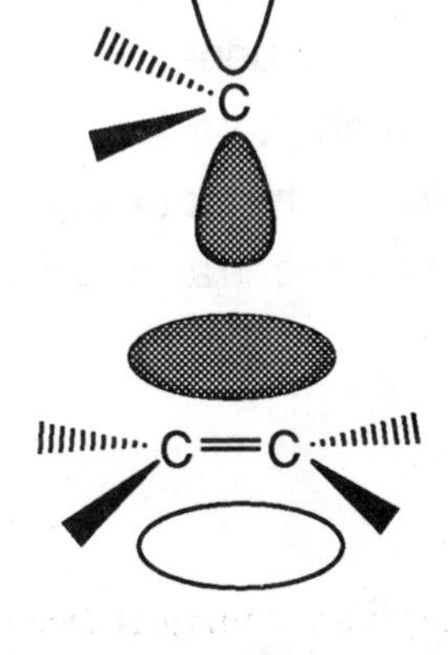

although this would lead to a product with an impossible geometry. It must be that the carbene twists by 90° during the course of reaction, i.e.,[1]

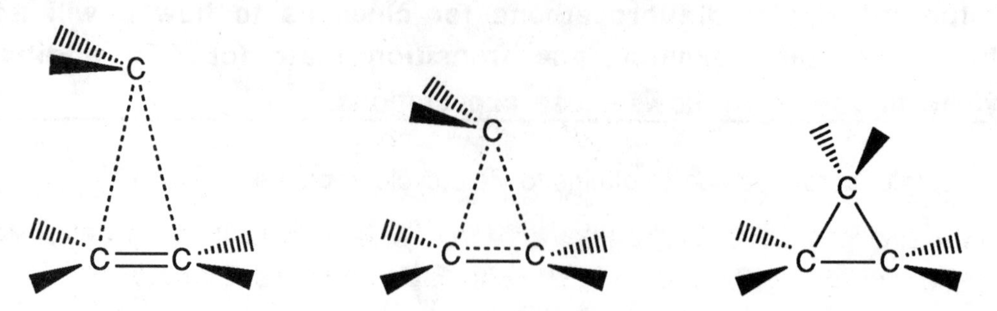

In this experiment, we first examine the highest-occupied and lowest-unoccupied molecular orbitals for singlet difluorocarbene, to see whether or not our qualitative picture is reasonable. We'll then obtain a transition state for addition of singlet difluorocarbene to ethylene and following this, examine in detail the pathway connecting reactants and product.

Procedure

Build CF_2 and optimize at the semi-empirical AM1 level. Request generation of the HOMO, the LUMO and the electrostatic potential encoded onto the total electron density surface. Once all the calculations have completed, examine both the HOMO and LUMO. Do these resemble the qualitative pictures? The electrostatic potential provides another way to anticipate the electrophilic or nucleophilic reactivity of a species such as dilfuorocarbene. As evaluated at the van der Waals contact this provides a measure of the charge distribution which the substrate (the olefin) would encounter upon initial contact with the reagent (the carbene). Display the electrostatic potential map. Relate what you see to the known nucleophilic and electrophilic character usually ascribed to singlet carbenes. [3]

Let's next locate the transition state for addition of singlet difluorocarbene to ethylene, and following this examine the pathway connecting reactants and product. As a guess for the geometry of the transition state, we will use a "distorted" difluorocyclopropane.

---

[1] Lowry and Richardson, p. 556.

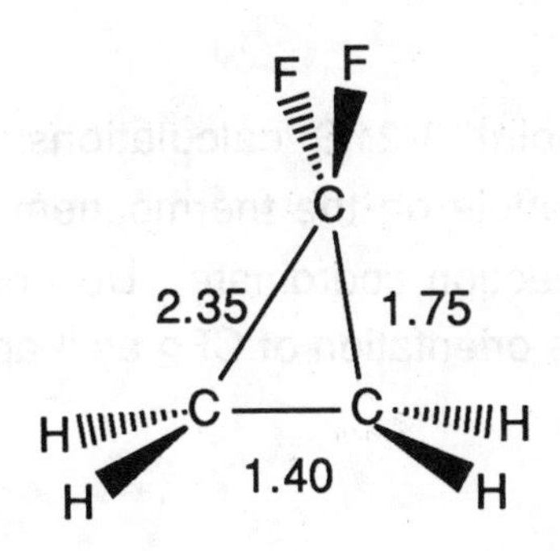

This is easily constructed by "constraining" the CC bond lengths to the above values. **[14]** Using this starting geometry, determine the transition state at the AM1 level.

> One important reason that transition states are more difficult to locate from calculations than equilibrium structures is an almost complete lack of knowledge of detailed geometries. Often crude guesses like that provided above are the best we can do.

Be certain to specify that a normal-mode analysis is to be performed following optimization. This will provide vibrational frequencies and associated normal-mode coordinates in order to verify that we have indeed located a transition structure, and furthermore will allow animation of the motion along the reaction coordinate. When the calculations have completed, examine the final transition structure. In light of earlier discussion regarding the orientation of filled and empty molecular orbitals on the carbene with the π orbital on ethylene, would you describe your structure as indicating an "early" or "late" transition state? Is this consistent with the Hammond postulate? You will need to obtain AM1 energies for the product, 1,1-difluorocyclopropane, as well as for reactants, CF_2 and ethylene, to properly address this question. Perform the required AM1 optimizations and record the heats of formation in the table below.

AM1 heats of formation (kcal/mol) and 3-21G energies (hartrees)		
	AM1	3-21G
difluorocarbene		
ethylene		
transition state		
1,1-difluorocyclopropane		

Optionally, perform single-point 3-21G calculations on all species (using AM1 geometries) to get a better handle on the thermochemistry. Animate the vibrational mode corresponding to the reaction coordinate. Describe the motion, with particular emphasis on the change in the orientation of CF_2 as it approaches the double bond.

Experiment 45: Do Singlet Carbenes Behave as Electrophiles or as Nucleophiles in Additions to Olefins?

We use AM1 semi-empirical calculations to examine the dependence of rate of carbene additions to olefins both on the carbene and on the olefin, in order to determine whether singlet carbenes act as electrophiles or as nucleophiles.

Singlet carbenes possess both a high energy filled σ-type molecular orbital and a low-energy unfilled p-type molecular orbital [see also **Experiment 44**].

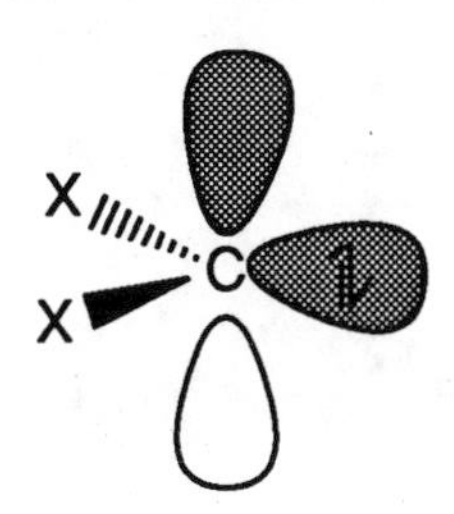

This suggests that singlet carbenes could behave either as nucleophiles or as electrophiles (or both) in additions to olefins. It also suggests that their behavior might be different for different carbenes and might alter with substitution on the olefin.[1] Here we examine such possibilities.

This experiment is divided into three parts. In the first, we examine HOMO and LUMO energies for ethylene, tetramethylethylene and tetracyanoethylene to verify that substitution by π-electron-donor groups increases the attractiveness of ethylene for electrophiles, while substitution by π-electron-withdrawing groups increases the attractiveness for nucleophiles. In the second part, we look at the frontier orbital energies of difluorocarbene and dichlorocarbene to ascertain which of these is the better electrophile and which is the better nucleophile. In the last part, we determine activation energies for six different combinations of reactants (difluorocarbene and dichlorocarbene with ethylene, tetramethylethylene and tetracyanoethylene, respectively). Relative rates as a function of the carbene and of the olefin, together with previous information characterizing carbenes and olefins, should answer our question about the identity of the carbenes in their additions to olefins.

---

[1] Carey and Sundberg B, p. 512; Lowry and Richardson, 556.

Procedure

Build ethylene, tetramethylethylene and tetracyanoethylene. Optimize at the AM1 level, and be certain to request printing of the molecular orbitals and associated orbital energies. As each job completes, write down the HOMO and LUMO energies in the table below:

AM1 heats of formation (kcal/mol), orbital energies (eV) and electrostatic potentials (kcal/mol)				
	ΔH_f°	E_{HOMO}	E_{LUMO}	electrostatic potential
tetramethylethylene				
ethylene				
tetracyanoethylene				
difluorocarbene				σ: π:
dichlorocarbene				σ: π:

Also compute and display electron density surfaces onto which the electrostatic potential has been encoded. Measure the potential in the vicinity of the olefin π system and record in the table. On the basis of the orbital energy and electrostatic potential data, what is the ordering of electrophilicities and of nucleophilicities of the three olefins? Is your ordering consistent with conventional wisdom regarding the effects of methyl and of cyano substituents? 3,8]

Build difluorocarbene and dichlorocarbene and optimize at the AM1 level. Obtain HOMO and LUMO energies as well as electrostatic potentials (encoded on electron density surfaces), both in the vicinity of the lone pair (σ) and in the π system, and record in the table above. On the basis of your data, what is the ordering of electrophilicities and of nucleophilicities of the two carbenes?

Obtain transition states for the six carbene addition reactions (difluorocarbene and dichlorocarbene with ethylene, tetramethylethylene and tetracyanoethylene, respectively). If you have already completed **Experiment 44**, use the transition state for difluorocarbene addition to ethylene as a template for the remaining systems. If you have not completed this experiment, obtain this transition state following the directions given in **Experiment 44**, and then use this transition state as a template. Record the transition state heats of formation in the table below.

AM1 heats of formation (kcal/mol)		
	+ difluorocarbene	+ dichlorocarbene
tetramethylethylene		
ethylene		
tetracyanoethylene		

Work out activation energies using these data and the previously obtained heats of formation for the reactants and record below.

AM1 activation energies (kcal/mol)		
	+ difluorocarbene	+ dichlorocarbene
tetramethylethylene		
ethylene		
tetracyanoethylene		

For which carbene (difluorocarbene or dichlorocarbene) is the reaction with a given olefin more facile? Does this follow the increase in electrophilicity or increase in nucleophilicity of the carbenes? For which olefin (tetramethylethylene, ethylene or tetracyanoethylene) is the reaction with a given carbene most facile? Does this follow the increase in electrophilicity or increase in nucleophilicity of the olefins? Overall, would you conclude that carbenes behave as electrophiles or as nucleophiles in their additions to olefins?

Optional

Repeat your investigations using data from 3-21G *ab initio* calculations which have already been collected. Total energies, orbital energies and electrostatic potentials for the three ethylenes and for the two carbenes are tabulated below.

3-21G energies and orbital energies (hartrees) and electrostatic potentials (kcal/mol)				
	E	E_{HOMO}	E_{LUMO}	electrostatic potential
tetramethylethylene	-232.88241	-0.323	0.201	-24
ethylene	-77.60099	-0.380	0.187	-22
tetracyanoethylene	-442.42947	-0.439	-0.046	
difluorocarbene	-235.37481	-0.475	0.087	σ: -23 π: 56
dichlorocarbene	-952.33002	-0.403	0.026	σ: -35 π: 35

Do these provide the same or different picture of the relative electrophilicities/nucleophilicities of the olefins and of the carbenes?

Transition state energies corresponding to the six addition reactions are tabulated below.

3-21G transition state energies (hartrees)		
	+ difluorocarbene	+ dichlorocarbene
tetramethylethylene	-468.23793	-1185.20888
ethylene	-312.93294	-1029.92001
tetracyanoethylene	-677.75652	-1394.73728

Use these data, and the energies for the reactants provided above, to compute activation energies. Tabulate below.

3-21G activation energies (kcal/mol)		
	+ difluorocarbene	+ dichlorocarbene
tetramethylethylene		
ethylene		
tetracyanoethylene		

Do these exhibit the same orderings (with respect to change in carbene and change in olefin) as provided by the AM1 semi-empirical calculations? Does your previous conclusion regarding the behavior of carbenes (as electrophiles or as nucleophiles) remain the same?

Experiment 46: Selectivity in Carbene Additions to Olefins

We examine the highest-occupied molecular orbital in a variety of olefins obtained from AM1 semi-empirical calculations to assign both site selectivity and stereochemistry in dichlorocarbene additions.

Addition of singlet carbenes to olefins occurs selectively. For example, singlet dichlorocarbene adds preferentially to the center double bond in the triene **1**, while further addition to **2** occurs preferentially with *anti* stereochemistry.[1]

Cl Cl :CCl_2 :CCl_2 Cl Cl Cl Cl

1 **2**

The latter result at least is not at all unexpected in view of obvious steric considerations. Dichlorocarbene additions to asymmetric propelladienes, e.g., **3**, also occur with *anti* stereochemistry, and preferentially to the double bond closer to the Cl substituent, i.e.,

H Cl :CCl_2 H Cl Cl Cl

3 **4**

In this experiment, we examine the highest-occupied molecular orbital in compounds **1-3** for evidence of selectivity in carbene additions. As detailed in **Experiments 44** and **45**, the HOMO of a singlet carbene is a lone pair in the plane of the molecule, while the LUMO is an *out-of-plane* p-type orbital.

---

[1] B. Halton and S.G.G. Russell, J. Org. Chem., **56**, 5553 (1991).

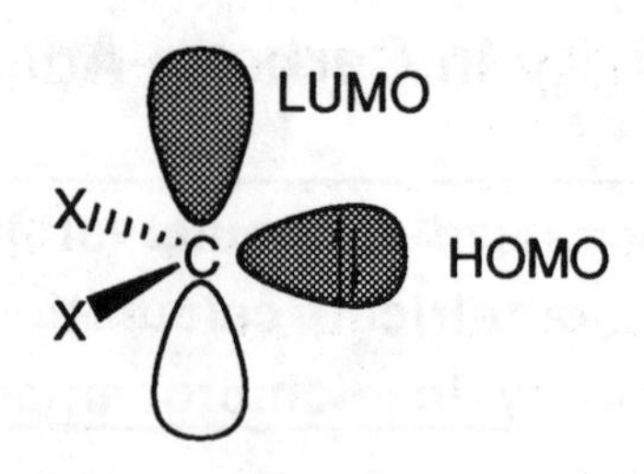

In the early phase of reaction, it is clearly advantageous for the carbene LUMO to align itself with the olefin π system, and for the HOMO of the carbene to point away from the π system, i.e.,

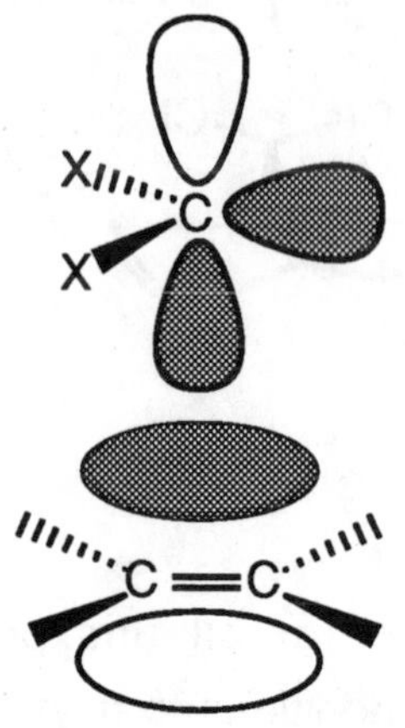

This allows for favorable interaction between the olefin HOMO and carbene LUMO, at the same time as minimizing any unfavorable interactions between the olefin HOMO and the carbene HOMO. If we assume that product selectivity occurs at this early stage, then it will be dictated by the disposition of the highest-occupied molecular orbital on the olefin substrate. This is the basis for the approach examined in this experiment.

Procedure

Build **1** and **3**. Optimize at the AM1 level, and specify generation of the highest-occupied molecular orbital and (optionally) of the highest-occupied orbital encoded onto the total electron density surface. Upon completion, display the HOMO's for both systems (or alternatively the HOMO's encoded onto the density surface). Describe what you see. Specifically, do the graphics show the observed site selectivity in **1**. Do they anticipate the site selectivity and stereochemistry for dichlorocarbene addition to **3**? Why do you suppose that carbene additions to **3** occur onto the double bond closer to the Cl substituent?

Experiment 47: Regioselectivity in Hydroboration of Olefins[1]

We use MNDO semi-empirical calculations to investigate regioselectivity in hydroboration of asymmetrically-substituted alkenes.

Hydroboration of propene may either occur at the terminal carbon (C_1) giving rise (eventually) to n-propanol, or onto the internal olefin position (C_2) giving rise to isopropanol.

$$CH_3CH{=}CH_2 + BH_3 \xrightarrow{\text{attack at } C_2} \underset{\text{internal}}{CH_3CH(BH_2)\text{-}CH_3} \xrightarrow{\text{"reagents"}} CH_3CH(OH)\text{-}CH_3 \quad (1)$$

$$CH_3CH{=}CH_2 + BH_3 \xrightarrow{\text{attack at } C_1} \underset{\text{terminal}}{CH_3CH_2\text{-}CH_2(BH_2)} \xrightarrow{\text{"reagents"}} CH_3CH_2\text{-}CH_2OH \quad (2)$$

Similarly, hydroboration of isobutene can either result in final production of isobutanol (terminal attack) or *tert*-butanol (internal attack). Experimentally, terminal attack is generally preferred, the magnitude of the preference increasing with increasing alkyl substitution.

In this experiment, we apply the semi-empirical MNDO molecular orbital method to investigate the regiochemistry of hydroboration of propene, 3,3-dimethylbut-1-ene and isobutene.

Our experience has shown that the MNDO method is generally superior to AM1 in dealing with simple boron compounds.

We will examine transition states for six different reactions, (1) and (2) above for additions to propene, (3) and (4) for additions to 3,3-dimethylbut-1-ene and (5) and (6) for additions of borane to isobutene, respectively.

[1] Carey and Sundberg B, p. 200; Lowry and Richardson, p. 584; March, 702; for a review, see: H.C. Brown, **Organic Synthesis Via Boranes**, Wiley, New York, 1975.

$$(CH_3)_3CCH{=}CH_2 + BH_3 \rightarrow (CH_3)_3C\overset{BH_2}{\overset{|}{C}}H\text{-}CH_3 \qquad (3)$$

$$(CH_3)_3CCH{=}CH_2 + BH_3 \rightarrow (CH_3)_3CCH_2CH_2BH_2 \qquad (4)$$

$$(CH_3)_2C{=}CH_2 + BH_3 \rightarrow (CH_3)_2\overset{BH_2}{\overset{|}{C}}\text{-}CH_3 \qquad (5)$$

$$(CH_3)_2C{=}CH_2 + BH_3 \rightarrow (CH_3)_2CH\text{-}CH_2BH_2 \qquad (6)$$

Procedure

Let's start with a structure which approximates the transition state for addition of borane to ethylene. Build the following "four-membered ring" and constrain distances [14] to the values below,

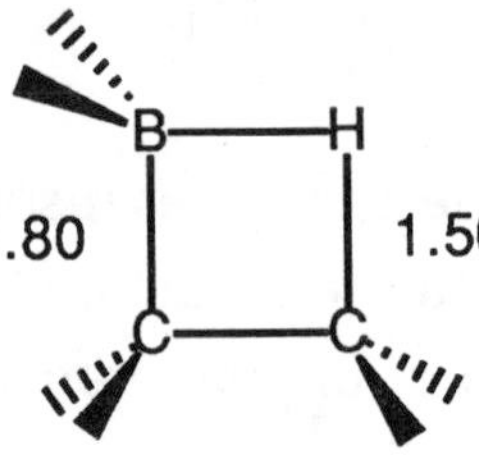

B—H, 1.80 (B–C), 1.50 (H–C), C—C

Minimize using molecular mechanics. Specify a transition state optimization at the MNDO level and request that a normal-mode analysis be performed following completion of the optimization. When the calculations have completed, display the [7] motion along the reaction coordinate (the one characterized by an imaginary frequency). Describe this motion. Does it appear to be synchronous (bond making and breaking going on more or less at once) or asynchronous with one bond made or broken well in advance of other changes? Describe the geometry of the transition state you have found. Is it more like reactant or more like product?

Use the transition state for addition of borane to ethylene as a template for the transition states for additions to propene, to 3,3-dimethylbut-1-ene and to isobutene. (Modify the structures accordingly in the builder but do not minimize at the mechanics level. You already have a very good guess at the transition state geometry.)

As each calculation completes, enter the heat of formation in the table below.

MNDO heats of formation (kcal/mol)		
transition state for reaction of borane with:	internal	terminal
propene		
3,3-dimethylbut-1-ene		
isobutene		

Also build the reactants, borane, propene, 3,3-dimethylbut-1-ene and isobutene, optimize at the MNDO level and enter the heats of formation below.

MNDO heats of formation (kcal/mol)	
borane	
propene	
3,3-dimethylbut-1-ene	
isobutene	
isopropylborane	
n-propylborane	
2-(BH_2)-3,3-dimethylbutane	
1-(BH_2)-3,3-dimethylbutane	
tert-butylborane	
isobutylborane	

Use these data and the heats calculated for the six transition states to obtain activation energies. Enter these below.

MNDO heats of formation (kcal/mol)			
transition state for reaction of borane with:	activation energy		regioselectivity
	internal	terminal	
propene			
3,3-dimethylbut-1-ene			
isobutene			

For each reaction, identify the preferred product (internal or terminal addition) and calculate the regioselectivity. Is the direction in accord with experimental evidence? Do you see increased regioselectivity with increasing asymmetry of the olefin? Is it better to have a single bulky substituent, e.g., a *tert*-butyl group, or two smaller groups, e.g., methyl groups?

Optional

One after the other, build the products in equations **1-6**. Optimize at the MNDO level. Enter the heats of formation in the table above. From the heats of formation work out reaction energies. Enter these in the table below.

MNDO reaction energies (kcal/mol) and BC bond lengths (Å)				
reaction of borane with:	internal		terminal	
	ΔE	r_{BC}	ΔE	r_{BC}
propene				
3,3-dimethylbut-1-ene				
isobutene				

Also enter the BC bond distance calculated at the transition state as a measure of how far the reaction has proceeded. By comparison of reaction energies and bond lengths, comment on the validity of the **Hammond postulate** in these systems. Are trends in transition state energies reflected in the overall thermodynamics of the reactions?

Experiment 48: Stereochemistry of Base Catalyzed Elimination

We examine the relative dispositions of the total electron density and the lowest-unoccupied molecular orbital in norbornyl chloride obtained from 3-21G *ab initio* calculations to assign the stereochemistry of base-catalyzed elimination of HCl leading to norbornene.

Elimination of hydrogen chloride from norbornyl chloride in the presence of strong base is known to proceed with *syn* stereochemistry, i.e.,[1]

Cl D H H — t-BuOK / triglyme → H H + H D

94 : 6

Given that the mechanism for the reaction involves first abstraction of a proton by the base, leading to an intermediate carbanion, followed by rapid elimination of Cl^-, i.e.,

Cl H H H — t-BuOK / triglyme → Cl - H H — $-Cl^-$ → H H

then the problem of assigning stereochemistry is simply one of identifying which proton, *syn* or *anti*, is the more acidic.

In this experiment, we model the abstraction of a proton from norbornyl chloride by a strong base. The best approach of the base to norbornyl chloride will be that which minimizes steric interactions between the filled molecular orbitals on norbornyl chloride and the electron pair on the base, and at the same time which maximizes interactions between the empty molecular orbital on norbornyl chloride and the electron pair on the base, i.e.,

---

[1] R.A. Bartsch and J.G. Lee, J. Org. Chem., **56**, 212 (1991).

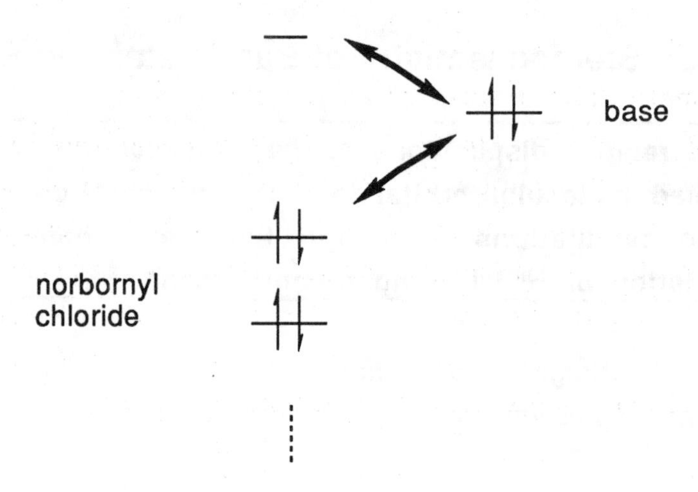

This is the same model previously applied to the description of stereoselectivity in nucleophilic additions to norbornyl cation and norcamphor [see **Experiment 40**].

Procedure

Build norbornyl chloride. First minimize at the AM1 semi-empirical level and then perform a single-point calculation using the 3-21G *ab initio* method. Be certain to use direct methods. Before you submit the *ab initio* calculation, request Mulliken charges, the LUMO isosurface and the total electron density isosurface onto which the value of the LUMO has been encoded. [1]

Examine the Mulliken atomic charges. Do these distinguish between *syn* and *anti* hydrogens? Is the ordering of charges consistent with the *syn* proton being the more acidic? Turn on display of the LUMO encoded onto the total density surface. Alternatively turn on simultaneous display of the total electron density (without the LUMO encoded) as a mesh or as a transparent solid and the LUMO as a solid. Based on inspection of either or both of these graphics, which proton (*syn* or *anti*) would you expect to be the more labile to base? Is your observation consistent with the known stereochemistry of base catalyzed elimination? [3]

Optional

1. Inspect one or both of the graphics you have produced for evidence of the lability of other protons of norbornyl chloride. Describe what you find. Is there evidence from the Mulliken charge analysis to support the graphical models? To what products would their abstraction lead? Are such products observed experimentally?

2. In **Experiment 23** we successfully correlated electrostatic potentials with acidities. Let's see if this same approach can properly reproduce the observed relative acidities of *syn* and *anti* hydrogens in norbornyl chloride. Calculate an electron density surface for norbornyl chloride (at 3-21G) onto which the electrostatic potential has been encoded. Can you distinguish between the *syn* and *anti* hydrogens adjacent to the chlorine? According to this measure, which proton is the more acidic? **[3]**

3. Base catalyzed elimination from **1** leads predominately to a single product.[2]

Me SO_2R

1

Me

not

or

Me

Does the orbital model support the experimental result? Perform 3-21G calculations (AM1 geometry) on **1** (R=Me), and simultaneously examine the total electron density and the lowest-unoccupied molecular orbital.

[2] M. Sellen, J.E. Bäckvall and P. Helquist, J. Org. Chem., **56**, 835 (1991).

Experiment 49: Regiochemistry of Cycloadditions of Azomethine Ylides

We obtain structures and relative stabilities for isomers of a disubstituted azomethine ylide using semi-empirical AM1 and *ab initio* 3-21G calculations, and identify factors which dictate the relative ordering of stabilities. Finally, we examine frontier molecular orbitals to anticipate the regioselectivity of the cycloaddition reaction of the ylide with acrylonitrile.

Azomethine ylides, a class of 1,3 dipoles, serve as useful reactive intermediates in organic synthesis. They are presumed to undergo $4\pi_s + 2\pi_s$ cycloaddition reactions with olefins leading to nitrogen heterocycles, e.g.,[1]

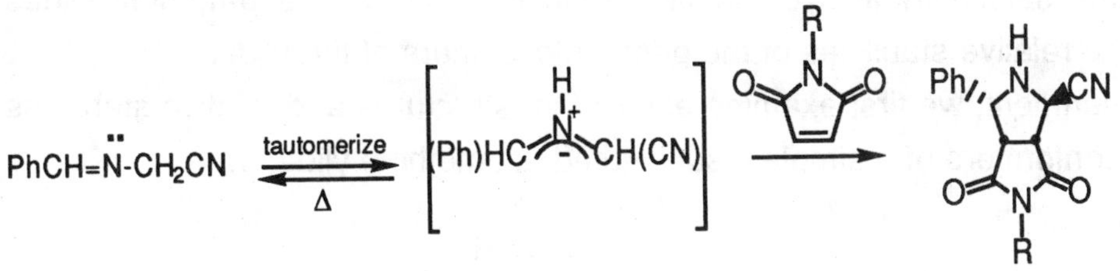

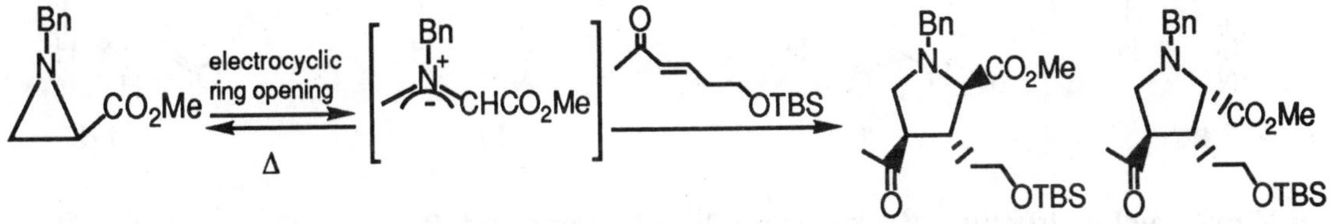

$$PhCH{=}\ddot{N}{-}CH_2CN \underset{\Delta}{\overset{\text{tautomerize}}{\rightleftharpoons}} \left[(Ph)HC{\overset{H}{\overset{|+}{N}}}CH(CN)\right] \xrightarrow{\text{N-R maleimide}} \text{Ph, CN-substituted bicyclic pyrrolidine (N-H; N-R imide)}$$

$$\text{N-Bn aziridine-}CO_2Me \underset{\Delta}{\overset{\text{electrocyclic ring opening}}{\rightleftharpoons}} \left[{\overset{Bn}{\overset{|+}{N}}}CHCO_2Me\right] \xrightarrow{\text{enone-OTBS}} \text{pyrrolidine isomers} \quad 1 : 11$$

These reactions generally proceed regio- and/or stereospecifically, which further enhances their synthetic utility.[1-3] Selectivity depends upon the substitution patterns and geometry of both the ylide and olefin. In this respect, it needs to be noted that moderately low rotational barriers (~20 kcal/mol) about the ylide carbon-nitrogen bond may render the ylide susceptible to geometric isomerization, i.e.,

---

[1] O. Tsuge and S. Kanemasa, Adv. Heterocyclic Chem., **45**, 232 (1989).
[2] O. Tsuge, K. Veno, S. Kanemasa and K. Yorozu, Bull. Chem. Soc. (Japan), **59**, 1809 (1986).
[3] P. Deshong, D.A. Kell, D. Sidler, J. Org. Chem., **50**, 2309 (1985).

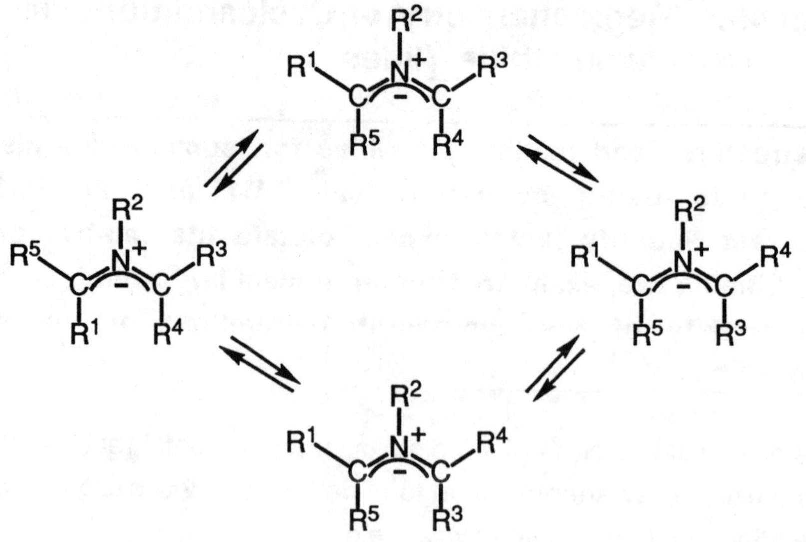

This suggests that selectivity in cycloaddition reactions involving azomethine ylides will depend on the relative stabilities of the geometric isomers of the ylide.

In this experiment, we first examine equilibrium structures and relative stabilities of four different conformers of a simple disubstituted azomethine ylide, **1**.

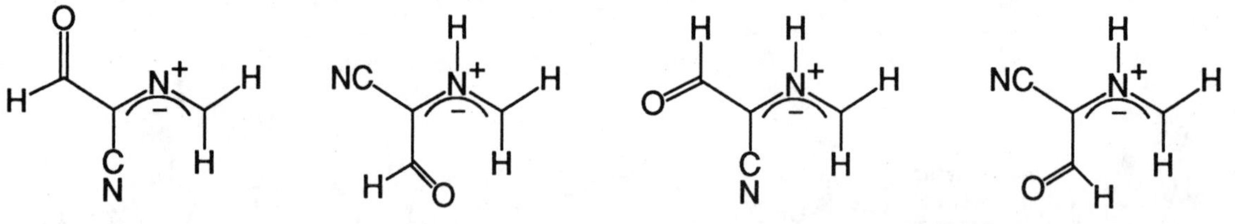

1a **1b** **1c** **1d**

The X-ray crystal structure of a closely related compound, **2**,

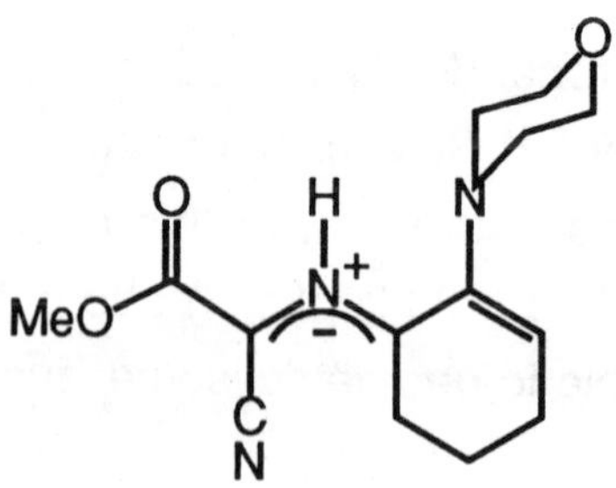

2

is available, and permits assessment of the computational model.[4] Following this, we examine frontier orbital interactions involving the azomethine ylide, **1a**, and acrylonitrile as a dipolarophile, and try to anticipate the preferred regiochemistry of the cycloaddition, i.e.,

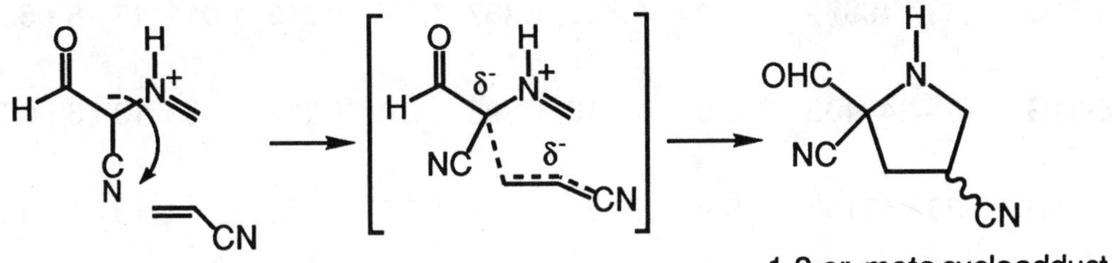

1,3 or *meta* cycloadduct

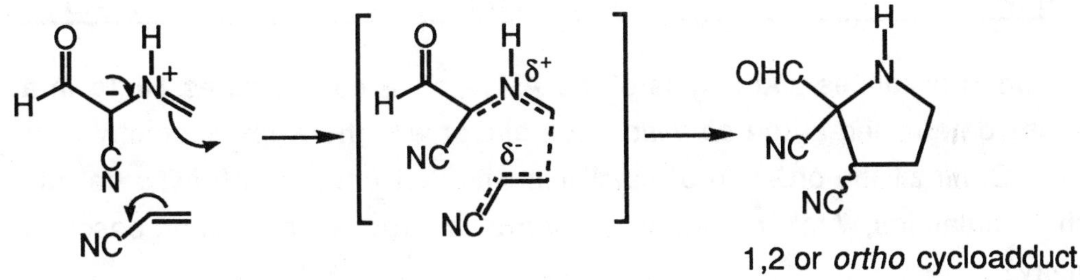

1,2 or *ortho* cycloadduct

Specifically, we examine to what extent the highest-occupied molecular orbital on the ylide complements the lowest-unoccupied molecular orbital on acrylonitrile.

Procedure

Build ylides **1a-1d** and **2**, and optimize at the semi-empirical AM1 level. Request calculation of the electric dipole moment, and record this along with the relevant bond distances in the table below. Compare with the 6-31G* *ab initio* structures for **1a-1d** which have been supplied, as well as with the experimental X-ray structure for **2**.

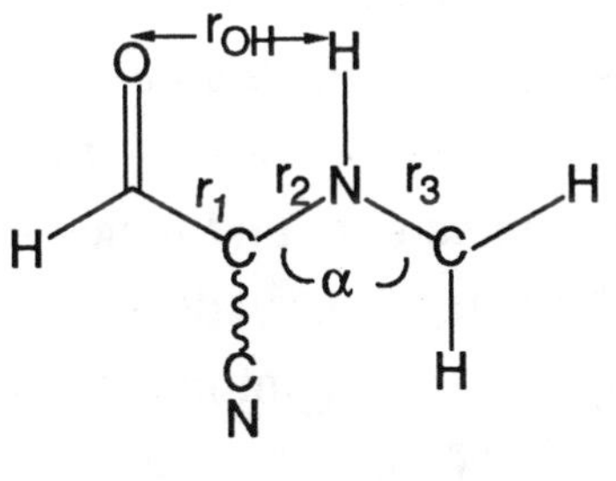

[4] L. Toupet and Y. Delugeard, Acta Cryst., **B35**, 1935 (1979).

	AM1 heats of formation (kcal/mol), 3-21G energies (hartrees), relative energies (kcal/mol), bond lengths (Å), angles (°), and dipole moments (debyes)									
	level	energy	relative energy	r_1	r_2	r_3	r_{CO}	r_{NH}	α	μ
1a	AM1									
	6-31G*	-337.48879	0.0	1.420	1.387	1.267	1.212	1.011	131.8	5.33
1b	AM1									
	6-31G*	-337.48400	3.0	1.416	1.398	1.274	1.212	1.003	130.6	6.08
1c	AM1									
	6-31G*	-337.47158	10.9	1.429	1.381	1.275	1.196	1.004	131.1	9.56
1d	AM1									
	6-31G*	-337.46466	15.2	1.435	1.383	1.277			133.9	9.77
2	X-ray			1.45	1.43	1.30			134.0	

Are the bond distances and angles of the AM1 optimized structures **1a**-**1d** in accord with those determined at the *ab initio* level, and/or with the X-ray geometry known for ylide **2**? Contrast the ordering of stabilities with that from the *ab initio* calculations. Which calculations, AM1 or 3-21G, appears to provide the better description of geometry?

Given that the van der Waals radii of oxygen and hydrogen are 1.7Å and 1.2Å, respectively, is the OH distance in **1a** (2.09Å at the 6-31G* level) shorter than the sum of the van der Waals radii? Examine the NH and CO bond distances in dipole **1a** (use **1c** as a standard). Is the lengthening and shortening of the NH and CO bonds consistent with the presence of an intramolecular hydrogen bond?

To explore the origin of the preferred stabilities, examine the dipole moments for these ylides. In terms of bond dipole schemes [see **Experiment 28**], can you account for the preferred stability of **1a** over **1c**? Is the orientation of the geminal formyl and cyano substituents likely to be the same or different in the gas phase and in the solid state? Would you expect any changes from the gas phase to solution?

Build acrylonitrile and optimize at the AM1 level. Construct a graphic depicting [3] the value of the LUMO mapped onto on the total electron density surface. Also, obtain the corresponding graphic for the HOMO mapped onto the electron density in **1a**. View the two graphics together on screen, and match the end of the 1,3-dipole having the larger HOMO contribution for the ylide with the end of the acrylonitrile (dipolarophile) have the larger LUMO contribution. What regioselectivity do you anticipate for the cycloaddition of ylide **1** and acrylonitrile? Does this agree or disagree with the experimental observations?

Experiment 50: Stereochemistry in Diels Alder Cycloadditions

We use AM1 semi-empirical calculations to assign the preferred facial and *endo/exo* stereochemistry of Diels-Alder cycloadditions of 5-substituted cyclopentadienes and acrylonitrile.

Additions of 5-substituted cyclopentadienes with acrylonitrile can lead to four distinct stereoproducts, in which the substituent on cyclopentadiene is *syn* or *anti* to the dienophile, and in which the nitrile functionality is *endo* or *exo*.

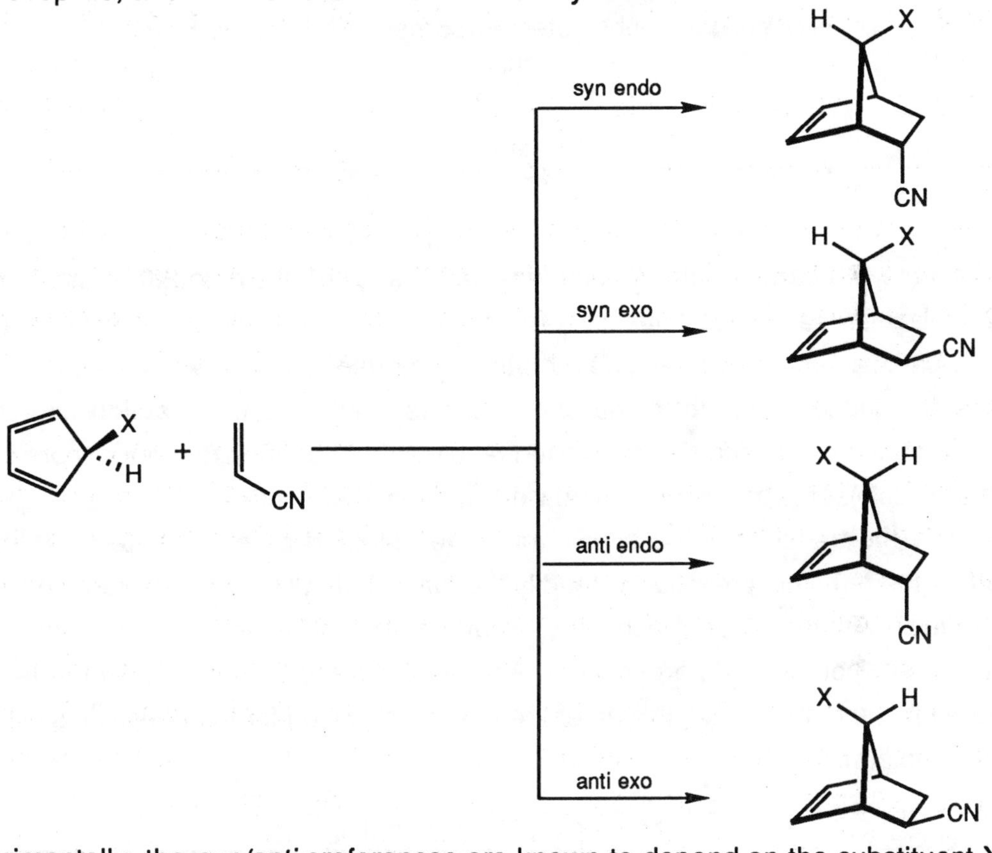

Experimentally, the *syn/anti* preferences are known to depend on the substituent X. In particular, if X is alkyl, *anti* products are preferred (in line with obvious steric dictates), while *syn* products are favored for X=alkoxy.[1] In general, *endo* adducts are favored over *exo* adducts. In this experiment, we relate AM1 transition state energies for reactions of 5-methylcyclopentadiene and 5-fluorocyclopentadiene with acrylonitrile as a function of stereochemistry to kinetic product distributions.

---

[1] For a review of the experimental and theoretical literature, see: S.D. Kahn and W.J. Hehre, J. Am. Chem. Soc., **109**, 663 (1987); T. Chao, PhD thesis, University of California, Irvine, 1992.

We use a fluorine substituent to model the effects of alkoxy. Both are σ acceptors and π donors and should show similar stereoelectronic properties.

Procedure

As all the possible transition structures are likely to be similar, the best way to build the whole set is to build and fully optimize one of them and, having done so, use this structure as a guess to the remaining transition states. Build the transition state for cycloaddition of 5-fluorocyclopentadiene with acrylonitrile in a *syn*, *endo* arrangement. The easiest way is to build the substituted norbornene (the product),

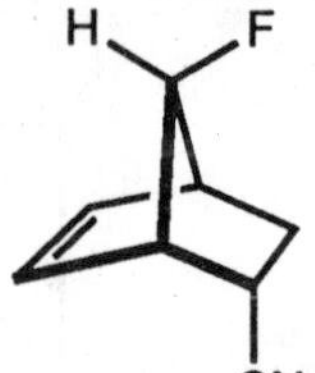

H F

CN

constrain the two carbon-carbon bond lengths "a" and "b" above to 2.0Å, and minimize using molecular mechanics. Specify a transition state calculation at the AM1 level, and request calculation of normal-mode vibrational frequencies. Once the calculation has completed, animate the vibrational mode corresponding to the reaction coordinate. Does the motion suggest a fully concerted reaction (both bonds are formed more or less simultaneously), or is one bond formed well ahead of the other?

Use the transition state which you have obtained as a template for transition states for the remaining reactions. Modify the pattern of substituents as required but do not minimize with molecular mechanics. Your template is already a good guess. Setup each for transition state determination. As the jobs complete write down the heats of formation in the table below (also enter the heat of formation for the transition state used as the template).

	AM1 heats of formation (kcal/mol)			
	anti-endo	*anti-exo*	*syn-endo*	*syn-exo*
R=F				
R=Me				

Pick out the lowest energy pathway for each of the two reactions. Are your results consistent with the experimental *syn/anti* stereoselectivity? Do they correctly reproduce the observed *endo/exo* selectivity?

Experiment 51: The Origin of the Barrier in the Diels-Alder Reaction

We use AM1 semi-empirical and (optionally) 3-21G *ab initio* calculations to factor out that component of the overall activation energy in a simple Diels-Alder reaction due to geometrical distortion of reactants.

What is the origin of the activation energy in a simple chemical transformation such as a Diels-Alder cycloaddition? Does it arise from having to distort the reactants away from equilibrium positions or does it come about because of unfavorable steric and/or electrostatic interactions between the reactants before they bind? Are there stabilizing interactions at the transition state which partially overcome these destabilizing forces? In this experiment, we use calculations to provide insight into the mix of forces which sum up to make the overall reaction barrier. Specifically, we examine transition states for cycloaddition of acrylonitrile and 1-methylcyclopentadiene leading to both "*ortho*" and "*meta*" products,

CH_3 + CN → H_3C CN *ortho* + CH_3 CN *meta*

and then separate intramolecular (reactant distortion) terms from intermolecular (electrostatic and steric) terms by "dissecting" the transition state into two parts, corresponding to the two reactants, and computing their energies.[1] For expediency, we use AM1 semi-empirical calculations to obtain reactant and transition state structures and (optionally) follow these by single-energy calculations at the 3-21G *ab initio* level.

[1] T. Chao, PhD thesis, University of California, Irvine, 1992.

Procedure

Build transition states corresponding to Diels-Alder cycloaddition of 1-methylcyclopentadiene with acrylonitrile, leading both to *ortho* and *meta* products and with *endo* stereochemistry. The easiest way to do this is to follow the procedure given in **Experiment 50**, and start with the appropriate substituted norbornene (the product) in which two of the bonds (marked "a" and "b" in the figure below) have been constrained at 2.0Å.

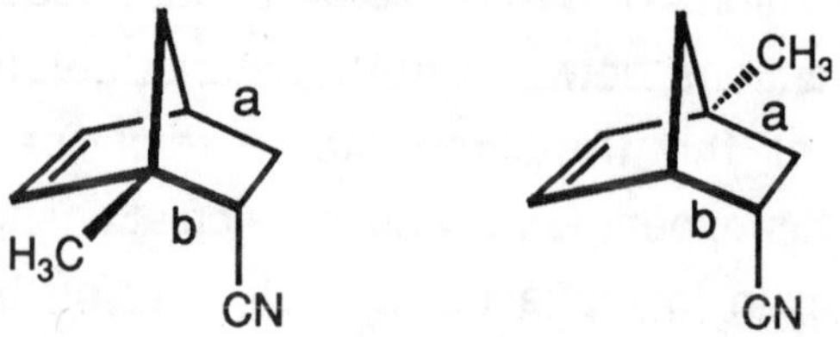

You might want to do one of these transition states first and then use it as a template for the remaining structure.

When the calculations have completed, write down the heats of formation in the table below.

AM1 heats of formation (kcal/mol) and 3-21G energies (hartrees)				
	ortho		*meta*	
	AM1	3-21G	AM1	3-21G
transition state				
1-methylcyclopentadiene				
equilibrium			--	--
distorted				
acrylonitrile				
equilibrium			--	--
distorted				

Also build and optimize at the AM1 level, 1-methylcyclopentadiene and acrylonitrile. Enter the heats of formation into the table under the heading "equilibrium". Finally, perform single-point AM1 calculations on the 1-methylcyclopentadiene and acrylonitrile fragments incorporated into the transition state structures. Obtain these from the transition states by "clipping away" those parts which do not correspond to the reactant of interest. Record the heats of formation in the table under the heading "distorted".

Compute activation energies for Diels-Alder reactions leading to *ortho* and *meta* products and record in the table below.

AM1 and 3-21G activation energies and reactant distortion energies (kcal/mol)				
	ortho		*meta*	
	AM1	3-21G	AM1	3-21G
activation energy				
distortion energy				

Which product (*ortho* or *meta*) is the favored according to the AM1 calculations? Is this consistent with what is known experimentally [see also **Experiment 50**]?

Sum the energies for the distorted reactants for structures corresponding to each of the *ortho* and *meta* transition states. Subtract these sums from the sum of the energies of normal (non-distorted) reactants to obtain the distortion component of the overall activation energy. Is the distortion component smaller or larger than the overall activation energy for the two reactions? Does your result imply that remaining (intermolecular) interactions are stabilizing or destabilizing in net?

Optional

Perform single-point 3-21G *ab initio* calculations (using the AM1 geometries) on the two transition state as well as the equilibrium and "distorted" reactants. Record these in the first table. As you did using the AM1 data, calculate both activation and distortion energies, and record these in the second table. Have any of the conclusions reached using the AM1 changed?

Experiment 52: S_N2 Reactions in the Gas Phase and in Water

We use the AM1-SM2 solvation model of Cramer and Truhlar to correct reactant, complex and transition state energies for the S_N2 displacement of fluoride from methyl fluoride by fluoride calculated at the 6-31+G* *ab initio* level for the effects of aqueous media. We examine differences between gas- and aqueous-phase reaction profiles.

The S_N2 reaction, which involves attack of a nucleophile, X^-, onto tetrahedral carbon opposite a leaving group, Y^-, i.e.,

$$X^- + \;\rangle C{-}Y \longrightarrow X{-}C\langle\; + Y^-$$

leads to inversion.[1] The rates of S_N2 reactions depend on the steric demands of the substrate, the nucleophile and leaving group as well as on the solvent. Here, we examine the role of solvent in altering the profile of the gas-phase S_N2 reaction.

Procedure

First examine the energetics of a simple symmetrical S_N2 reaction in the gas phase:

$$F^- + CH_3F \rightarrow [F{-}{-}{-}{-}CH_3F]^- \rightarrow [F{-}{-}{-}{-}CH_3{-}{-}{-}{-}F]^{-\neq} \rightarrow [FCH_3{-}{-}{-}{-}F]^- \rightarrow CH_3F + F^- \quad (1)$$

$[F{-}{-}{-}{-}CH_3F]^-$ and $[FCH_3{-}{-}{-}{-}F]^-$ are intermolecular complexes and $[F{-}{-}{-}{-}CH_3{-}{-}{-}{-}F]^{\neq}$ is the transition state. Build all the species involved in (1). The complex, like methyl fluoride, has C_{3v} symmetry and the transition state has D_{3h} symmetry. The symmetry of the latter allows us to perform geometry optimization rather than searching for a transition state structure. Optimize at the 6-31+G* level; be certain to use direct methods on the larger systems. Record the energies in the table below, and use the data to construct a reaction coordinate diagram for the S_N2 reaction in the gas phase, setting the zero in energy to the total energy of the reactants (F^- + CH_3F). [1]

---

[1] Carey and Sundberg, p. 261; Lowry and Richardson, p. 327; March, p. 256; for a recent discussion of theoretical work on S_N2 reactions, see: S.S. Shaik, H.B. Schlegel and S. Wolfe, **Theoretical Aspects of Physical Organic Chemistry; the SN2 Mechanism**, Wiley, New York, 1992.

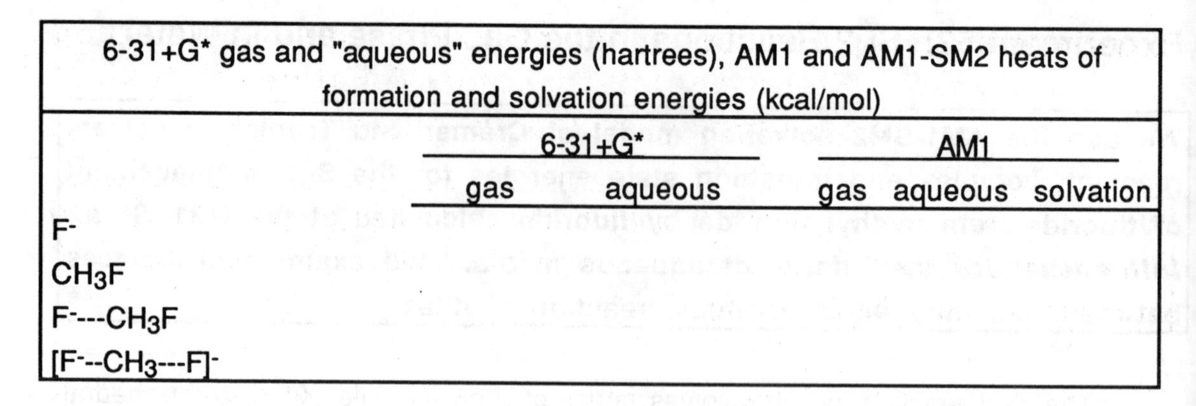

6-31+G* gas and "aqueous" energies (hartrees), AM1 and AM1-SM2 heats of formation and solvation energies (kcal/mol)					
	6-31+G*		AM1		
	gas	aqueous	gas	aqueous	solvation
F^-					
CH_3F					
F^----CH_3F					
[F^---CH_3---F]$^-$					

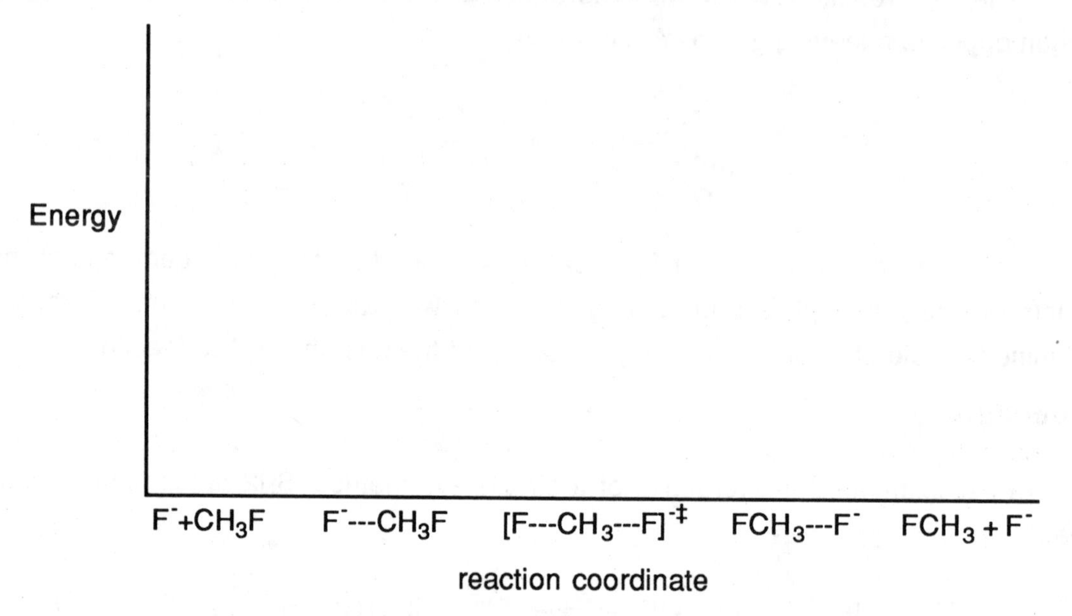

Do the calculations show a barrier to the reaction as written? Explain.

Set up single-point energy calculations (using the 6-31+G* geometries) for all molecules in (1) using both AM1 (gas phase) and AM1-SM2 (aqueous-phase) models. Once completed enter the heats of formation in the table above and compute the solvation energy (ΔH_f(aqueous) - ΔH_f(aqueous)). Enter this in the table, and add it to the gas-phase energy tabulated at the 6-31+G* level. You will need to convert from kcal/mol to hartrees (1 hartree=627.5 kcal/mol). Enter the sum in the table. Work out a reaction coordination diagram for the S_N2 displacement in water, and place it on the same figure (and on the same scale) as the diagram for the gas-phase reaction. Point out any significant differences between the gas- and aqueous-phase reaction coordinate diagrams, in particular, differences in overall barrier.

Experiment 53: Substituent Effects on the Regio- and Stereochemistry and Relative Rates of 1,3-Dipolar Cycloadditions

We use semi-empirical AM1 calculations to model the regio- and stereochemistry and relative rates of dipolar cycloadditions of substituted azomethine ylides with acrylonitrile.

1,3 dipolar cycloadditions of azomethine ylides with electron-deficient alkenes (dipolarophiles) lead to a variety of possible regio- and stereoproducts, e.g.,

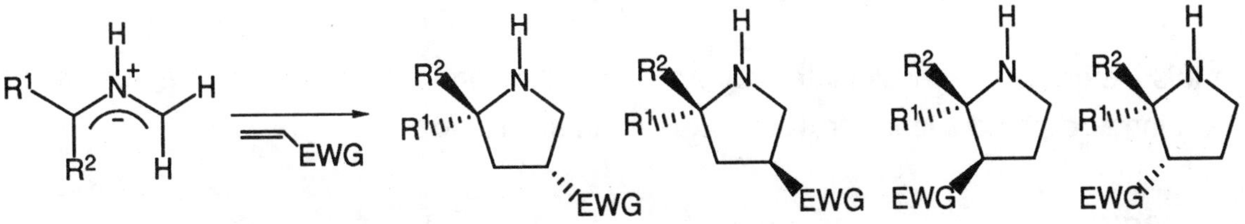

The distribution of products in 1,3 dipolar cycloadditions may be modeled either by matching frontier molecular orbitals on 1,3-dipoles and dipolarophiles [see **Experiment 49**], or by considering the relative energies of transition states leading to the different possible products. The latter approach allows elucidation of the relative rates of cycloadditions as a function of substitution, i.e., by examining changes in activation barriers, as well as permits *endo/exo* selectivity to be modelled. The results of the calculations may then be compared with experimental observations, e.g.,[1]

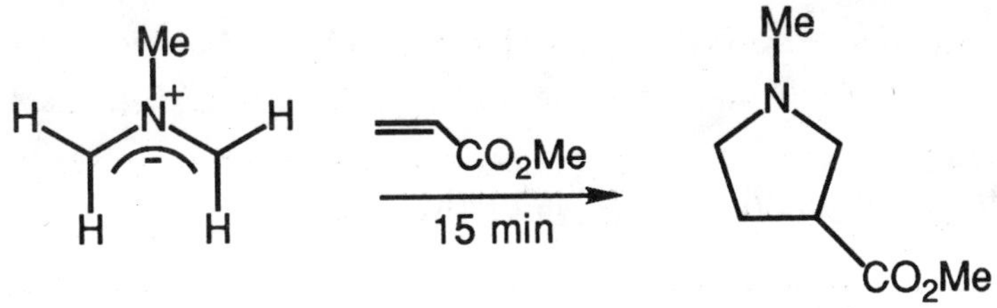

15 min

---

[1] O. Tsuge, S. Kanemasa, M. Ohe and S. Takenaka, Chem. Lett., 973 (1986); S. Husinec, V. Savic and A. Porter, Tetrahedron Lett., 6649 (1988).

In this experiment, we calculate product selectivities and relative rates for a number of 1,3-dipolar cycloadditions for which experimental data are available.

Procedure

Build and optimize at the AM1 level the dipoles, **1-3**, as well as the dipolarophile, acrylonitrile.

Record the heats of formation in the table below.

	AM1 heats of formation (kcal/mol)
1	
2	
3	
acrylonitrile	

We'll construct the various transition states of interest based on a "template" corresponding to cycloaddition of parent azomethine ylide (**1**) with ethylene.

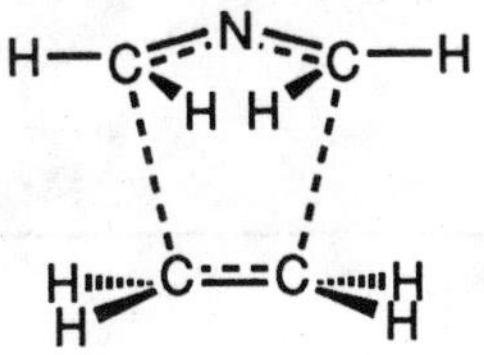

This has been artificially constrained to mimic a reasonable transition state. Setup for transition state optimization at the AM1 level and be certain to request calculation of vibrational frequencies. After the transition state optimization has completed, examine the calculated frequencies to verify that the geometry located actually corresponds to a reasonable transition structure for the cycloaddition. Animate the motion corresponding to the reaction coordinate. **[17]** **[7]**

Using the template, build *endo* and *exo* transition states for addition of azomethine ylide to acrylonitrile,

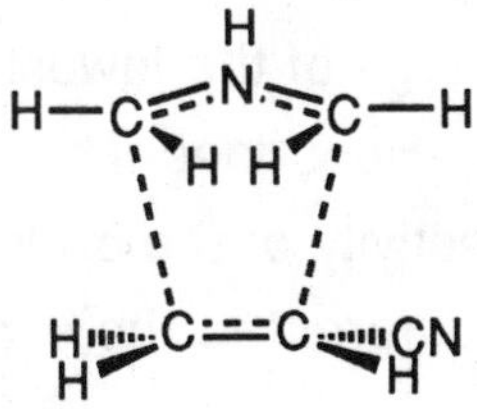

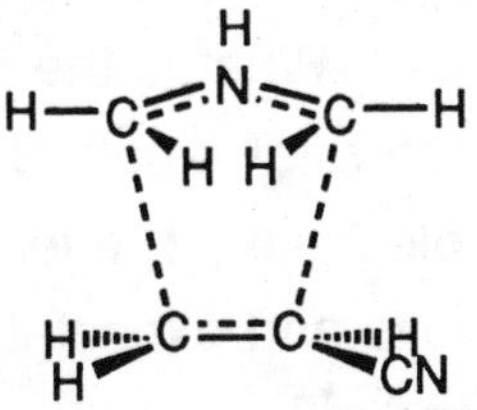

and the four possible transition states for addition to the substituted azomethine ylides **2** and **3** (corresponding to *endo* and *exo* stereochemistry and *ortho* and *meta* regiochemistry), e.g., for **2**.

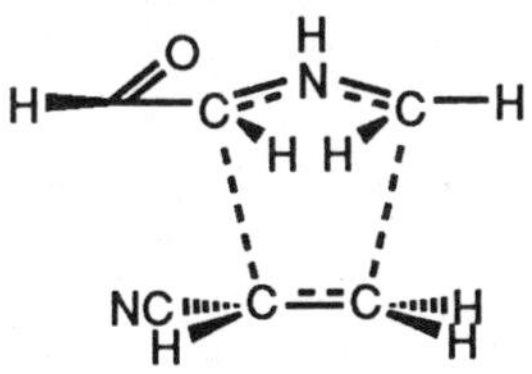

ortho-endo 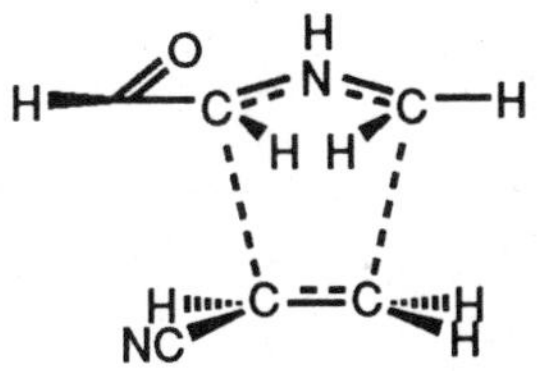 ortho-exo 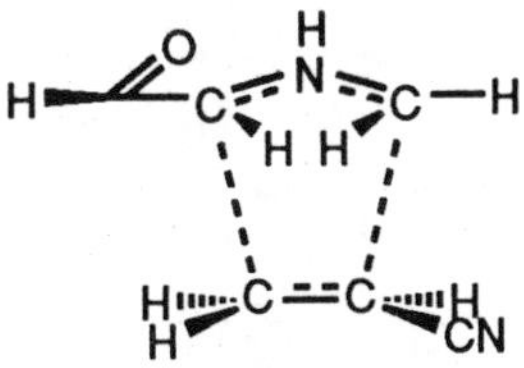 meta-exo 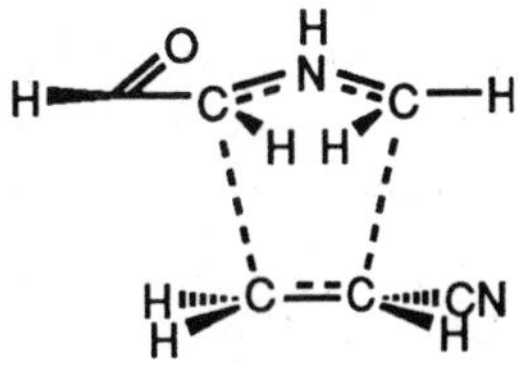 meta-endo

Submit each for transition state optimization at the AM1 level. When completed, record the heats of formation in the table below.

AM1 heats of formation (kcal/mol)				
reaction of acrylonitrile with:	*meta, endo*	*meta, exo*	*ortho, endo*	*ortho, exo*
1			--	--
2				
3				

Compute the activation energies as a function of regio- and stereochemistry. Record in the table below.

AM1 activation energies (kcal/mol)				
reaction of acrylonitrile with:	*meta, endo*	*meta, exo*	*ortho, endo*	*ortho, exo*
1			--	--
2				
3				

Based on your data, what is the effect of substituting the 1,3 dipole with electron-withdrawing groups? What is the difference in energy of the lowest energy *ortho* and *meta* transition states for dipole **2**? for dipole **3**? How does the addition of a cyano substituent to dipole **2**, i.e., **3**, effect the stereoselectivity of the cycloaddition reaction? How are your results and expectations similar or different to the experimental relative rates presented earlier?

Appendix A. Assistance in Using SPARTAN

1. Direct SCF methods, while significantly more costly computationally than in-memory SCF methods, do not make large memory demands and are generally the only alternative for most *ab initio* calculations performed on typical workstations. In-memory Hartree-Fock calculations on systems comprising 50-60 basis functions are practical for workstations comprising 32 mbytes of available memory and 80-90 basis functions for workstations with 64 mbytes of available memory.

2. The easiest way to build 1,3,5-cyclohexatriene is to enter the *expert* builder screen, bring up phenyl and then change the six "aromatic" ring bonds to alternating single and double bonds. Select the appropriate bond icon, and then *double click* on the bond to be changed. Minimization should result in a structure with C_{3h} symmetry and three ring bonds of length 1.507Å (single bonds) and three of length 1.320Å (double bonds).

3. The color scale used for display of a property encoded onto an isosurface ranges from red for the minimum value of the property through orange, yellow and green to blue for the maximum value of the property. Surfaces with the same property encoded displayed simultaneously on screen may all be brought onto the same scale by adjusting the range inside the **Surfaces** dialog (under the **Display** menu). First decide on minimum and maximum values of the property for the entire set of displays, and then for each display, enter these values into the text boxes to the right of **From:** and **To:**. Display values may be returned to their original values by *clicking* on **Reset**.

4. Conformational searching in ring systems is initiated by entering the **Conformer Search** dialog under the **Build** menu and *double clicking* on any of the bonds incorporated into the ring. Conformational searching in acyclic systems is specified by *double clicking* on one or more single bonds. Then enter the appropriate (**Mechanics**, **Semi-Empirical** or **Ab Initio**) dialog under the **Setup** menu and select conformation under task. When the search has completed, you can examine the individual conformers by reentering the **Conformer Search** dialog under the **Build** menu. Individual conformers may be named and saved using **Save As** under the **File** menu inside the dialog. They are then treated as separate molecules.

5. Hybrid orbital analysis is performed using the Natural Bond Orbital (NBO) procedure. This is accessed by entering the **Properties** dialog under the **Setup** menu and then *clicking* inside the box to the left of **Hybrid**.

6. Constraints on dihedral angles are introduced in the builder by selecting **Constrain Dihedral** from the **Geometry** menu, *clicking* on the four atoms (or three bonds), and typing in desired dihedral angle. Sigma (which may be changed from the default) controls the weight given to the constraint (for minimization in the builder). The larger the value, the more closely will the constraint be satisfied. Minimize in the builder. Once inside the appropriate setup dialog, *click* inside the box to the left of **Constraints** to ensure that the dihedral constraint is applied to the optimization.

7. Animation is accomplished by entering the **Vibration** dialog (**Display** menu), *clicking* on the entry in the text box corresponding to the normal mode of interest and then *clicking* on **OK**. Any molecular model may be animated, although any but wire frame models may tax low-end graphics workstations.

8. To determine the value of a property encoded onto an isosurface, e.g., the electrostatic potential encoded onto the total electron density surface, first display the surface, then select **Properties** under the **Display** menu and **Surfaces** from the sub menu which appears. Position the cursor on the surface region of interest and *click*. The value of the property at that region will be reported in a text box.

9. To "measure" the :NN: dihedral angle, enter the builder, select tetrahedral carbon from the list of atom types and, one after the other, *double click* on the two nitrogens. "Carbon" now replaces nitrogen and a free valence replaces the "lone pair", allowing the dihedral angle to be measured (using the **Dihedral** function under the **Geometry** menu inside the builder). When done, exit the builder without saving the changes to the structure.

10. Constraints on bond angles are introduced in the builder by selecting **Constrain Angle** from the **Geometry** menu, *clicking* on three atoms (or two bonds) and typing in the desired angle. Sigma (which may be changed from the default) controls the weight given to the constraint (for minimization in the

builder). The larger the value, the more closely will the constraint be satisfied. Minimize in the builder. Once inside the appropriate setup dialog, *click* inside the box to the left of **Constraints** to ensure that the angle constraint is applied to the optimization.

11. Isotopic substitution (deuterium for hydrogen only) is accomplished by first identifying the hydrogen of interest (**Display Labels** under the **Model** menu), followed by entering the text string "D=atom number" (where atom number is the number of the atom in the list of atoms) in the text box in the **Properties** dialog under the **Setup** menu. It will then be necessary to rerun the frequencies calculation (this will be quick as the Hessian has not changed).

12. The text output file provides excitation energies (in eV) and associated oscillator strengths. Choose the lowest excitation energy and add this value to the ground state heat of formation to obtain a heat of formation for the lowest excited state. You will need to know that 1 eV=23.06 kcal/mol.

13. Start with benzene and delete two adjacent free valences. Constrain the distance between the carbons from which the free valences were removed to be 1.22Å (see footnote 14). Minimize in the builder. The molecule should possess C_{2v} symmetry.

14. Constraints on bond lengths are introduced in the builder by selecting **Constrain Distance** from the **Geometry** menu, *clicking* on two atoms (or on a bond) and typing in the desired bond distance. Sigma (which may be changed from the default) controls the weight given to the constraint (for minimization in the builder). The larger the value, the more closely will the constraint be satisfied. Minimize in the builder. Once inside the appropriate setup dialog, *click* inside the box to the left of **Constraints** to ensure that the distance constraint is applied to the optimization.

15. The identity of the π orbitals of benzyne could have been obtained from inspection of symmetry labels on the molecular orbitals or the *structures* of the orbitals. Enter the **Properties** dialog under the **Setup** menu and *click* inside the box to the left of **MOs**. Once the calculations have completed, select **Output** from the **Display** menu. Find the HOMO (orbital no. 20) and, working

backward, look for orbitals where most of the entries in the column vector are zero (only those corresponding to contributions from 2p type orbital are non-zero). Find the other occupied orbitals with "similar" structure. You should also be able to locate the π^* orbitals.

16. A clearer image will result from using a value of 0.003 electrons/au^3 for the electron density surface rather than the default value of 0.002 electrons/au^3. This change is accomplished by entering the **Surfaces** dialog under the **Setup** menu and first specifying calculation of the density isosurface in the usual way. This will enter the request into the large text box at the top of the dialog. Next, *click* on this line and then *click* on the **Expert** button at the top right of the dialog; this will lead to a small text box at the bottom of the dialog in which the line "surface=density..." will appear. *Click* inside the box and enter an additional text string **value=0.003** onto the end of the line. *Click* on **Add** and then on **Save**.

17. Build a cyclopentyl ring with C_s symmetry. Locate the plane of symmetry. Convert the tetrahedral carbon which lies in this plane to a planar nitrogen using the atom replacement function in the *expert* builder. Identify the two carbon-carbon bonds linking azomethine ylide to ethylene in the transition state and constrain these to be 2.0Å. Minimize.

Appendix B. Practical Application of Electronic Structure Methods

Here we discuss a number of practical aspects relating to the application of electronic structure methods. These include finding and verifying equilibrium and transition state geometries, applying solvent corrections and making efficient use of energy data resulting from the calculations. Our treatment is very brief. Further details may be found in **Practical Strategies for Electronic Structure Calculations** available from Wavefunction, Inc.

Establishing Equilibrium Geometry

The energy of a molecule depends on its geometry. Even small changes in structure can lead to quite large changes in total energy. Proper choice of molecular geometry is therefore quite important in carrying out computational studies. What geometry should we use? Experimental structures would seem the best choice, given that they are available and are accurate. The trouble is that accurate experimental structures are often not available. Accurate gas-phase structure determinations using such techniques as microwave spectroscopy are very tedious and have generally been restricted to very small molecules. X-ray determinations on solid samples, while becoming evermore routine, are not as accurate and generally do not provide full geometrical information. Finally, only a few experimental structures exist for reactive or otherwise short-lived molecules. Use of experimental geometries in computational studies is not usually a viable alternative.

Another approach might be to employ *idealized* or otherwise *standard* geometries. This should be acceptable given the very high degree of systematics exhibited by a large range of structures, in particular, structures of organic molecules. One trouble with this approach is that energies and other properties are often very sensitive to subtle changes in geometry. For example, the fact that the dipole moment of trimethylamine is smaller than the dipole moment in ammonia is due in large part to a small change in the local geometry about nitrogen; were both ammonia and trimethylamine constrained to incorporate a tetrahedral nitrogen, then the relative magnitudes of the two dipole moments might not be properly reproduced. Another problem with the use of standard geometries is that the structures of many of the most interesting molecules differ greatly from the norm. Assumed or standard geometries also do not offer a good solution.

In the final analysis, we have little choice but to obtain geometries directly from calculation. This is not as difficult a chore as it might appear, at least if we have a reasonable guess geometry from which to start. More important, it is a chore which can be fully automated, requiring no more human effort than a calculation utilizing an experimental or standard geometry.

Geometry optimization is an iterative process. The energy and its first derivative with respect to all geometrical coordinates are calculated for the guess geometry, and this information is then used to project a new geometry. This process needs to continue until the lowest energy or *optimized* geometry is reached. Several criteria must be satisfied before a geometry is accepted as optimized. First, successive geometry changes must not lower the total energy by more than a specified (small) value. Second, the energy gradient (first derivative of the energy with respect to geometrical distortions) at the optimized geometry must closely approach zero. This tells us that we are on a *flat* region of the energy surface. Third, successive iterations must not change any of the geometrical parameters, i.e., bond lengths, angles, etc., by more than a specified (small) amount.

Geometry optimization does not guarantee that the final structure has a lower energy than any other structure of the same molecular formula. All that it guarantees is a *local minimum*, that is, a geometry the energy of which is lower than that of any similar geometry, but which may still not be the lowest energy geometry possible for the molecule. Chemists usually distinguish between sets of local minima which are interconnected by (low energy) rotations about single bonds (**conformers**), and sets of local minima, interconversion among which requires significant bond reorganization (**isomers**). Although chemists have usually treated the problem of finding conformational minima independently of the problem of identifying and finding isomers, they are really the same. In either case, finding the absolute or *global minimum* requires repeated optimization starting with different initial geometries.

Locating and Verifying Transition States

There are several reasons why transition state geometries are inherently more difficult to locate than equilibrium geometries:

i) Finding a first-order saddle point is more difficult than finding a minimum.

ii) The potential energy surface in the vicinity of a transition state is generally more "flat" than that in the vicinity of a minimum. Small energy changes may correspond to large changes in geometry, and even subtle differences in molecular composition and/or theoretical model may lead to large differences in transition-state geometries.

iii) Transition states often involve bond making and breaking, and simple levels of calculation may not lead to acceptable results. In particular, semi-empirical models may not always lead to reasonable transition state geometries.

iv) We know remarkably little about the geometries of transition states, compared with extensive knowledge of equilibrium structures. Our ability to guess reasonable starting geometries is therefore very limited. The hope is that with experience, transition state determinations will become as routine and as reliable as equilibrium structure determinations are today.

The key to finding a transition structure is to provide a suitable initial guess. While there is no "best way" to do this, in order of preference, a number of reasonable alternatives are:

i) Base the guess on the transition structure of a closely related system as obtained at the same level of calculation, or on the transition structure for the same system based on a lower level of calculation.

ii) Base the guess on reactant and product geometries (**Linear Synchronous Transit Method**).

iii) Base the guess on "chemical intuition". In this case, try not to impose symmetry as you do not want to bias the outcome.

In the absence of a closely related structure (option (i) above), it is generally (but not necessarily always) a good idea to precede transition state optimization at *ab initio* levels by optimization at a semi-empirical level. In this case, a full Hessian (matrix of second energy derivatives) should be obtained at the semi-empirical level before going on with optimization using *ab initio* methods.

Once a transition state has actually been located there are two tests which need to be performed to verify that it indeed corresponds to an acceptable structure.

i) Verify that the Hessian corresponding to the structure yields one and only one imaginary frequency. Experience suggests that the magnitude of this frequency will typically be in the range of 800-2000 cm^{-1}. It is possible that you will also find several very small (<100 cm^{-1}) imaginary frequencies, especially for molecules with several methyl groups or other rotors. These correspond to rotations and can probably be disregarded.

ii) Verify by animation that the normal coordinate corresponding to the imaginary frequency smoothly connects reactants and products.

Computing Solvent Corrections

Models now exist allowing consideration of the effect of solvent on gas-phase calculations. These pertain only to semi-empirical calculations.[1] To correct *ab initio* data for solvent effects, the following strategy is recommended:

i) Perform both semi-empirical gas-phase and solvent phase calculations using the same structures employed in the *ab initio* calculations.

ii) Add the difference in solvent-phase and gas-phase heats of formation to the *ab initio* energies (you need to pay attention to units).

Using Energy Data from Calculations

Energies obtained from theoretical calculations are themselves not usually of direct interest. Rather, they need to be used to establish relative stabilities of isomeric systems or more generally energies of chemical reactions. Energy comparisons can be broken down into different categories depending on the extent to which bonding is maintained. From the most difficult to the easiest to accurately describe, the these are:

---

[1] C.J. Cramer and D.G. Truhlar, Science, **256**, 213 (1992); R.W. Dixon, J. Leonard and W.J. Hehre, J. Am. Chem. Soc., submitted for publication.

i) Reactions in which the total number of electron pairs (chemical bonds or lone pairs of electrons) is not conserved. The simplest example is homolytic bond dissociation, e.g.,

$$H_3C\text{-}CH_3 \rightarrow 2CH_3^{\bullet}$$

Here the CC bond has been cleaved.

ii) Reactions in which the total number of electron pairs is conserved but the number of chemical bonds is not conserved. The simplest example is heterolytic bond dissociation where an electron-pair bond is exchanged for a lone pair, e.g.,

$$Na\text{-}Cl \rightarrow Na^+ + \ddot{C}l^-$$

Here the NaCl bond has been replaced by a lone pair of electrons residing on chlorine.

iii) Reactions in which both the number of chemical bonds and the number of lone pairs of electrons are conserved, but the numbers of each type of chemical bond and/or of each type of lone pair are not conserved. A simple example is the comparison of structural isomers, e.g., vinyl alcohol vs. acetaldehyde.

$$H_2C{=}CH\text{-}\ddot{O}H \longrightarrow H_3C\text{-}CH{=}\ddot{O}$$

Here an OH bond and a CC π bond have been replaced by a CH bond and a CO π bond.

iv) Reactions in which the total numbers of each kind of chemical bond and of each kind of lone pair are conserved, and only the local environments are altered. These reactions are termed *isodesmic* reactions. A good example is the bond-separation reaction, e.g.,

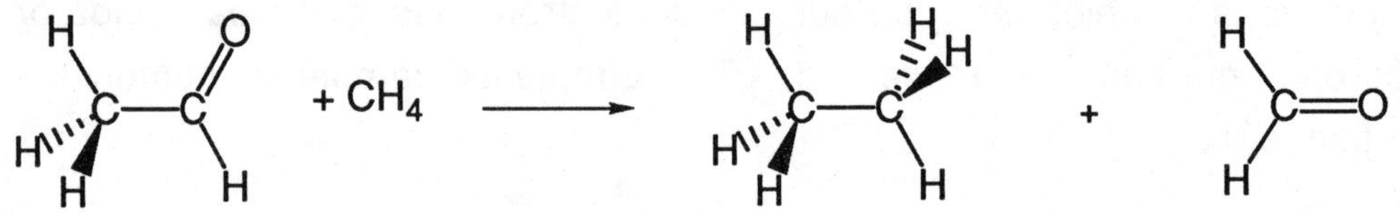

v) Reactions which involve no change in bonding but only conformational change. An example is the equilibrium between *trans* and *gauche* n-butane.

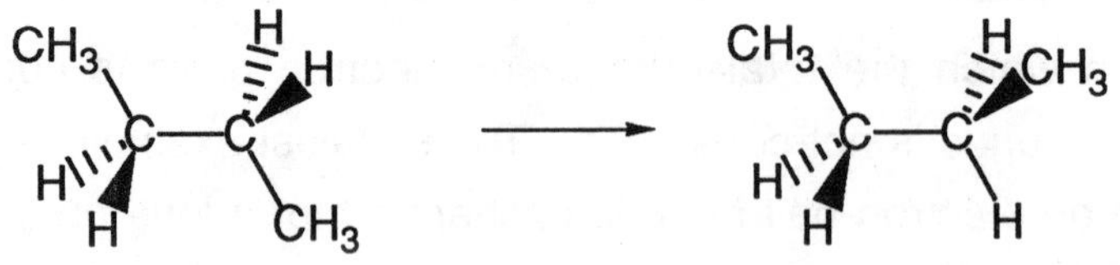

While critical assessment of the performance of theoretical methods is beyond our present scope[2] , a few general comments are in order. *Ab initio* models with large basis sets (beyond the 3-21G level encountered in most of the exercises in this book) and with explicit consideration of electron correlation are required to provide accurate descriptions of the energetics of homolytic bond dissociation (and to some extent heterolytic bond dissociation as well). Here, Hartree-Fock and semi-empirical models do not generally provide acceptable results An important consequence of this is that these models need to be used with caution in describing absolute activation energies. Transition states are likely to involve a significant degree of bond making and breaking.

Ab initio Hartree-Fock models are moderately successful in describing the relative energies of molecules which contain the same number of electron-pair bonds, although basis sets beyond minimal STO-3G representations are generally required. Semi-empirical models are generally not satisfactory.

Comparisons among molecules with the same number of each kind of electron-pair bond (*isodesmic* reactions) are generally satisfactory for Hartree-Fock models even with small basis sets. Semi-empirical models do not provide a reliable account.

Conformational energy differences are generally well described using both *ab initio* and semi-empirical methods.

---

[2] W.J. Hehre, L. Radom, P.v.R. Schleyer and J.A. Pople, **Ab Initio Molecular Orbital Theory**, Wiley, New York, 1986

Appendix C: Answers to Computational Experiments

Answers to all computational experiments follow. Only numerical results, e.g., geometries, energies and charge distributions, and not the results of graphical models, have been provided. As such, answer keys for experiments which rely entirely on graphical models have not been included.

1. Aromaticity in Pyrrole, Furan and Thiophene

AM1 heats formation (kcal/mol) and 3-21G (3-21G(*)) energies (hartrees)				
		X=NH	X=O	X=S
(saturated ring)	AM1	-10.43	-58.40	-16.51
	3-21G	-209.95942	-229.68372	-550.92487
(one double bond)	AM1	20.06	-24.69	10.18
	3-21G	-208.78312	-228.50585	-549.74037
(two double bonds)	AM1	39.88	2.96	27.44
	3-21G	-207.64199	-227.34430	-548.58664

AM1 and 3-21G (3-21G(*)) hydrogenation energies and aromatic stabilization energies (kcal/mol)				
		X=NH	X=O	X=S
(one double bond)	AM1	-25.3	-24.5	-21.5
	3-21G	-33.4	-34.5	-38.6
(two double bonds)	AM1	-14.6	-22.5	-12.1
	3-21G	-11.4	-24.2	-19.3
aromatic stabilization	AM1	10.7	2.0	9.4
	3-21G	20.0	10.3	9.3

AM1 bond distances (Å).

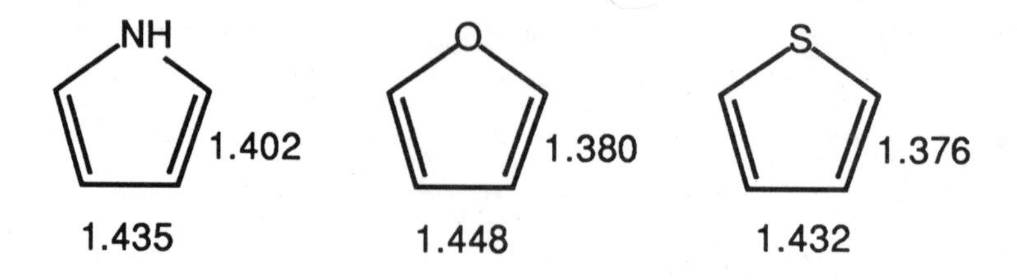

2. 1,3,5-Cyclohexatriene

AM1 heats of formation (kcal/mol) 3-21G energies (hartrees) and relaxation energies (kcal/mol)		
	AM1	3-21G
benzene	22.02	-229.41563
1,3,5-cyclohexatriene	44.73	-229.38729
"relaxation"	22.7	17.8

3. Ring Strain in Cycloalkanes and Cycloalkenes

AM1 heats of formation (kcal/mol)			
cyclopropane	17.78	propane	-24.26
cyclobutane	-0.99	n-butane	-31.13
cyclopentane	-28.80	n-pentane	-37.97
cyclohexane	-35.83	n-hexane	-44.82
cycloheptane	-40.75	n-heptane	-51.67

AM1 hydrogenation energies (kcal/mol)	
cyclopropane	-36.9
cyclobutane	-25.0
cyclopentane	-4.0
cyclohexane	-3.8
cycloheptane	-5.7

AM1 heats of formation (kcal/mol)	
cyclopropene	74.81
cyclobutene	45.76
cyclopentene	2.97
cyclohexene	-10.06
cis cycloheptene	-12.98
trans cycloheptene	16.76

AM1 hydrogenation energies (kcal/mol)	
cyclopropene	-51.8
cyclobutene	-41.6
cyclopentene	-26.6
cyclohexene	-20.6
cis cycloheptene	-22.6
trans cycloheptene	-52.3
cis 2-butene	-23.7

4. Bredt's Rule

AM1 heats of formation (kcal/mol), 3-21G energies (hartrees) and energy differences (kcal/mol)

	AM1	3-21G
2	25.96	-269.36142
3	79.80	-269.25617
ΔE	53.8	66.0
4	-2.82	-308.19372
5	50.45	-308.08766
ΔE	53.3	66.6
6	-10.88	-347.00261
7	16.14	-346.95288
ΔE	27.0	31.2
8	-16.25	-385.80913
9	-4.71	-385.78802
ΔE	11.5	13.2

5. π Bond Strengths in Olefins and Olefin Analogues

MP2/6-31G* (UMP2/6-31G*) energies (hartrees)	
ethylene	-78.28411
ethyl radical	-78.83517
ethane	-79.49430

MP2/6-31G* (UMP2/6-31G*) energies (hartrees)	
silaethylene	-329.24998
methylsilyl radical	-329.85118
silylmethyl radical	-329.82763
silaethane	-330.48506

MP2/6-31G* (UMP2/6-31G*) energies (hartrees)	
acetylene	-77.06466
vinyl radical	-77.60174
ethylene	-78.28411

MP2/6-31G* π-bond strengths (kcal/mol)	
ethylene	68
silaethylene	35
acetylene	91

6. Substituent and Solvent Effects on Tautomeric Equilibria

AM1 heats of formation and relative energies (kcal/mol)

	ΔH_f°	rel. energy
1a (R=H)	39.87	0
1b (R=H)	50.51	10.6
1c (R=H)	48.58	8.7
1a (R=Cl)	46.76	20.3
1b (R=Cl)	27.95	1.4
1c (R=Cl)	26.51	0

AM1 and AM1-SM2 heats of formation and relative energies (kcal/mol) and AM1 dipole moments (debye)

	AM1			AM1-SM2	
	ΔH_f°	rel. energy	μ	ΔH_f°	rel. energy
2a	-11.77	0	1.4	-20.32	1.8
2b	-11.31	0.5	3.9	-22.11	0

7. Glycine in the Gas Phase and in Water

AM1 and AM1-SM2 heats of formation (kcal/mol), solvation energies (kcal/mol) and gas and "aqueous" 3-21+G energies (hartrees)

	heat of formation		solvation energy	3-21+G energy	
	AM1	AM1-SM2		gas	"aqueous"
1	-97.90	-110.22	12.3	-281.28985	-281.30945
2	-59.17	-96.92	37.7	-281.26146	-281.32154
ΔE	38.7 (**1**)	13.3 (**1**)		17.8 (**1**)	7.6 (**2**)

Comparison of AM1 geometries for methylammonium ion and acetate ion with that of the zwitterionic form of glycine. ([ ] indicates average.)

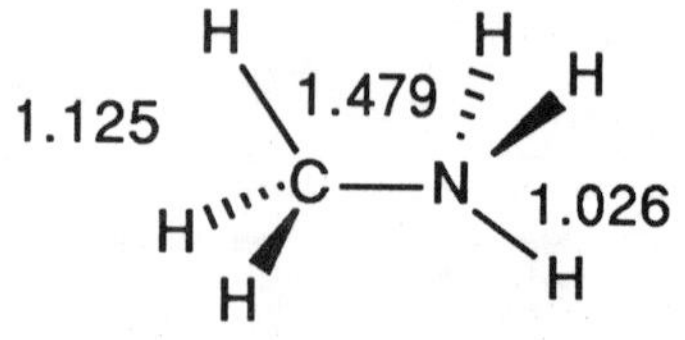

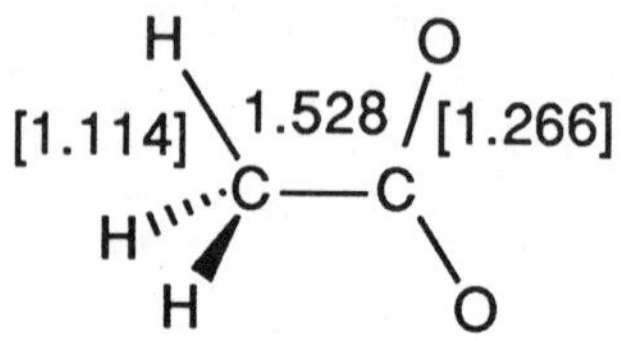

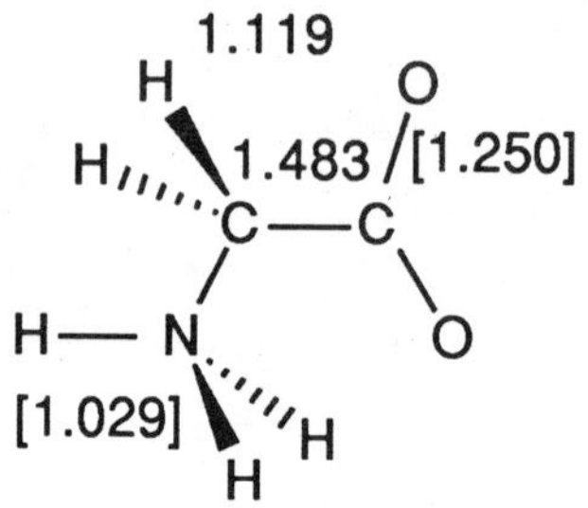

H, H, H, H, H, H, C, N; 1.125, 1.479, 1.026

H, H, H, C, C, O, O; [1.114], 1.528, [1.266]

H, H, H, H, H, C, C, N, O, O; 1.119, 1.483, [1.250], [1.029]

Comparison of 3-21+G//AM1 atomic charges based on fits to electrostatic potentials for methylammonium ion and acetate ion with those for the zwitterionic form of glycine. ([ ] indicates average.)

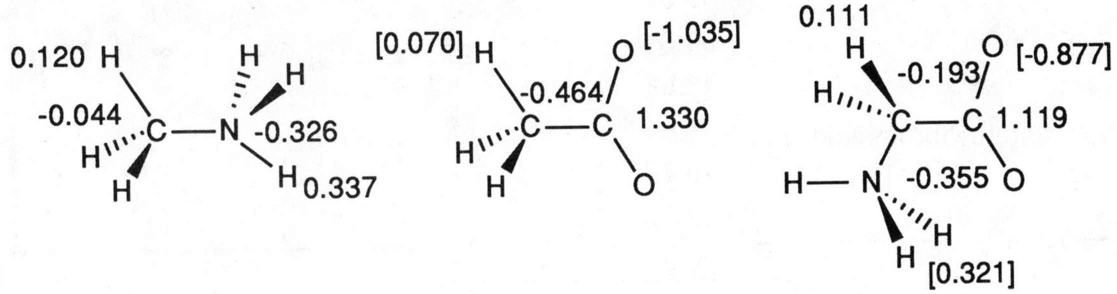

0.120 H H H
-0.044 H C—N -0.326
H H 0.337

[0.070] H O [-1.035]
-0.464
H C—C 1.330
H O

0.111
H O [-0.877]
-0.193
H C—C 1.119
H— N -0.355 O
H H
[0.321]

8. Site of Protonation in Amides

AM1 heats of formation (kcal/mol) and 3-21G energies (hartrees)		
	AM1	3-21G
N-protonated formamide	132.49	-168.29257
O-protonated formamide	122.66	-168.32031
ammonia	-7.28	-55.87138
ammonium ion	150.58	-56.23380
formaldehyde	-31.49	-113.22009
protonated formaldehyde	161.31	-113.50897
formamide	-44.76	-167.98157
N-protonated N,N-dimethylformamide	135.10	-245.93736
O-protonated N,N-dimethylformamide	124.58	-245.95526
N-protonated acetamide	121.24	-207.13467
O-protonated acetamide	110.56	-207.16143

AM1 and 3-21G proton affinities and differences in N- and O-proton affinities (kcal/mol)			
		AM1	3-21G
formamide	N	188	175
	O	208	215
	ΔE(O-N)	20	30
N,N-dimethylformamide	ΔE(O-N)	21	24
acetamide	ΔE(O-N)		

9. Atomic Hybridization and Bond Lengths

AM1 CH bond lengths (Å) and hybridizations		
	r_{CH}	n in sp^n
ethane	1.117	2.99
ethylene	1.098	2.15
acetylene	1.061	1.06
methylene	1.103	4.26
cyclopropane	1.104	2.36
cyclobutane	1.110	2.65

AM1 CC bond lengths (Å) and hybridizations		
	CC single bond length	m, n in sp^m, sp^n
butadiyne	1.356	1.16
but-1-yne-3-ene	1.405	1.13, 2.27
1-butyne	1.433	1.13, 3.10
1,3-butadiene	1.451	2.20
1-butene	1.484	2.23, 3.02
n-butane	1.514	3.07
cyclopropane	1.501	3.94
cyclobutane	1.543	3.42
cyclopropene	1.489	3.06, 4.16
cyclobutene (C_3C_4)	1.522	2.60, 3.45
(C_2C_3)	1.567	3.60

STO-3G TiH bond lengths (Å) and hybridization at titanium		
	r_{TiH}	n in sd^n
titanaethane	1.676	1.97
titanaethylene	1.698	1.29
titanaethyne	1.752	0.24

10. Molecular Recognition: Hydrogen-Bonded Base Pairs

PM3 heats of formation (kcal/mol)	
1-methylcytosine	-14.27
1-methylthymine	-76.85
9-methyladenine	54.58
9-methylguanine	6.22
N-naphthridinylacetamide	9.56
6-amino-2-pyridone	-18.04

PM3 complex energies (kcal/mol) and experimental association constants				
	$\Sigma\Delta H_{PM3}$ (monomers)	ΔH_{PM3} (complex)	$\Delta\Delta H_{PM3}$	$K_{association}$
1	-153.70	-157.81	4.1	3.2
2	-22.27	-28.81	6.5	1.3×10^2
3	109.16	105.46	3.7	3.1
4	12.45	1.88	10.6	5×10^3
5	-8.05	-19.77	11.7	5×10^4
6	-8.48	-18.55	10.1	1.7×10^4 [a]

a) data for closely related substituted system

11. Conformational Isomerism in n-Butane

AM1 heats of formation and relative conformer energies (kcal/mol) of n-butane			
ideal CCCC dihedral angle	actual CCCC dihedral angle	heat of formation	rel. energy
0°	0.0	-25.39	5.74
30°	30.0	-28.98	2.15
60°	60.0	-30.25	0.88
90°	90.0	-30.20	0.93
120°	120.0	-29.60	1.53
150°	150.0	-30.39	0.74
180°	180.0	-31.13	0.00

3-21G total energies (hartrees) and relative conformer energies (kcal/mol) of n-butane		
CCCC dihedral angle	total energies	rel. energy
0°	-156.41638	10.10
30°	-156.42670	3.62
60°	-156.43106	0.88
90°	-156.42958	1.81
120°	-156.42673	3.60
150°	-156.42963	1.78
180°	-156.43247	0.00

12. Conformational Preferences Involving Multiple Bonds

3-21G energies (hartrees) and rotational barriers (kcal/mol)			
	eclipsed	staggered	barrier
propene	-116.42401	-116.42119	1.77
acetaldehyde	-152.05525	-152.05344	1.14

3-21G energies (hartrees) and relative conformer energies (kcal/mol) of 1-butene			
ideal CCCC dihedral angle	actual CCCC dihedral angle	energy	rel. energy
0°	0.0	-155.24194	0.82
30°	30.0	-155.24045	1.75
60°	60.0	-155.23975	2.19
90°	90.0	-155.24208	0.72
120°	120.0	-155.24324	0.00
150°	150.0	-155.24157	1.05
180°	180.0	-155.23984	2.13

3-21G energies (hartrees) and relative conformer energies (kcal/mol) of propanal			
ideal CCCO dihedral angle	actual CCCO dihedral angle	energy	rel. energy
0°	0.0	-190.87779	0.00
30°	30.0	-190.87602	1.11
60°	60.0	-190.87352	2.68
90°	90.0	-190.87381	2.50
120°	120.0	-190.87498	1.76
150°	150.0	-190.87462	1.99
180°	180.0	-190.87390	2.44

13. Conformational Isomerization in 1,3-Butadiene

3-21G energies (hartrees) and relative conformer energies (kcal/mol) of 1,3-butadiene			
ideal CCCC dihedral angle	actual CCCC dihedral angle	energy	rel. energy
0°	0.0	-154.05394	3.46
30°	30.0	-154.05500	2.80
60°	60.0	-154.05404	3.40
90°	90.0	-154.05093	5.35
120°	120.0	-154.05170	4.87
150°	150.0	-154.05688	1.62
180°	180.0	-154.05946	0.00

3-21G energies (hartrees) and relative conformer energies (kcal/mol) of E-1-methyl-1,3-butadiene		
CCCC dihedral angle	energy	rel. energy
0°	-192.87238	6.28
30°	-192.87454	4.93
60°	-192.87514	4.55
90°	-192.87336	5.67
120°	-192.87388	5.34
150°	-192.87768	2.96
180°	-192.88239	0.00

14. Conformational Equilibria in Substituted Cyclohexanes

AM1 heats of formation and axial-equatorial energy differences (kcal/mol) and steric parameters					
	heat of formation		relative energies		A
	axial	equatorial	axial	equatorial	
methylcyclohexane	-42.28	-43.70	1.4	0.0	1.8
tert-butylcyclohexane	-49.08	-54.17	5.1	0.0	>4.5
fluorocyclohexane	-83.17	-84.42	1.3	0.0	0.25
chlorocyclohexane	-44.87	-45.71	0.8	0.0	0.5
cyanocyclohexane	-4.80	-5.94	1.1	0.0	0.2

AM1 heats of formation and relative energies (kcal/mol)				
	heat of formation		relative energies	
	a/a	e/e	a/a	e/e
trans-1,2-dimethylcyclohexane	-45.91	-47.71	1.8	0.0
trans-1,2-difluorocyclohexane	-127.19	-128.68	1.5	0.0
cis-1,3-dimethylcyclohexane	-44.65	-48.84	4.2	0.0
cis-1,3-difluorocyclohexane	-126.31	-129.40	3.1	0.0

3-21G energies (hartrees) and relative energies (kcal/mol)				
	energies		relative energies	
	axial	equatorial	axial	equatorial
methylcyclohexane	-271.72137	-271.72541	2.5	0.0
tert-butylcyclohexane	-388.15860	-388.17186	8.3	0.0
fluorocyclohexane	-331.22899	-331.23053	1.0	0.0
chlorocyclohexane	-689.73222	-689.73386	1.0	0.0
cyanocyclohexane	-324.12453	-324.12483	0.2	0.0

3-21G energies (hartrees) and relative energies (kcal/mol)				
	total energies		relative energies	
	a/a	e/e	a/a	e/e
trans-1,2-dimethylcyclohexane	-310.53701	-310.54242	3.4	0.0
trans-1,2-difluorocyclohexane	-429.54926	-429.54930	0.0	0.0
cis-1,3-dimethylcyclohexane	-310.53223	-310.54524	8.2	0.0
cis-1,3-difluorocyclohexane	-429.54753	-429.55267	3.2	0.0

15. The Anomeric Effect

AM1 heats of formation and axial-equatorial energy differences (kcal/mol)			
	axial	equatorial	axial-equatorial
chlorocyclohexane	-44.87	-45.71	0.8
2-chlorotetrahydropyran	-73.07	-69.45	-3.6

AM1 heats of formation and axial-equatorial energy differences in 2-X-tetrahydropyrans (kcal/mol)			
X	axial	equatorial	axial-equatorial
SiH_3	-55.23	-61.01	5.8
CF_3	-222.46	-221.82	-0.6
NO_2	-64.33	-58.48	-5.9
CN	-30.86	-29.13	-1.7
F	-119.95	-118.03	-1.9
Br	-57.30	-54.78	-2.5

AM1 CO and CCl bond lengths (Å) in axial and equatorial conformers of 2-chlorotetrahydropyran.

1.428 O 1.408 H 1.795 Cl

1.426 O 1.426 Cl 1.769 H

16. Conformational Isomerism in Hydrazine. Keeping Lone Pairs out of Each Other's Way

3-21G energies (hartrees), relative energies (kcal/mol) and orbital energies (hartrees) in hydrazine					
ideal ω(:NN:)	actual ω(:NN:)	energy	relative energy	E_{HOMO}	E_{HOMO-1}
0°	0.0	-110.52935	12.0	-0.326	-0.482
30°	30.0	-110.53451	8.7	-0.336	-0.465
60°	60.0	-110.54380	2.9	-0.363	-0.429
90°	90.0	-110.54844	0.0	-0.389	-0.400
120°	120.0	-110.54706	0.9	-0.353	-0.442
150°	150.0	-110.54377	2.9	-0.327	-0.484
180°	180.0	-110.54231	3.8	-0.317	-0.510

17. Configurational Stability in Amines

PM3 heats of formation (kcal/mol), HNH bond angles (°) and orbital energies (eV) for ammonia		
	pyramidal	planar
ΔH_f	-3.07	6.92
∠ (HNH)	108.0	120.0
E (HOMO)	-9.70	-8.59
E (HOMO-1)	-15.10	-15.12
E (HOMO-2)	-15.10	-15.12
E (HOMO-3)	-28.79	-28.88

PM3 heats of formation (kcal/mol), XNX bond angles (°) and pyramidal-planar energy differences (kcal/mol)				
	pyramidal		planar	pyramidal-planar
	ΔH_f	$\angle$ (XNX)	ΔH_f	
ammonia	-3.07	108.0	6.92	10.0
trimethylamine	-10.87	112.3	-2.47	8.4
trifluoroamine	-24.40	105.0	10.67	35.1
tricyanoamine	132.57	115.2	134.92	2.4

PM3 heats of formation and pyramidal-planar energy differences (kcal/mol)			
	pyramidal	planar	pyramidal-planar
aziridine	31.61	51.13	19.5
dimethylamine	-7.90	0.47	8.4

18. Stereodynamics of Dimethylisopropylamine

PM3 heats of formation and relative energies and experimental relative free energies of dimethylisopropylamine (kcal/mol)			
structure	heat of formation	relative energy	experimental relative free energy
1a	-20.46	1.2	0.7
1b	-21.68	0.0	0.0
1c	-21.68	0.0	0.0
1d	-18.91	2.8	4.5
1e	-17.50	4.2	5.2
1f	-14.22	7.5	--

19. Hydrazine Conformations by Photoelectron Spectroscopy and Molecular Orbital Calculations

PM3 :NN: dihedral angles (°), orbital energies, difference in orbital energies and difference in experimental ionization potentials (eV)					
	:NN: dihedral angle	E_{HOMO}	E_{HOMO-1}	ΔE	IP_1-IP_2
1	96.3	-9.19	-9.42	0.23	0.55
2	134.6	-9.06	-10.36	1.30	2.04
3	138.3	-8.76	-10.08	1.32	2.30
4	137.1	-8.87	-10.14	1.27	1.78
5	177.2	-8.53	-10.06	1.53	2.11
6	106.4	-9.18	-9.62	0.44	0.73

20. Structures and Stabilities of *meta* Cyclophanes

AM1 heats of formation and hydrogenation energies (kcal/mol)			
n	ΔH_f°		$\Delta H_{dehydrogenation}$
	cyclohexadiene	*meta* cyclophane	
4	26.65	72.50	40.7
5	8.20	37.71	24.3
6	-2.09	12.07	9.0
7	-14.57	-6.02	3.4

21. Infrared Spectrum of Acetic Acid

PM3 heats of formation for acetic acid conformers (kcal/mol).

CH_3—C(=O)—O-H

-102.0

CH_3—C(=O)—O—H

-99.4

Experimental and PM3 infrared frequencies (cm $^{-1}$) and intensities					
Observed			Calculated		
description of vibration		frequency (intensity) [a]	description of vibration	frequency	intensity
a'	OH stretch	3583 (m)		3853	
	CH_3 d-stretch	3051 (vw)		3091	
	CH_3 s-stretch	2944 (vw)		3175	
	C=O stretch	1788 (vs)		1982	
	CH_3 d-deform	1430 (sh)		1387	
	CH_3 s-deform	1382 (m)		1456	
	OH bend	1264 (m)		1240	
	C-O stretch	1182 (s)		1355	
	CH_3 rock	989 (m)		977	
	CC stretch	847 (w)		962	
	OCO deform	657 (s)		467	
	CCO deform	581 (m)		395	
a"	CH_3 d-stretch	2996 (vw)		3083	
	CH_3 d-deform	1430 (sh)		1385	
	CH_3 rock	1048 (w)		1009	
	C=O op-bend	642 (s)		570	
	C-O torsion	534 (m)		507	
	CH_3 torsion	93		42	

a) vs=very strong; s=strong, m=medium; w=weak; vw=very weak; sh=sholder

22. Charges on Atoms in Molecules

Mulliken and electrostatic fit charges (electrons)						
	MNDO	AM1	PM3	STO-3G	3-21G	6-31G*
Mulliken						
C_1	0.038	-0.217	-0.116	-0.188	-0.672	-0.575
C_2	0.317	0.306	0.375	0.314	0.820	0.760
O_1	-0.365	-0.361	-0.398	-0.276	-0.611	-0.585
O_2	-0.295	-0.321	-0.310	-0.315	-0.711	-0.713
H_1	0.030	0.117	0.075	0.082	0.251	0.217
H_2=H_3	0.032	0.117	0.075	0.083	0.255	0.212
H_4	0.211	0.243	0.227	0.218	0.413	0.472
Fits to Electrostatic Potentials						
C_1	-0.199	-0.370	-0.173	-0.499	-0.573	-0.381
C_2	0.887	0.790	0.803	0.804	1.028	0.879
O_1	-0.594	-0.556	-0.588	-0.462	-0.661	-0.636
O_2	-0.635	-0.608	-0.608	-0.580	-0.791	-0.699
H_1	0.048	0.112	0.052	0.471	0.147	0.106
H_2=H_3	0.058	0.124	0.065	0.138	0.177	0.134
H_4	0.377	0.382	0.384	0.344	0.495	0.462

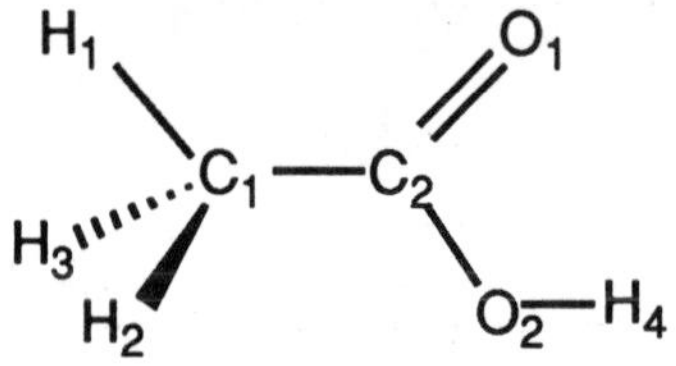

23. Electrostatic Potentials as Indicators of Acidity

3-21G electrostatic potentials (kcal/mol) and hydrogen charges (electrons)		
	value of the electrostatic potential	charge on acidic hydrogen
ethane	13.2	0.02
ethylene	21.8	0.16
acetylene	50.4	0.28

3-21G electrostatic potentials (kcal/mol) and hydrogen charges (electrons)		
	value of the electrostatic potential	charge on acidic hydrogen
propane	13.2	0.06
cyclopropane	19.3	0.12

3-21G electrostatic potentials (kcal/mol) and hydrogen charges (electrons)		
	value of the electrostatic potential	charge on acidic hydrogen
acetylene	50.4	0.28
propyne	40.3	0.32
trifluoropropyne	66.7	0.29

3-21G electrostatic potentials (kcal/mol) and hydrogen charges (electrons)		
	value of the electrostatic potential	charge on acidic hydrogen
ethanol	63.3	0.42
acetic acid	80.8	0.49
nitric acid	100.9	0.49

24. UV Spectra of Conjugated Carbonyl Compounds

AM1 absorption maxima (nm)					
	expt	AM1		expt	AM1
 O	209	224	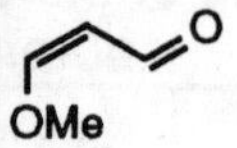 O, OMe	239	264
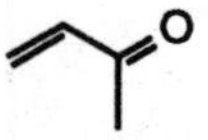 O	215	224	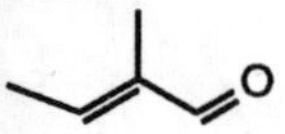 O	241	253
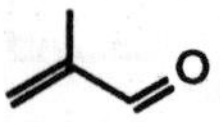 O	219	237	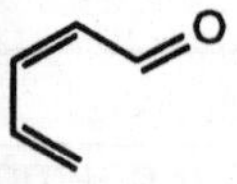 O	251	281
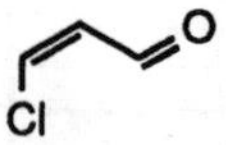 O, Cl	221	239	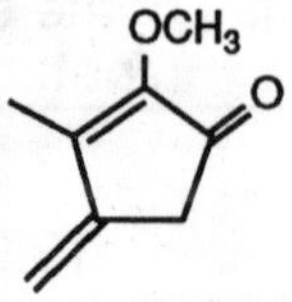 OCH_3, O	259	322
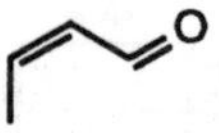 O	221	238	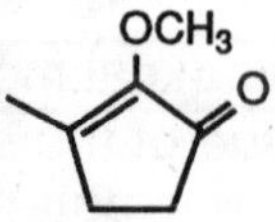 OCH_3, O	266	296
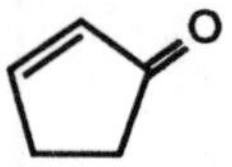 O	219	240	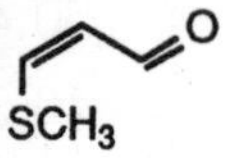 O, SCH_3	294	348
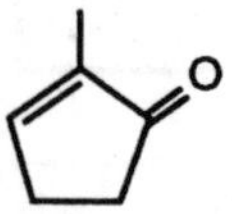 O	229	250	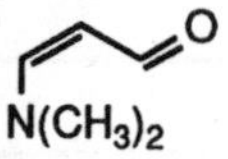 O, $N(CH_3)_2$	304	328

25. Gas and Aqueous Phase Basicities of Alkylamines

AM1 heats of formation and solvation energies (kcal/mol) and STO-3G energies (hartrees)

	AM1			STO-3G	
	ΔH_f^{gas}	ΔH_f^{aq}	$E^{solv.}$	E^{gas}	E^{aq}
NH_3	-7.28	-11.57	4.29	-55.45542	-55.46227
CH_3NH_2	-7.38	-13.49	6.11	-94.03286	-94.04258
$(CH_3)_2NH$	-5.63	-9.80	4.17	-132.61220	-132.61889
$(CH_3)_3N$	-1.71	-4.17	2.46	-171.19192	-171.19590
NH_4^+	150.58	71.13	79.45	-55.86885	-55.99475
$CH_3NH_3^+$	148.75	76.83	71.92	-94.46063	-94.57441
$(CH_3)_2NH_2^+$	149.22	86.87	62.35	-133.05002	-133.14946
$(CH_3)_3NH^+$	152.00	99.07	52.93	-171.63695	-171.72109

STO-3G relative proton affinities (kcal/mol)

	ΔE^{gas}	ΔE^{aq}
NH_3	0	0
CH_3NH_2	9.0	-0.4
$(CH_3)_2NH$	15.3	-1.2
$(CH_3)_3N$	19.8	-5.6

26. Reduction Potentials in Substituted Quinones

AM1 orbital energies and experimental reduction potentials (eV)

	E_{LUMO}	reduction potential
1	-1.73	0.010
2	-1.68	0.023
3	-1.62	0.067
4	-1.56	0.165
5	-1.51	0.235

AM1 orbital energies and experimental reduction potentials (eV)		
	E_{LUMO}	reduction potential
1	-1.73	0.715
6	-1.66	0.783
7	-1.55	0.484
8	-1.52	0.576
9	-1.44	0.401
10	-1.43	0.401
11	-1.39	0.154

27. Structure and Infrared Spectrum of Water Dimer

3-21G OH bond lengths (Å) and vibrational frequencies (cm^{-1})			
	OH bond length	frequency	description of vibrational motion
water	0.967	1799	bend
		3813	symmetric stretch
		3946	asymmetric stretch
water dimer	0.967 (O_1H_1)	1798	bend ($H_1O_1H_2$)
	0.967 (O_1H_2)	1854	bend ($H_3O_2H_4$)
	0.973 (O_2H_3)	3729	symmetric stretch (O_2H_3, O_2H_4)
	0.966 (O_2H_4)	3834	symmetric stretch (O_1H_1, O_1H_2)
		3909	asymmetric stretch (O_2H_3, O_2H_4)
		3963	asymmetric stretch (O_1H_1, O_1H_2)

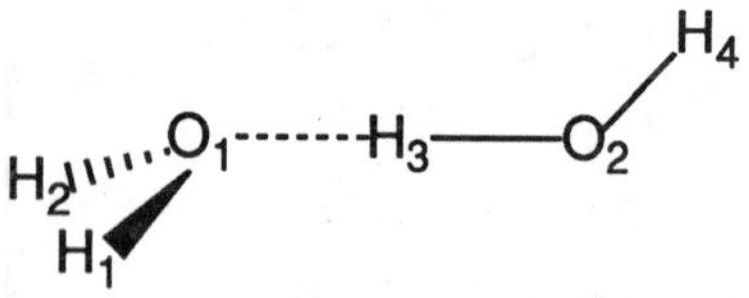

28. Atomic Charges and Electric Dipole Moments

CO bond distance (Å), Mulliken charges (electrons) and dipole moments (debyes)				
	r_{CO}	q(C)	q(O)	μ
linear CO_2	1.156	1.083	-0.541	0.0
"bent" CO_2	1.209	0.949	-0.474	1.91

29. Rates of Electrophilic Additions to Alkenes

AM1 orbital energies (eV) and experimental relative rates for *para* -substituted phenylacetylenes		
X	E(HOMO)	relative rate
H	-9.291	1
F	-9.258	1.40
CH_3	-9.060	17.3
OCH_3	-8.813	1840
NO_2	-10.161	.0030

30. Aqueous Phase pKa's of Organic Acids

AM1 electrostatic potentials (kcal/mol) and experimental pKa's		
	maximum value of the electrostatic potential	aqueous phase pKa
1	43.4	0.70
2	44.3	1.23
3	41.1	1.48
4	40.6	2.45
5	39.6	2.85
6	39.7	3.10
7	37.8	3.51
8	35.1	3.75
9	36.1	3.79
10	32.4	4.19
11	32.2	4.41
12	31.0	4.70
13	33.9	4.75
14	31.8	5.03

31. Acidities and Basicities of Excited State Molecules

AM1 and AM1/CI heats of formation (kcal/mol)		
	S_0	S_1
2-naphthol	-3.34	71.95
2-naphthoic acid	-49.29	28.08
2-naphthoxy anion	-28.94	24.49
2-naphthyl carboxylate	-70.36	48.84

32. Hyperconjugation and the Structures and Stabilities of Alkyl Cations

AM1 heats of formation and relative energies for *tert* amyl cation (kcal/mol)			
ideal dihedral angle	actual dihedral angle	ΔH_f°	rel. energy
0 (in-plane)	0.0	167.6	0.5
30	29.9	167.1	0.0
60	60.0	168.0	0.9
90 (out-of-plane)	90.0	168.3	1.2

AM1 heats of formation and relative energies for $H_3SiCH_2CMe_2^+$ (kcal/mol)			
ideal dihedral angle	actual dihedral angle	ΔH_f°	rel. energy
0 (in-plane)	0.0	176.0	8.2
30	30.0	173.7	5.9
60	60.0	169.8	2.0
90 (out-of-plane)	90.0	167.8	0.0

33. Structures and Stabilities of Allyl, Benzyl and Cyclopropylcarbinyl Cations

AM1 heats of formation and relative energies (kcal/mol)			
		ΔH_f°	rel. energy
allyl cation	(planar)	226.2	0
	(perpendicular)	244.8	19
benzyl cation	(planar)	222.1	0
	(perpendicular)	253.2	31
cyclopropylcarbinyl cation	(bisected)	232.4	0
	(eclipsed)	244.8	12

34. Directing Effects in Electrophilic Aromatic Substitution

AM1 heats of formation (kcal/mol)			
σ-complex resulting from nitration of:	*ortho*	*meta*	*para*
toluene	221.5	224.5	219.0
aniline	203.0	230.6	202.0
nitrobenzene	259.1	256.1	260.1
trifluorotoluene	95.2	90.2	93.6

35. Free Radical Substitution Reactions of Alkenes

AM1 heats of formation (kcal/mol)	
1	45.37
2	45.23
3	40.52
4	19.02
5	33.25
6	13.92
7	-5.32
8	28.30
9	9.11

36. *Ortho* Benzyne

3-21G equilibrium bond lengths (Å)

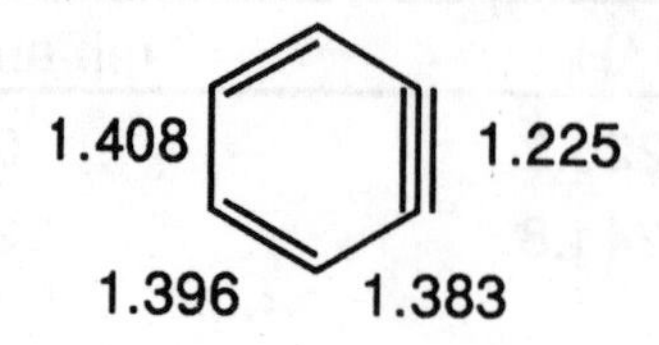

3-21G LUMO energies (hartrees)	
acrylonitrile	0.104
acrolein	0.096
ortho benzyne	0.088

3-21G C≡C stretching frequency (cm^{-1})

2210

37. Stabilization of Reactive Intermediates

3-21G energies (hartrees)				
X	XCH_3	XCH_2^+	XCH_2^-	$XCH_2^\bullet$
H	-39.97688	-39.00913	-39.23940	-39.34261
Li	-46.75248	-45.91361	-46.05483	-46.13337
CH_3	-78.79395	-77.87261	-78.06125	-78.16365
NH_2	-94.68166	-93.86284	-93.95307	-94.06305
CN	-131.19180	-130.21045	-130.54632	-130.57555

3-21G stabilization energies (kcal/mol)			
X	XCH_2^+	XCH_2^-	$XCH_2^\bullet$
H	0	0	0
Li	81	25	9
CH_3	29	3	2
NH_2	93	6	10
CN	-9	58	11

3-21G energies (hartrees) and stabilization energies (kcal/mol)				
	energies		stabilization energies	
X	$X\ddot{C}H$	$X\dot{C}H\bullet$	$X\ddot{C}H$	$X\dot{C}H\bullet$
H	-38.65185	-38.70907	0	0
Li	-45.45800	-45.53234	19	30
CH_3	-77.48475	-77.53370	10	5
NH_2	-93.45252	-93.43428	60	13
CN	-129.88133	-129.95645	9	21

38. Rates of Electrophilic Additions to Alkenes

AM1 electrostatic potentials (kcal/mol)	
ethylene	-11.35
propene	-14.29
1-butene	-15.30
iso-butene	-16.23
tetramethylethylene	-20.12
cyclopropene	-11.66
cyclobutene	-15.87
cyclopentene	-19.22
cyclohexene	-19.06
cis-cycloheptene	-18.12
trans-cycloheptene	-20.58

39. Structure and Reactivity of Cyclic Bromonium Ions

AM1 equilibrium bond lengths (Å) and natural atomic charges (electrons)

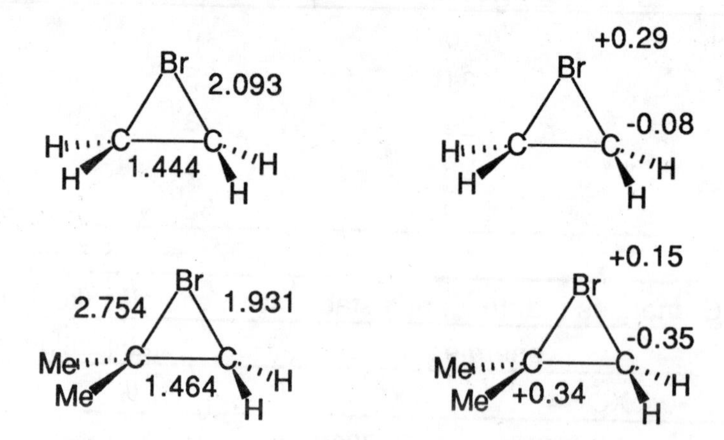

STO-3G equilibrium bond lengths (Å) and natural atomic charges (electrons)

Br 2.001, 1.481 | Br +0.35, +0.04

2.143, 1.965, 1.486 | Br +0.24, +0.30, -0.04

40. Stereochemistry in the Synthesis of Bicyclic Alcohols

(no tabulated results)

41. Acid-Catalyzed Ring Opening of Epoxides

AM1 CO bond lengths (Å)

1.594, 1.546 (CH_3, CH_3)

42. Nucleophilic Addition to α,β-Unsaturated Carbonyl Compounds

AM1 bond lengths (Å).

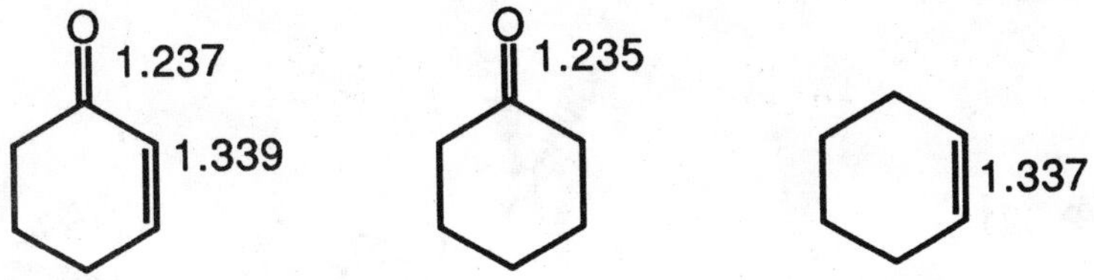

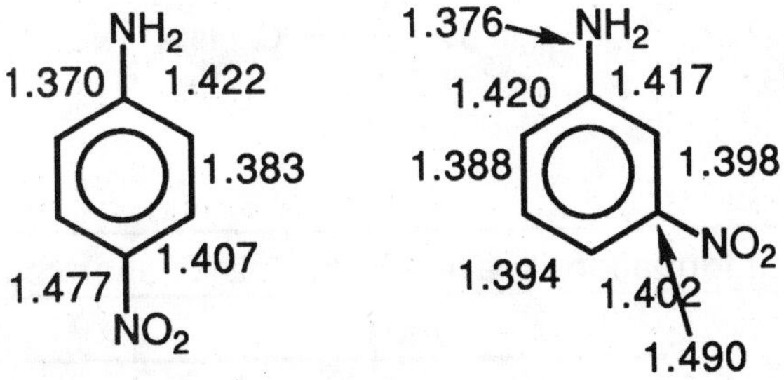

43. Activated Dienophiles in Diels Alder Reactions

	3-21G orbital energies (hartrees)
ethylene	0.183
acrylonitrile	0.098
trans-1,2-dicyanoethylene	0.032
cis-1,2-dicyanoethylene	0.034
1,1-dicyanoethylene	0.044
tricyanoethylene	-0.013
tetracyanoethylene	-0.054

	Electrostatic potential on the π system (kcal/mol)
ethylene	-22.0
acrylonitrile	-3.7
trans-1,2-dicyanoethylene	13.0
cis-1,2-dicyanoethylene	10.5
1,1-dicyanoethylene	11.7
tricyanoethylene	23.6
tetracyanoethylene	34.1

44. Addition of Singlet Dichlorocarbene to Ethylene

AM1 bond lengths (Å).

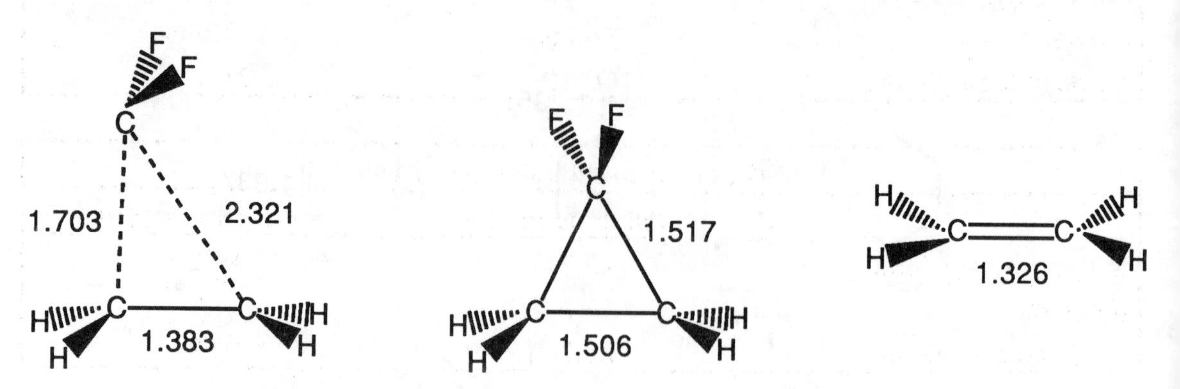

AM1 heats of formation (kcal/mol) and 3-21G energies (hartrees)		
	AM1	3-21G
difluorocarbene	-67.96	-235.37439
ethylene	16.47	-77.59899
transition state	-34.59	-312.92612
1,1-difluorocyclopropane	-77.05	-313.03683

45. Do Single Carbenes Behave as Electrophiles or as Nucleophiles in Additions to Olefins

AM1 heats of formation (kcal/mol), orbital energies (eV) and electrostatic potentials (kcal/mol)				
	ΔH_f°	E_{HOMO}	E_{LUMO}	electrostatic potential
tetramethylethylene	-16.09	-8.96	1.15	-19.8
ethylene	16.47	-10.55	1.44	-11.2
tetracyanoethylene	152.38	-11.52	-2.53	28.9
difluorocarbene	-67.96	-0.30	3.60	σ: -29.7 π: 12.1
dichlorocarbene	48.45	-1.10	0.29	σ: -37.4 π: 18.0

AM1 heats of formation (kcal/mol)		
	+ difluorocarbene	+ dichlorocarbene
tetramethylethylene	-61.33	43.56
ethylene	-34.59	70.38
tetracyanoethylene	110.12	211.15

AM1 activation energies (kcal/mol)		
	+ difluorocarbene	+ dichlorocarbene
tetramethylethylene	22.7	11.2
ethylene	16.9	5.5
tetracyanoethylene	25.7	10.3

3-21G transition state energies (hartrees)		
	+ difluorocarbene	+ dichlorocarbene
tetramethylethylene	-468.23793	-1185.20888
ethylene	-312.93294	-1029.92001
tetracyanoethylene	-677.75652	-1394.73728

46. Selectivity in Carbene Additions to Olefins

(no tabulated results)

47. Regiochemistry in Hydroboration of Olefins

MNDO heats of formation (kcal/mol)		
transition state for reaction of borane with:	internal	terminal
propene	21.19	20.91
3,3-dimethylbut-1-ene	21.74	20.73
isobutene	20.40	19.33

MNDO heats of formation (kcal/mol)	
borane	11.72
propene	4.99
3,3-dimethylbut-1-ene	1.90
isobutene	-2.00
isopropylborane	-14.32
n-propylborane	-17.61
2-(BH_2)-3,3-dimethylbutane	-10.47
1-(BH_2)-3,3-dimethylbutane	-18.34
tert-butylborane	-11.55
isobutylborane	-18.32

MNDO activation energies and regioselectivities (kcal/mol)			
transition state for reaction of borane with:	activation energy		terminal
	internal	terminal	
propene	4.5	4.2	0.3 (terminal)
3,3-dimethylbut-1-ene	8.1	7.1	1.0 (terminal)
isobutene	10.7	9.6	1.1 (terminal)

MNDO reaction energies (kcal/mol) and BC bond lengths (Å)				
reaction of borane with:	internal		terminal	
	ΔE	r_{BC}	ΔE	r_{BC}
propene	-31.0	1.700	-34.3	1.658
3,3-dimethylbut-1-ene	-24.1	1.707	-32.6	1.657
isobutene	-21.3	1.727	-28.0	1.642

48. Stereochemistry of Base-Catalyzed Elimination

Mulliken hydrogen charges (electrons).

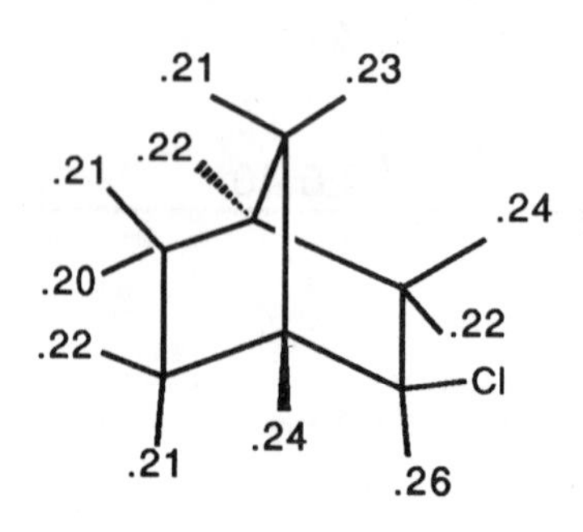

49. Regiochemistry of Cycloadditions of Azomethine Ylides

AM1 heats of formation (kcal/mol), 3-21G energies (hartrees), relative energies (kcal/mol), bond lengths (Å), angles (°), and dipole moments (debyes)										
	level	energy	relative energy	r_1	r_2	r_3	r_{CO}	r_{NH}	α	μ
1a	AM1	28.93		1.454	1.377	1.307	1.241	1.014	127.2	4.34
	6-31G*	-337.48879	0.0	1.420	1.387	1.267	1.212	1.011	131.8	5.33
1b	AM1	29.98		1.447	1.381	1.308	1.241	1.010	123.1	4.76
	6-31G*	-337.48400	3.0	1.416	1.398	1.274	1.212	1.003	130.6	6.08
1c	AM1	36.42		1.458	1.373	1.311	1.234	1.011	126.8	7.91
	6-31G*	-337.47158	10.9	1.429	1.381	1.275	1.196	1.004	131.1	9.56
1d	AM1	36.99		1.458	1.371	1.311	1.234	1.011	127.9	7.63
	6-31G*	-337.46466	15.2	1.435	1.383	1.277			133.9	9.77
2	X-ray			1.45	1.43	1.30			134.0	

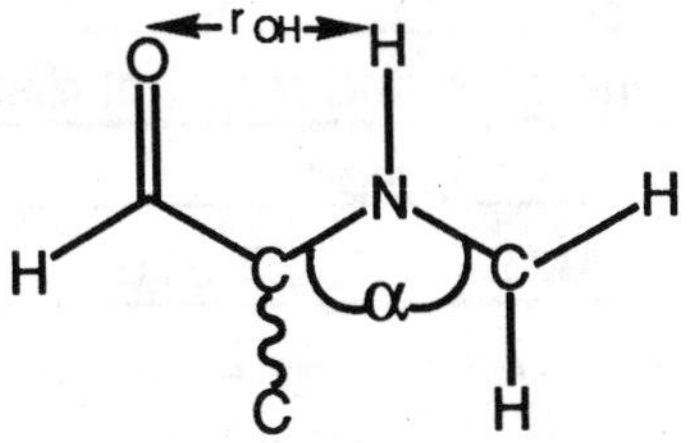

50. Stereochemistry in Diels Alder Cycloadditions

AM1 heats of formation (kcal/mol)				
	anti-endo	*anti-exo*	*syn-endo*	*syn-exo*
R=F	70.5	70.3	68.2	70.1
R=Me	107.4	107.0	109.4	110.3

51. The Origin of the Barrier in the Diels-Alder Reaction

AM1 heats of formation (kcal/mol) and 3-21G energies (hartrees)				
	ortho		*meta*	
	AM1	3-21G	AM1	3-21G
transition state	103.96	-399.30901	104.66	-399.30870
1-methylcyclopentadiene				
equilibrium	28.29	-230.53261	28.29	-230.53261
distorted	45.02	-230.49660	46.36	-230.49371
acrylonitrile				
equilibrium	44.96	-168.81673	44.96	-168.81673
distorted	56.17	-168.79682	56.66	-168.79633

AM1 and 3-21G activation energies and reactant distortion energies (kcal/mol)				
	ortho		*meta*	
	AM1	3-21G	AM1	3-21G
activation energy	30.7	25.3	31.4	25.5
distortion energy	28.0	35.1	29.8	37.2

52. S_N2 Reactions in the Gas Phase and in Water

6-31+G* gas and "aqueous" energies (hartrees), AM1 and AM1-SM2 heats of formation and solvation energies (kcal/mol)					
	6-31+G*		AM1		
	gas	aqueous	gas	aqueous	solvation
F^-	-99.41859	-99.58927	3.44	-103.61	-107.1
CH_3F	-139.04423	-139.04343	-58.79	-58.31	0.5
$[F^- \text{----} CH_3F]$	-238.48328	-238.61268	-64.06	-145.25	-81.2
$[F\text{----}CH_3\text{----}F]^-$	-238.45374	-238.56262	-20.75	-89.07	-68.3

53. Substituent Effects on the Regio- and Stereochemistry and Relative Rates of 1,3-Dipolar Cycloadditions

	AM1 heats of formation (kcal/mol)
1	43.38
2	-0.58
3	28.93
acrylonitrile	44.96

	AM1 heats of formation (kcal/mol)			
reaction of acrylonitrile with:	*meta, endo*	*meta, exo*	*ortho, endo*	*ortho, exo*
1	90.99	91.84	--	--
2	53.59	53.87	56.08	54.44
3	88.02	88.86	90.87	91.14

	AM1 activation energies (kcal/mol)			
reaction of acrylonitrile with:	*meta, endo*	*meta, exo*	*ortho, endo*	*ortho, exo*
1	2.6	3.5	--	--
2	9.2	9.5	11.7	10.1
3	14.1	15.0	17.0	17.3

Appendix D. Units

Geometry

Bond distances are given in Ångströms (Å) and bond angles and dihedral angles in degrees (°).

Energies and Heats of Formation

Total energies and orbital energies from *ab initio* calculations are given in atomic units (also termed hartrees).

Heats of formation from semi-empirical calculations are given in kcal/mol. Orbital energies are given in electron volts (eV).

Strain energies from molecular mechanics calculations are given in kcal/mol.

1 hartree = 627.5 kcal/mol

1 eV = 23.06 kcal/mol

1 hartree = 27.21 eV

Dipole Moments, Charges and Electrostatic Potentials

Dipole moments are given in debyes.

Atomic charges are given in electrons.

Electrostatic potentials are given in kcal/mol.

Vibrational Frequencies

Vibrational frequencies are given in wavenumbers (cm^{-1}).

Index (Bold type refers to experiment numbers.)